THE PFIZER GUIDE
PHARMACY CAREER OPPORTUNITIES

Second Edition

Published by Merritt Communications, Inc.

The Pfizer Guide: Pharmacy Career Opportunities is published for the Pfizer Laboratories, Pratt, and Roerig divisions of Pfizer Inc., New York, NY, by Merritt Communications, Inc., copyright © 1994. Reprinted 1999. The contents are determined independently and do not necessarily reflect the views of Pfizer Inc. or the publishers. No part of this publication may be reproduced in any form without prior written permission from the publisher. Correspondence should be addressed to *The Pfizer Guide,* c/o Merritt Communications, Inc., 123 Elm St., Old Saybrook, CT 06475.

ISBN 1-885031-00-9

Printed in The United States of America

Pfizer Inc
235 East 42nd Street
New York, NY 10017-5755

William C. Steere, Jr.
Chairman of the Board
Chief Executive Officer

Dear Pharmacy Student:

Since 1978, we have taken great pride in the publication of <u>Tomorrow's Pharmacis</u>
a magazine for pharmacy students.

During this period there has been a rapid increase in the range of career opportuniti
for pharmacists. Indeed, much of the popularity of <u>Tomorrow's Pharmacist</u> lies in i
many articles concerning new directions in pharmacy.

For these reasons we joined with several major pharmacy associations in 1986
develop the first edition of <u>The Pfizer Guide - Pharmacy Career Opportunities</u>. In th
way, each author was chosen by the professional group most knowledgeable in th
particular area. Now, accelerating changes in the role of the pharmacist have led ι
to create this new edition of <u>The Pfizer Guide</u>, again in cooperation with pharmac
associations.

We at Pfizer, and its Pfizer Labs, Pratt and Roerig divisions, are pleased to spons
this guide. We hope it will continue to be a valuable aid for every pharmacy stude
in making the critical decisions associated with career choice.

My best wishes for a long and successful professional career.

Sincerely,

William C. Steere, Jr.

TABLE OF CONTENTS

INTRODUCTION

INDEPENDENT PHARMACY

Contents

CHAIN PHARMACY

HOSPITAL PHARMACY

Contents

MANAGED CARE

Contents

Contents

Contents

New Horizons

Don Douglas
is manager of industry affairs for the
U.S. Pharmaceuticals Group, Pfizer Inc.

During recent years, there has been a vast expansion of opportunities in our profession. There is no doubt that it will continue. Independent pharmacists, who used to manage predictable businesses, are finding bold new ways to broaden their economic horizons. Institutional pharmacists, once limited in their practice activities, can now choose from an unprecedented number of recognized subspecialties. No longer restricted to the prescription counter, chain pharmacists are reaching into brand-new practice areas. Consultants? They can be found almost anywhere, performing a variety of professional activities. Throughout this expanding profession are abundant and exciting opportunities for students who carefully investigate their career options.

Despite the wide range of available opportunities, students often find the need for assistance when it comes time to evaluate their aptitude for specific careers and begin pursuing their goals. Most pharmacy educators agree that intelligent early planning can make the difference between an uneventful and even frustrating career and one that's filled with the excitement of recognized and seized opportunities.

Pfizer also recognizes the importance of sound planning in shaping successful careers. Our publication *Tomorrow's Pharmacist* regularly features articles on career development. We believe these articles make clear the educational steps one must take to achieve professional goals. Even more basic, we believe they help students establish goals. Not only can planning result in more rewarding work for pharmacists, it also helps them become better practitioners. Almost surely, it will lead to better health care for consumers.

In an effort to provide you with a complete compendium of career options as well as some insights into career planning, we have compiled this career guide. To do so, we turned to the profession.

In cooperation with several professional societies, we contacted successful pharmacists in nearly every practice area. We asked these professionals to describe their own careers, to tell how they got started, what they do on the job, what they envision for the future, and what they would do differently if they could start over again. The result is a practical guide that is intended to provide a perspective on the opportunities in contemporary pharmacy. But it's only a beginning.

After reading and reflecting on the articles in this book, students should discuss appealing career options with experts at their colleges and in their communities. Additionally, they should take advantage of the contacts and resources that are listed in the directory section of this guide. It might even be valuable to enlist the aid of the dean's office at one's own school in organizing formal career planning discussions. If the cooperation of our contributors is any indication, leading pharmacists in every community are proud of what they do and will be glad to discuss their professional activities with students.

Pfizer is grateful to the many pharmacists and association executives who devoted their time to this project. We join them in wishing you a rewarding career in pharmacy.

Making Career Plans

*Michael W. McKenzie, PhD, is
assistant dean of the College of Pharmacy at the
University of Florida, Gainesville.*

Changes within pharmacy have been dramatic over the past 50 years, and the profession continues to be an exciting and innovative field that provides new roles and opportunities for students who want to serve the health needs of society. The emphasis on drug information, patient education, and consultation services requires pharmacists to continually improve their professional expertise. In order to take full advantage of the opportunities created by these changes, pharmacists need to make wise decisions regarding educational preparedness and continuing education, keeping in mind the mobility and flexibility of career positions.

Career planning can speed the process of achieving your potential in pharmacy. And it should be done carefully because the type of work you do will shape your status and function in society.

Framework for decisions To make wise decisions about a particular career, you must have adequate information. The National Pharmaceutical Council, Inc., publishes a brochure entitled *Career Opportunities for Pharmacists in the Pharmaceutical Industry.* In addition, publications such as this Pfizer guide provide a broad perspective on various careers. The American Association of Colleges of Pharmacy and the American Pharmaceutical Association can provide further career information.

Additional information can be obtained directly from pharmacy faculty, counselors, and pharmacy practitioners. Some pharmacy schools and nearly every university have a career development center. Professional university counselors can provide aptitude tests and can arrange interviews and visits with pharmacy employers. Direct contact with individuals in a particular practice area can yield helpful insights. Attending local, state, regional, and national professional meetings can be another fruitful way to gain insight into pharmacy careers.

Work experience is an ideal way to measure your suitability for a career. But it requires an open mind. Work in one hospital pharmacy, for example, should not be taken as an indicator for all of this diverse practice area. If possible, pharmacy students should seek work experience in different professional settings. Within the limitations of an internship, students can arrange to work in both community and hospital pharmacy settings. Some boards of pharmacy allow internship credit through work experience. The National Pharmaceutical Council coordinates such a program for students interested in working in the pharmaceutical industry.

Once you have been introduced to one or more pharmacy careers, it would behoove you to assess your options from several viewpoints. A variety of factors should be examined, including an assessment of your own interests, aptitude, temperament, and expectations for working conditions, earnings, physical activities, and hours of work or travel. You should also learn what education and experience credentials are necessary for certain positions.

Assessing your interests Your career interests can be categorized into six sets of job-related activities:

Realistic   You prefer physical activities and projects to socializing. You seek concrete solutions to problems by trying out various possibilities. You avoid situations that involve a lot of discussion with other people, and you usually want to go beyond working out a problem in theory; you want to see your solutions work.

Investigative   You like to analyze situations and work with ideas to find concrete solutions. You prefer to work on your own and do not enjoy persuading others to accept your ideas.

Social   You enjoy being helpful and working in jobs that directly affect other people. You work and socialize well with others. Whenever possible, you avoid physical work.

Enterprising   You live to sell products and ideas. You want power, prestige, and high status. You have good language skills, and you like using them to control and influence others.

Artistic   You enjoy art, music, and literary activities. You usually show emotion more easily than other people, and you avoid rules and rigid situations.

Conventional   You feel comfortable working with details in structured situations. You want things neat and organized. You like working with forms, charts, and reports. You are self-controlled, and you identify strongly with status, authority, and power.

With these characteristics in mind, you can consider how a specific career would match your interests. If your interests include selling products, trying to convince people of the value of certain items, talking with people on the telephone, making appointments and arranging details, you are "enterprising" and may want to investigate career opportunities as a pharmaceutical company representative. If, as another example, you like to avoid a regimented routine, you may be happiest running your own business.

Factors that deserve a great deal of consideration before settling on a job include working conditions, earnings, hours of work/travel, and physical activities.

Working conditions have to do with the physical environment in which you perform your job. They can be critical factors in your future success. For example, even if you have the skills and knowledge to perform in the research laboratory, you may become dissatisfied if working conditions subvert your need to help patients directly.

Earnings Economic compensation for work is a strong motivating factor in career selection. For example, if income is a high priority and you enjoy being your own boss, then you might shape your goals toward ownership of a pharmacy operation or toward a position of authority within a company.

But income should not be the only basis for career decisions. Other factors are no less important in providing a balanced approach to the choice of a career. In fact, the most meaningful criteria are those relating to your own achievements. The opportunity to render professional help to those who need it is the true measure of success for many pharmacists.

Hours of work/travel Patterns of working hours or travel could cause job dissatisfaction. Night or weekend work may affect your lifestyle because such a schedule can be incompatible with family life. Some positions may require more than 40 hours of work each week. On the other hand, the opportunity to work more hours may be an advantage to some individuals. While the traveling that accompanies work as a pharmaceutical representative or a clinical research monitor for a pharmaceutical company may be exciting to some pharmacists, it can become a burden for others.

Physical activities Certain job activities may influence your choice of a career. Standing for long periods of time or sitting at a desk all day may take the pleasure out of an otherwise promising job. Some employees feel frustrated if their work fails to allow freedom of movement in their daily activities. Your comfort in making oral presentations is another factor that deserves consideration, especially if you are interested in teaching or in an administrative position.

Education Preparation for a career in pharmacy begins in the undergraduate curriculum. As a student, you can begin now to shape your future by selecting appropriate elective coursework. If you are interested in hospital pharmacy, sign up for courses in drug delivery systems, quality assurance, sterile products, and drug information retrieval. An early focus may prove helpful in preparing for this specialized practice environment.

Some curricula offer formally differentiated practice options such as community pharmacy practice, institutional pharmacy practice, advanced clinical pharmacy practice, nuclear pharmacy practice, and careers in research and industry. These options have designated electives in the didactic and clerkship courses that help a student enter the profession with a higher level of educational preparedness than the core curriculum provides.

Many jobs demand education and experience beyond the scope of an undergraduate curriculum. Even if advanced work is not required, the competition for such jobs may make your investment of time and money a wise one. Specialty residencies or fellowships are ways to gain advanced preparation.

Specialty training can be obtained in various areas of health care. The American Society of Hospital Pharmacists offers a residency in traditional hospital pharmacy. Similar programs include clinical pharmacy and specialized clinical residencies. Community pharmacy residencies have been developed by the American College of Apothecaries and the American Pharmaceutical Association. These – as well as specialty clinical residencies that are offered through hospital pharmacies and schools of pharmacy – allow graduates to obtain specific experience while improving their educational credentials for advanced positions. To compete for these residencies, students should perform at a distinguished academic level as undergraduates.

Further preparation can be obtained through fellowships in a school of pharmacy, hospital pharmacy, government organization, or pharmaceutical company. Fellowship training can enhance pharmacists' research credentials. It can also increase their appeal as applicants for jobs in academia and industry.

A student who fulfills the academic requirements of a doctor of pharmacy program, a residency, and a fellowship has laid a solid foundation for work as a clinical scientist. A pharmacist who earns a PhD in the pharmaceutical or medical sciences and completes a clinically oriented residency or fellowship and also meets the educational and experience requisites for a clinical science career is well on the way to success.

A third way to become a clinical scientist is by completing both PharmD and PhD programs. For people with this background, a postgraduate fellowship in research caps a set of excellent credentials for work in academia or the pharmaceutical industry.

Certificate programs are another way to gain the qualifications needed for specialty practice. Such programs in nuclear pharmacy, nutrition, and consultant pharmacy usually allow pharmacists to develop specialty skills and abilities within one year or less. This reduces the time investment required by formal degree programs.

Outstanding students interested in advanced positions in academia, industry, and administration should seriously consider pursuing graduate-level preparation. A variety of graduate programs are available.

The PhD is the highest degree available for researchers. In hospital pharmacy, an MS is the terminal degree. Multiple advanced degrees, even if they center on other fields, provide impressive credentials. A pharmacist with a JD, MBA, or MPH will likely be well rewarded by employers.

The purpose of advanced education is to provide the necessary knowledge and experience to perform scientific jobs in pharmacy. For that reason, students are wise to investigate prerequisite course work before making commitments. Career expectations should be reviewed with experts in a given field. Discussions with a director of a hospital pharmacy, a pharmaceutical corporation executive, or an academic specialist will provide insights into the realities of a prospective career. This kind of exploration will also clarify the commitment and preparation required for success. An early assessment of your desire for advanced training will let you begin tailoring educational courses and experience to the requirements of your future. The investment in advanced training should be weighed in the context of a 40- to 50-year professional career. If financial resources and other circumstances permit you to seek advanced training, the added preparation will likely pay dividends in career and personal satisfaction.

Future prospects The delivery of health care is constantly changing in America. Decisions about health issues, whether they're made by legislatures, governmental agencies, boards of pharmacy, local and national health care organizations, or private industry, will affect your career. Consequently, you must stay informed about these issues by taking an active part in professional organizations. As you plan for a job, you must weigh developments that will affect pharmacy in the future.

Preventive care, home care, and managed care are a few issues that define pharmacists' roles in society. Pharmacists in community practice may be called on to provide more preventive services in the future. The resulting responsibility may require some pharmacists to hone their skills by seeking additional clinical training.

Pharmacists should not be satisfied with employment that minimizes professional services and casts them only in technical roles. The absence of opportunity to apply your comprehensive knowledge and skills will result in disillusionment and frustration. Cultivate every opportunity to create change and to expand your professional services. Stick to your goals and continually evaluate your progress toward them. If you don't find satisfaction in one job, move to another, even if the salary is lower. Daniel Hussar, Remmington Professor of Pharmacy at the Philadelphia College of Pharmacy and Science said:

"Pharmacists should strive for excellence in each of their responsibilities. Although some might suggest that the realities of practice force them to compromise their professional ideals and values, they should endeavor to make changes that will permit them to practice at the highest professional level."

Career plans Both short-term and long-term career planning is recommended. A short-term career plan may cover a two- to five-year period. When making a plan for the near future, you should review such factors as type of work, responsibilities, work environment, earnings, requirements for continuing education, potential for advanced training, possibilities for promotion, job relocation, and type of community.

Covering from 10 to 20 years, a long-term career plan should focus on steps required to reach your highest goals. You must establish these goals thoughtfully and lay this plan with great care. Be realistic about your talents, opportunities for advancement, costs, and the effect of your ambition on family and personal life. Never aim low.

Most people underestimate their abilities. Within the above limitations, try to establish a goal that meets your personal needs while providing rewards for your family and for society at large.

When planning a pharmacy career you may be surprised to learn that job changes are common. It is not unusual for a pharmacist to have had five or more jobs within a 30- to 40-year period. A pharmacist may start out working in both community and hospital pharmacy environments and then select a pharmacy residency. Furthermore, it wouldn't be unusual for such a professional to obtain further education in preparation for a better job or for a position in another practice area.

Summary Ten important points to keep in mind when considering a pharmacy career:

- Prioritize your interests, aptitude, and temperament for specific career positions.
- Obtain professional guidance through counselors.
- Seek interviews with pharmacists and employers of pharmacists.
- Attend local and national pharmacy meetings if possible.
- Use the resources of professional societies.
- Outline long- and short-range career goals.
- Gain necessary professional experience via an internship.
- Obtain necessary credentials through residencies, fellowships, or graduate school.
- Assess the need for continuing education.
- Evaluate your options in terms of personal, family, and professional considerations.

The Job Search

Avis J. Ericson, PharmD, is
associate professor of clinical pharmacy and
director for the division of clinical
pharmacy at the St. Louis College
of Pharmacy, Missouri.

You're a short-timer. Dreams of that first job, a real paycheck, a new apartment, and a life to call your own run through your consciousness with increasing frequency. You're almost there.

Making the transition from the classroom to the work world creates high expectations – and anxiety too – for most of us. Our self-confidence sometimes gives way to questions such as: How do I launch my great career? Where do I find the right job? What if no one hires me? What will the competition be like? What do I really want to do with my life? How do I chart a course to the top?

You have invested five or more years in the training necessary to graduate from pharmacy school. It is only logical that a reasonable amount of time should now be invested in marketing yourself. In most instances, the right job doesn't just drop into the job-seeker's lap. It takes organization, planning, and hard work to land that ideal position.

Three key elements will help make your job search go smoothly and successfully: the curriculum vitae, the job search, and the interview.

The curriculum vitae The curriculum vitae (CV) outlines who you are, what you've accomplished, and what you hope to achieve. It introduces you to strangers who will use it to evaluate your suitability for a job. Rarely will your CV alone produce a job offer. Instead, it is a tool used for screening purposes. If the specific job requirements and your experience or aspirations match, an interview may be the next step. The interview is where most hiring decisions are made.

Creating your first CV is not a difficult task, but it should be done with care. The process is usually time-consuming. As well as you know yourself, it is still difficult to put yourself "on paper" in a concise and professional manner. Outlined below are several suggestions to consider for your CV. Many books and articles have been written on the "proper" way to create your CV. But even experts disagree on the best format or approach. Your CV should reflect you as an individual. Nevertheless, it is advisable to stay within commonly accepted guidelines.

Suggestions for an effective CV
- Keep it short. One page is best; two are recommended as the maximum.

- Be accurate. Check names, titles, dates, and all other data.
- Typing must be error free.
- Type should be clear and reproductions clean. A professional typist, offset printing, or professional reproductions may be worth the cost.
- Information should be balanced on the page. Be sure information is not crowded at the top or to one side. Information should flow smoothly over the page and spaced to make individual items easy to find at a glance.
- Choice of paper should reflect substance and quality. Use a good $8\frac{1}{2}$" x 11" bond paper. The same paper with matching envelopes may be used for your accompanying cover letter.
- Avoid abbreviations or jargon. Make sure your information is understandable.
- Quantify information about your job experiences. Such words as *managed*, *increased productivity*, *saved*, or *reduced* speak precisely of your accomplishments. Short, concise phrases using action verbs are preferred over long-winded job descriptions.
- Show consistency in the data as well as in the way you present them. If possible, avoid time gaps, but be prepared to account for gaps that occur. Some experts say dates should be in reverse-chronological order with most recent education, experience, publication, or presentation at the head of the list. Whether you use chronological or reverse-chronological order, it is important to be consistent throughout the document.
- Proofread and critique your CV at all stages of preparation. It will be useful to have a colleague or teacher assist in this process.
- Retain a "work copy" of your CV. A monthly review will allow you to update it easily. This may also remind you of your stated goals.
- In such fields as academia, consulting, or industry, it is wise to keep a detailed listing of all professional meetings attended, lectures and presentations made, and special projects attempted and completed. In time, these lists will become too cumbersome for the main body of your CV. Separate lists can be included with the CV when required.

The job search The world is waiting for you, but just where do you begin to search for the job of your dreams? There are many sources of information about potential jobs:

- friends, classmates, colleagues
- past employers and their associates
- college faculty and contacts made during externship and clerkship assignments
- school, professional, and commercial placement services
- contacts at local, state, and national professional meetings
- contacts within the pharmaceutical industry

- campus career days
- advertisements in professional journals or newsletters and local newspapers
- job agencies and professional placement companies

The best jobs seem to be found through word of mouth or personal contacts rather than through advertisements. The frequency of this observation should lead you to create and maintain a network of professional contacts. For that reason, attend local, state, and national professional meetings; maintain connections with school and fraternity alumni programs; and take time to cultivate contacts outside your immediate circle of acquaintances.

Once a possible position is located, you must contact the potential employer. The most professional way to do this is by sending your CV with a brief cover letter. Telephone calls and drop-in visits run the risk of intruding on your potential employer at an inconvenient time. Besides, it seems only fair to let an employer review your credentials before making direct contact. That will help set the stage for a productive interview.

Your cover letter should be brief and to the point. A lengthy rehash of your CV is unnecessary. Use this letter to highlight areas where the job you want matches areas of your expertise and experience. Include a paragraph that explains your professional goals. This is especially useful if your CV does not contain a formal goals statement.

Letters should be addressed to the name of the director or manager, not blindly to "Dear Sir." The *Hayes Directory* lists pharmacies in alphabetical order by state and shows the name of the manager or owner. With only a small amount of research, you can find the name and title of the person who will be responsible for hiring you. Be absolutely sure to get the spelling of this name and title correct.

Your letter's tone should be businesslike and polite. It must be well typed and error free. Some employers consider it in bad taste to use a letterhead from one institution when applying for work in another. Plain bond paper is always in good taste.

In closing the letter, indicate your willingness to come in for an interview or to meet for preliminary discussions. The employer should sense that you are truly interested in the position and will go an extra mile to prove you are the right person for the job.

The interim Patience is an important virtue while waiting for a first job contact to turn into an interview. If communication takes place by mail, allow at least 10 days before initiating follow-up. Hopefully, your application will have been acknowledged by return mail or phone. At the least, you can be certain it has arrived. If you remain interested in a position despite lack of acknowledgement, a follow-up letter can be sent or contact made by phone. In either case, the tone of the contact should be polite and inquiring, not demanding or belligerent.

The day will come when you are invited to an interview. When it does,

be sure you understand the ground rules:
- date, time, and exact location
- length of the interview (an hour or all day?)
- whether you will be required to make a presentation
- whether application forms must be completed in advance

Policies vary as to whether interview expenses are reimbursed in part, in full, or not at all. Generally, a larger company or institution inviting you for a full day or more of interviews that require travel and hotel accommodations will pay for most or all of the expenses. Shorter interviews occurring in your hometown or within reasonable driving distance may not be compensated. Meals that occur as part of the interview day are usually paid for by the host. It is always wise, however, to be prepared with enough spare cash to alleviate an awkward situation.

Airline tickets and hotel accommodations are best paid for by credit card. Many hotels will require cash in advance if a major credit card cannot be used to guarantee the stay. The time lag between charge and actual billing will provide a reasonable cushion to allow major expenses to be reimbursed by your interviewer. Submission of such bills should be prompt to ensure rapid reimbursement. Some companies may allow you to bill them directly for expenses.

It is wise to maintain an accurate record of all interview expenses. This will streamline the reimbursement process and provide you with accurate records of unreimbursed expenses. The costs of CV preparation and mailing as well as relocation expenses may also be tax deductible. Keep your receipts in addition to a list of unreceipted expenses.

As interview day approaches, you will want to prepare yourself both physically and psychologically. Allow time to address the items highlighted below. Take time to talk with your peers and associates who are well seasoned in job market strategy. Talking through your concerns and doing a "dry-run" interview in the presence of supportive friends will help ease your anxiety.

The interview This process can be traumatic – especially if you are not prepared. Follow these tips to ensure a smooth experience:
- Be prepared. Know the job that you are interviewing for. A job description should be made available, preferably in advance. Study this document. Be sure you understand it. If certain tasks are unfamiliar to you, inquire about on-the-job training. Know who your immediate supervisor will be, and be sure that duties are reviewed and understood while the interview is in progress.
- The interview is a two-way street. It is important that both interviewer and applicant learn as much as possible about each other. Your CV was screened and caused you to be given an interview. The company may also be checking your references and previous employers. As an applicant, you also need to do some preparation. Check on the company, its people, products, and reputation. Be

prepared to ask questions that demonstrate your interest in the job and your knowledge of the company.

- Realize that the interview process is a marketing opportunity. You are selling yourself and your skills to a potential employer. The interview puts you on stage. Be ready to sell your capabilities and your capacity for future achievements. First impressions are extremely important in this high-stakes marketing game. The first few minutes of the interview are crucial in establishing your credibility and visibility as a future employee.
- Be prompt. Allow time to arrive at the interview and find its exact location. Cutting your time to the minimum heightens anxieties at an already anxious time. Arriving early lets you observe the general surroundings and gives you time to collect your thoughts.
- Be well dressed and well groomed. Neat, businesslike attire creates the best possible impression. Flashy clothes or too much jewelry or makeup do not inspire confidence in one's professionalism. Employers look for evidence of dependability, responsibility, and professionalism; the perception of those attributes can be enhanced by the clothes you wear.
- Maintain a positive, open-minded attitude. The duration of an interview can range from less than one hour to more than a day of intense meetings, depending on the position. It can be difficult to keep your enthusiasm level high as time wears on, but this is your principal chance to make a positive impression. Approach each new interviewer in a fresh manner.
- A firm handshake and friendly smile help set a positive tone.
- Relax and let your natural friendliness shine through.
- Maintain eye contact during the interview.
- Body language can speak volumes; be sure that your own gestures and stance reflect interest, enthusiasm, and self-confidence.
- The courtesy of saying please and thank you, and of waiting to be asked to sit are also standard expectations. Distractions may occur in the course of your interview. Wait quietly and politely until the event is over and then be ready to continue where you left off. A brief recap of the interrupted conversation may help things move smoothly back to the main flow of conversation.

The interview usually unfolds as a series of questions. Anticipating them in advance will help you answer them with confidence and in a manner that doesn't require much on-the-spot thinking. Traditional questions include:

- How would you describe yourself?
- Why have you applied for this position?
- What are your plans for the next 5, 10, or 20 years?
- What is your biggest fault?
- How do you plan to achieve your career goals?

- Why did you leave your previous position?
- What were your biggest frustrations in previous positions?
- What did you particularly like or dislike about school (or a job)?
- Why did you choose pharmacy?
- What motivates you?
- What do you think you can contribute to this company?

Practice answering these questions with a friend who can critique your answers and coach your responses. Know the points you want to make and be ready to expand on each answer with concrete examples if asked. These questions are important to your career decisions; they are not intended to be an aggravating exercise just for the interview process. Your answers will reflect your overall career plan.

If you do not understand a question, ask for clarification before attempting an answer. Never lie, exaggerate, or try to fake an answer – it's too easy for an experienced interviewer to spot such maneuvers, which may cause you to lose your credibility and the job prospect as well.

Be prepared. Expect the unexpected, and be ready to think quickly. A surprise question may be tactfully considered and even put off for later in the conversation if you need time to ponder. An honest "I don't know," or "I'm not sure, but I could find out" can also serve to avert an unexpected question.

Interviewers can be informal and conversational, they may prefer a highly structured interview with a laundry list of questions, or they may decide to conduct a "stress interview" to see how well you respond.

Some questions are difficult to answer without seeming to put yourself at a disadvantage. Questions that probe your weaknesses or your reasons for leaving other positions will probably make you feel uncomfortable. Seasoned professionals can turn such apparent weaknesses into strengths. We've all been in bad situations or made mistakes. Emphasizing what we have learned from such experiences is better than dwelling on the negative side. In reality, job changes may reflect a move toward challenges and opportunities rather than a move away from less-than-ideal conditions. It serves no purpose to be harshly negative about previous employers or experiences. Your answers should reflect ambition, drive, maturity, and sincerity combined with the ability to pull the best out of a bad situation.

Some areas of questioning are generally avoided during an interview. Topics that touch on a person's politics, religion, sex, marital status, children, and occupation of spouse, for example, are not appropriate and may be illegal. Politely decline to answer or deflect such questions.

Issues of salary, starting date, vacation time, health and life insurance, retirement packages, and other fringe benefits may be made known to you in one of three main ways:

- Information is given before the interview takes place. Salary may be mentioned in the job description. Information on other benefits may be sent along with a job application form to be reviewed before the interview day.

- These details may be handled only by a personnel department. A meeting may be scheduled for you with a member of that department when you have reached the stage of serious consideration.
- Negotiations are handled by the pharmacy director or manager but are not discussed with you until a preliminary decision has been made about your suitability for the position.

In all cases, the interviewer should be the first to broach these topics. If that does not happen, the applicant may request, in a general way, information about the benefits package. That may prompt discussions that reveal salary information.

Once an interview draws to a close, make sure you have answers to the following questions:

- What will be the next step?
- When will a decision be made?
- Should you call the company, or when can you expect to hear from the interviewer or the personnel department?

All interviews should end on a courteous, businesslike note. Thank-yous, both at the close of the interview and in a follow-up letter will make a good impression. If it is clear that the position is not for you, it is appropriate to politely ask that your name be removed from future con-sideration for the position. This is most easily done in the follow-up letter.

There are two final points to be kept in mind as you proceed through the maze of interviews:

- An interview may be scheduled to last from 2 to 3 PM. In reality, the interview is in progress as long as you interact with, or are even casually observed by, someone related to the position in question. A bit of discretion and a mature professional attitude may be vital in keeping your job prospects alive before and after the actual interview. This can be especially true for interviews conducted at a national professional meeting. Opportunities for chance observa-tions in convention sessions, hospitality suites, or just around the town are not uncommon.
- The pharmacy community remains a tight network of individuals with far-reaching loyalty. Such relationships are often not readily apparent to the casual observer who may feel that there are no common threads to be found between individuals who live and work thousands of miles apart. By contrast, however, it is amazing when you finally realize the ties that do exist among faculty at the various schools, pharmacy directors and managers of large and small insti-tutions and enterprises, and even staff people. Exploring the family tree of "Who went to school together," "Who has previously worked together," or "Who regularly attends major conventions together" would produce a web of connections easily disregarded if you look only at geography. The network exists, and it can be an invaluable

source of information and contacts.

Suggested reading

American Society of Hospital Pharmacists – Personnel Placement Services materials: "The Interview," "Important Skills In Interviewing," and "What Can and Cannot Be Asked During a Job Interview."

Angel JL: *The Complete Resume Book and Job Getters Guide.* New York, Pocket Books, 1980.

Bolles R: *What Color Is Your Parachute?* Berkeley, Calif., Ten Speed Press, 1984.

Enright SM, Enright SJ: Tips for making the job search productive and enjoyable. *Am J Hosp Pharm.* 41:924-7, May 1984.

Eolis W: *How to Write Acceptable Resumes: For Professionals and Executives.*

Lathrop R: *Who's Hiring Who?*

Mackowiak J, Eckel F: Career management: An active process. *Am J Hosp Pharm.* 42:554-60, March 1985.

Mackowiak J, Eckel F: Career management: An ongoing process. *Am J Hosp Pharm.* 42:1058-62, May 1985.

Mackowiak J, Eckel F: Career management: Understanding the process. *Am J Hosp Pharm.* 42:297-303, February 1985.

Marketing Yourself: The Catalyst Guide to Successful Interviews and Resumes. New York, Bantam Books, 1981.

Mathis PK: Prohibited employee interview questions. *Am J Hosp Pharm.* 41:443-4, 1984.

Medley HA: *Sweaty Palms: The Neglected Art of Being Interviewed.* Belmont, Calif., Lifetime Learning Publications, 1978.

Poteet GW: The employment interview: Avoiding discriminatory questioning. *J Nurs Admin.* 14:38-42, April 1984.

Siecker B: After graduation: Tips on getting that first job. *Tomorrow's Pharmacist.*

White SJ: Recruiting, interviewing, and hiring pharmacy personnel. *Am J Hosp Pharm.* 41:928-934, May 1984.

Careers in Independent Pharmacy

Charles M. West, PD,
is executive vice president of NARD: Representing
Independent Retail Pharmacy.

There are a number of different places where pharmacists practice their profession, including hospitals, chain drugstores, drug manufacturers, and government agencies. However, one of the most professionally and financially rewarding ways to practice pharmacy is in an independent pharmacy.

An independent drugstore is the place that most often comes to mind when we think about the practice of pharmacy – a neighborhood drugstore with its helpful and trusted pharmacist. Frequently, the pharmacist a patient sees in an independent pharmacy is the owner.

The key word is *independent*. Pharmacists who choose to practice in this setting are uniquely able to practice their profession in the ways they choose. They are able to respond quickly to changing consumer needs and to have a real and lasting impact in the communities they serve. No other practice setting gives pharmacists the dual opportunity to interact with patients every day and to decide for themselves how they will practice their profession.

That kind of independence has spawned great diversity. Some independent pharmacies are large and offer consumers a wide range of products. Others center their efforts almost exclusively on prescription and over-the-counter drugs and health care products. Many independents have branched out to provide home care products and services to meet the pharmacy needs of nursing homes, hospices, and even small hospitals. Some provide home oxygen therapy and high-tech home infusion therapy. The opportunities to offer specialized pharmacy services are expanding, and independents are especially well positioned to fill these emerging niches in health care.

Independent pharmacy is a powerful economic force:

- With 44,000 stores, 70 percent of the nation's retail pharmacies are independents.
- Each day, the nation's independent pharmacies serve 18 million patients.
- Independent retail pharmacies have total sales of nearly $45 billion per year.
- The typical independent pharmacy dispenses 102 prescriptions per day – nearly 33,000 new and renewed prescriptions per year.
- The typical independent pharmacist makes nearly 4,000 over-the-

counter drug recommendations each year.
- Independent pharmacy owners, on average, own 1.5 pharmacies.
- Independent pharmacists are community leaders and are actively involved in health, civic, and volunteer projects. Many hold local elected offices; others are members of state legislatures.

Independent pharmacists offer a variety of health care products and high levels of customer service:
- A survey found that nearly 60 percent of consumers who patronize independent pharmacies agree with the statement "The pharmacist knows me and my family." For pharmacists in other retail settings, the figure was 22 percent. In the same survey, seniors reported that their independent pharmacist was more than four times as likely as other retail pharmacists to speak to them personally and to give them professional advice.
- Another survey of consumers in all age groups found that independents provide face-to-face prescription drug counseling twice as often as other retail pharmacists.
- More than 77 percent of independents provide home health care pharmacy services, and more than 44 percent dispense prescriptions and consult in long-term care facilities. In fact, independents are the major providers of pharmacy services to the nation's nursing homes.
- More than 98 percent of independent pharmacists counsel their patients directly.
- In a typical day, an independent pharmacist has conversations with 23 physicians and spends nearly two hours counseling patients.
- 74 percent provide health screening products.
- 89 percent make home deliveries.
- 78 percent provide 24-hour emergency services.

Independent pharmacy contains extraordinary opportunities for professional fulfillment and economic prosperity. For example, in 1991, the average independent pharmacy had sales of more than $1 million, and the average owner earned $88,050. Most important, as business owners, independent pharmacists are able to expand their operations, open new locations, and diversify into related fields as they see fit.

Many independent owners enter partnership agreements with young staff pharmacists, allowing them to build an ownership stake and, eventually, assume full ownership of the pharmacy. Only independent pharmacy can provide such career opportunities.

Perhaps best of all, independent pharmacy lets its practitioners apply their specialized knowledge as intensely as they choose. Indeed, owning your own pharmacy will challenge all your skills, because you alone will decide where you will work, what your pharmacy will look like, and what services you will provide – because it's your pharmacy.

If you're ready to explore a career in independent pharmacy, there are many places to go for help. For example, local, state, and national pharmacy associations will provide valuable information and contacts that can help you learn more about independent pharmacy.

NARD is a national association that exclusively represents the professional and proprietary interests of the independent retail pharmacist. NARD can give you up-to-date professional information on pharmacy locations, financing, and management. In addition, NARD has programs that help pharmacists find career opportunities in independent practices.

This association has a special membership category for students interested in learning more about independent pharmacy practice. For a membership application and more information, write NARD, Student Outreach Program, 205 Daingerfield Road, Alexandria, VA 22314.

The NARD Foundation, a not-for-profit organization that is committed to the growth of independent pharmacy, also is dedicated to helping pharmacists pursue careers in independent practice.

Organized in 1953 to honor John W. Dargavel, executive secretary of NARD from 1933 to 1961, the foundation was established to make low-interest loans to pharmacy students, to help pharmacy owners in times of business catastrophe, and to promote the interests of independent pharmacy through educational programs and other activities.

Today, the NARD Foundation's student loan program is the most successful of its kind. Since its inception, it has provided more than $4 million to support the education of future pharmacists. Moreover, the foundation has a scholarship program and a grant award program for pharmacy students to conduct research projects and develop manuscripts related to independent pharmacy. These programs demonstrate the foundation's commitment to the future of independent pharmacy.

Students who are interested in a career in pharmacy and would like to have more information on the student loan, scholarship, and research grant programs should contact the NARD Foundation, 205 Daingerfield Road, Alexandria, VA 22314.

Independent pharmacy has a strong tradition of being highly responsive to the changing needs of patients. The flexibility ownership affords enables independent pharmacists quickly to modernize and broaden the scope of their practices in order to take advantage of innovations in health care delivery.

The aging of America's population has resulted in greater use of prescription drugs than ever before. And the fact that many elderly people take multiple medications requires face-to-face counseling and regular monitoring by their neighborhood pharmacist.

A high level of patient services has always enabled independents to maintain a loyal patient base. Now, many independents are expanding their practices to accommodate the demand for more specialized services, including home health care products and services, hospice care, home infusion therapy, and nursing home pharmacy services.

All of these services are broadening the scope of independent pharmacists' role in patient care. At the same time, they are challenging pharmacists to expand their expertise. In addition to enhancing the quality of patient care, this trend is raising the earning potential in independent pharmacy.

If you aspire to build your own pharmacy practice, if you want to decide for yourself how to apply your education in caring for patients, and if you want to make a real difference in your community, a career in independent pharmacy offers great professional satisfaction. NARD will be pleased to help make it a reality.

Joseph A. Mosso, PS,
is president of Mosso's Pharmacy
in Latrobe, Pennsylvania.

Owning Your Own Pharmacy

Through ownership, pharmacists can enjoy a level of professional freedom that does not exist in other practice settings and an income that is limited only by their abilities and willingness to work to achieve their goals. Ownership allows pharmacists to reap the benefits of their hard work, while making significant contributions to the health of their patients.

Students and young pharmacists often believe that establishing or buying a pharmacy is an unrealistic objective in today's competitive environment. Industry data indicate otherwise. There are now 44,000 independent pharmacies in the United States, and these operations set the standard for community pharmacy practice. Only as an independent will you have the opportunity to be your own boss, counsel patients as you were trained to do, and explore a wide range of professional opportunities.

A new generation of independent pharmacy entrepreneurs is facing the challenges of today's business climate. Most say they plan to buy or open more pharmacies in the future.

The focused nature of retail pharmacy makes establishing a new pharmacy less risky than start-up ventures that depend on new products or services. Even so, ownership isn't for everyone. The independent pharmacy owner must be able to set standards, communicate well, handle unstructured or poorly defined situations, know how to use limited resources effectively, and be able to organize information and record keeping. Most important, a pharmacist entrepreneur has to possess a high level of motivation and maturity.

Wholesalers are good resources for pharmacists who want to go into business for themselves. Some provide assistance in location analysis, store design, inventory, pricing, and shelf planning, and will help the prospective owner develop marketing approaches targeted to the demographics of a particular market. A wholesaler also may offer programs in clerk training, computerization, and security.

Opportunities to buy an established pharmacy abound in almost every state, and the number is expected to rise steadily throughout the 1990s.

Many independent pharmacists are nearing retirement age. At the same time, most young pharmacists are embarking on careers in chains and hospitals. The net result is that a steady supply of independent pharmacies are for sale.

Professors who teach courses in ownership engage in a continuing debate over whether it's better to start a new pharmacy or buy an existing one. Most independent pharmacists have their own opinion on the subject as well. Usually, it's biased toward the route they followed into business for themselves.

In general, buying an existing pharmacy is the more expensive course because in addition to buying fixed assets, the purchaser pays for a store's customer base under the heading of good will. On the other hand, an established, strong customer base – even though it may be costly – reduces start-up risks. The new owner must be careful not to make changes that upset customer relationships the previous owner spent years building.

While there are several ways to arrive at a realistic price, most selling prices are based on a reevaluation of the book value of the assets or on a multiplier of the earning potential. In most cases, a final price is reached through negotiations regarding the pharmacy's potential to make money, which, in turn, affects the new owners' estimated return on investment.

Price also can be affected by how much of the deal the seller is willing to finance and how quickly payback is required. Typically, a buyer can structure a five- to 10-year loan with a previous owner.

Some pharmacy graduates never even consider independent pharmacy as a career because they believe that buying a pharmacy requires a great deal of capital. It doesn't. Many recent graduates have become full or part owners of a pharmacy without having to put any money down.

The buy-out process, also known as a junior partnership, gives younger pharmacists (or junior partners) the opportunity to purchase a preset percentage of a practice over a certain number of years. This eases the financial burden of buying a pharmacy outright.

In most cases, junior partnerships are structured so that buyers gradually build equity by taking part of their salary in stock. This gives young pharmacists a chance to learn about the business and management sides of retail practice while gradually assuming ownership.

Just as important, junior partnerships also make it possible for the seller to relinquish ownership in an orderly fashion, and a primary benefit of this is that it allows the pharmacy's patients to become accustomed to the new owner. The arrangement also lets older pharmacists continue their practices as independents and perpetuate their legacy.

When most people think about independent retail pharmacy, they visualize a corner drugstore with several aisles of personal-hygiene products, convenience items, and cards and gifts that lead to the rear of the pharmacy, where a friendly, easy-going pharmacist is working behind the prescription counter.

Only part of that image still is accurate. Yes, independent pharmacists still enjoy talking with and counseling their patients, many of whom they know by name. And, yes, patients still can stock up on health and beauty aids and over-the-counter medicines while having a prescription dispensed.

But the graying of America and a shift in the delivery of health care from institutional settings to patients' homes have dramatically expanded the opportunities independent pharmacists have to become more directly involved in patient care. Today, independents offer specialized services that are redefining their role on the health care team. In fact, 77 percent of independent pharmacies currently provide some form of health care services.

In 1984, NARD became the first pharmacy association to establish a department of home health care service. Recently, the association expanded its commitment to independents by launching a separate division of Home Health Care Pharmacy Services.

The home care market is currently estimated at $12 billion and is growing by approximately 10 percent each year. Today's independents offer a wide range of home care services, including home infusion therapy, durable medical equipment, orthotic and prosthetic supplies, ostomy and wound care, respiratory therapy, and convalescent aids. The $4.3 billion home infusion industry, one of pharmacy's fastest-growing specialty areas, is expected to double in size by 1996. In fact, independents are the primary providers of home infusion services in this nation. The National Home Infusion Association, which was created by NARD in 1991, is dedicated to ensuring educational programs, marketing opportunities, and legislative and regulatory representation for this growing specialty.

An increasing number of independents – 44 percent of NARD members – have built highly successful practices providing prescription services to nursing homes and consulting on the patients' drug regimens. Because of continuing growth in this area, NARD recently established a division of long-term care pharmacy services.

Still other independents have returned to pharmacy's roots by establishing themselves as specialists in compounding.

All of these specialty practices require a great deal of clinical expertise and one-on-one patient contact, both of which produce significant rewards. In a real sense, these independent pharmacy specialists and entrepreneurs are pushing the boundaries of our profession and preparing us to accept the challenge of the 21st century.

John R. Carson, PD,
is owner and president of
Oakdell Pharmacy Inc.,
Home Intensive Care Pharmacy Inc.,
and Southwest Ostomy Supply Inc.,
in San Antonio, Texas.

The Home Care Pharmacist

Pharmacy runs in my family: I have four uncles and two cousins who were independent pharmacists, and I always knew I would have my own store some day. There was never any question about what my career would be. However, when I graduated from pharmacy school in 1964, who could have predicted that I would eventually own four retail pharmacies, a long-term care pharmacy, a home health care agency, and an ostomy supply business?

Home health care, which is central to all of my businesses, encompasses drugs, supplies, and services needed by patients in their own homes. Compared with hospitalization, home health care has many advantages. First, it's cheaper to care for a patient at home than in the hospital. For that reason, insurance companies prefer home care when it is a viable alternative. In addition, patients usually do better at home than in the hospital because their families are close at hand and they are happier. This tends to speed their recovery.

Home care became a viable industry in the late 1960s and early 1970s when Medicare began to reimburse for the cost of durable medical equipment. Since then, the industry has been government driven – the market expands when the government decides to provide reimbursement for a particular service or product. Because patients are being sent home "quicker and sicker" these days, there is a great need for our services. Also, more and more terminally ill patients are being treated at home, and many need pain management. Under certain circumstances, even chemo-therapy can be provided in the home.

The growth of my own practice has been steady since I opened my first community pharmacy in 1969. One of the first steps I took was to expand into long-term care by providing consultation to nursing home facilities and small hospitals. Since then, I have maintained a fairly large long-term care division.

In 1970, my pharmacy was the first in San Antonio to go into the ostomy supply business. For years, we were the largest ostomy-products dealer in Texas, and this part of the practice is still successful. Until an intra-stromal therapist moved to San Antonio, we did all of our ostomy fittings on patients in area hospitals.

In 1971, we were one of the first pharmacies in the area to make durable medical equipment (DME) available to patients in the home. The demand was so great that I operated a separate DME company for many years. Cuts in Medicare reimbursement over the years have had a significant impact on the DME business, and now I no longer operate a separate company. Instead, I provide DME equipment through my retail pharmacies. In 1984, we began offering home IV services.

The only way to get home care business is through referrals. This depends on direct marketing to physicians, hospitals, discharge planners, insurance companies, and other home care providers that don't provide infusion services. Our marketing team is charged with developing a highly professional profile for our companies.

The team's marketing efforts count on our ability to provide comprehensive pharmacy care. I want my business to be known as a home care supermarket. I want physicians to know that we can set up a completely equipped hospital room in a patient's home. We can dispense prescriptions and IVs, and we can provide any necessary supplies. Should professional nursing be needed, we can provide that, too.

The home care pharmacist is directly involved in patient care and works closely with physicians and nurses. In fact, where home infusion therapy is concerned, it is the pharmacist who really manages the patient. It is the pharmacist who assesses the patient's needs and resources, reviews all of the lab reports, and makes recommendations to the physician about therapy.

Here's how it works. A physician, hospital discharge planner, nurse, insurance company, or another home health care agency calls us and asks us to take a case. If it's a complex IV case, the pharmacist will go to the hospital before the patient is discharged and examine the patient's chart. The pharmacist also consults with nurses and the physician in order to verify the dosages and administration schedule.

Once the patient goes home, the pharmacist assesses the environment there to determine how much support the patient can expect from the family and what the patient is able to do independently. If IV services will be needed for an extended period, the pharmacist trains the patient and another family member to manage the IV properly. If the patient does not have adequate family support and cannot manage the IV alone, a nurse is assigned.

Thanks to portable pump technology, some patients can remain ambulatory while receiving infusion therapy. Some even continue to perform their jobs. Every situation is a little bit different, and it's up to the pharmacist to take all the variables into account.

I attribute my success to the philosophy that the patient comes first and deserves the best care possible. We deliver our services in the most professional way possible, and we work hard to project that image. If physicians are confident that we take extremely good care of their patients, we will never want for referrals. To make sure the quality of our work is maintained, I am very selective about the professionals I hire. They have to be exceptionally good "people people."

If you are thinking of going into business for yourself, I suggest that you first gain practical experience as a staff pharmacist in a chain or independent pharmacy. Your professional education will not end when the graduation ceremonies are over, because there are many things left to be learned – business principles and management skills in particular – by working for someone else. There is no better preparation for business success than spending two, three, or even four years in an independent or chain pharmacy. I recommend working in both settings and being less concerned about the paycheck than about what can be learned.

After I graduated from pharmacy school, I worked for a chain for six months and then for an independent for four years before opening my own pharmacy. The independent pharmacist I worked for was the Texas Pharmaceutical Association's Pharmacist of the Year, so I had an excellent role model. In retrospect, I can see that my early experience has kept me from making a lot of mistakes as an entrepreneur. I'm glad that pharmacy schools are now providing more pharmacy administration courses than they did when I went to school. I had to turn to a business school for courses in accounting, marketing, and management.

When you do open your practice, never stop trying to be innovative. Even though pharmacy should remain the hub of your operation, you should send spokes out in various directions. If you aren't afraid to take chances, you will find many opportunities for expansion, whether in the latest biotech innovations, new products or services for home health care, or a support clinic for people with diabetes. Never be reluctant to change, because there is enormous opportunity for independent pharmacists who are willing to try something new.

Donald L. Moore, PD,
is president and owner of Moore Drugs
in Kokomo, Indiana.

Owning a Large Independent Pharmacy

Owning a pharmacy has given me just about all I could have asked for in life. It has provided security for my family and exciting challenges for me. It's also been fun – a lot like coaching a football team, I imagine. I have 36 employees, including four pharmacists, a registered nurse, and a licensed practical nurse. If I train and manage my team properly, it's amazing to watch them develop.

Many pharmacists decided on their careers after being inspired by a kindly old druggist. Not me. I never thought about pharmacy before college, and then I was attracted by the science and the opportunity to work with people that I thought the profession would give me. As a student, I didn't even spend my summers working in drugstores, because I was raising a family and was able to make more money elsewhere.

I knew one thing for certain: I wanted to be my own boss and have my own store. But I was smart enough to realize I needed to get practical experience first. As a result, I went to work for a chain and stayed there for two years.

During the second year, I was promoted to store manager. From a business standpoint, I learned more in that job than I had during all the years I spent at Purdue. I learned principles of merchandising and advertising, and I got invaluable experience in managing people. I don't think I would have been able to succeed in my own store if I hadn't acquired such a foundation first.

One day, a pharmaceutical salesman stopped in to visit. "Say, I hear the Marsh grocery chain is looking for someone to put in a pharmacy next to a new supermarket," he said. My ears perked right up and I knew he was describing an opportunity I had to pursue. A refrigeration salesman who called on my dad knew the Marsh people, and the salesman was able to get me an appointment. Before long, at the ripe age of 25, I was the proud owner of Moore's Rexall Drugs.

I started with 4,800 square feet. Since then, I have worked hard to expand, because it's easier to run a big pharmacy than a small one. After a business reaches a certain size, you can afford a bookkeeper to reconcile the accounts. You can hire a manager to take care of the floor. You can hire other pharmacists to share the work load. In other words, you can start to be more efficient. The owner of a small operation does everything alone – from bookkeeping to bottle washing.

Now, we occupy the entire 12,000-square-foot building that used to house the supermarket. We are active in home care with IV services. We have oxygen and durable medical equipment. We do a great deal of compounding. We also have sundries and sections that sell automotive, electrical, photographic, and plumbing supplies. Our original soda fountain is long gone, but I won't be surprised if it makes a comeback someday. Conceivably, we'd be better off if we concentrated only on professional services, but I enjoy merchandising too much to stop.

I think the handwriting is on the wall for independent pharmacists, and the message is that smaller practices are going to find it more and more difficult to keep their heads above water. Any pharmacy that grosses less than $1,000,000 is going to be hard-pressed, unless it is highly specialized. This means that most pharmacies should have 5,000 to 8,000 square feet.

Especially for independents, retail pharmacy has become a complex business. Even so, a young person today can still do what I did more than 30 years ago. However, I would offer this advice: Take as many electives as you can in business and computer sciences. After graduation, spend a couple of years working for a chain. Then go looking for a good pharmacist who is ready for retirement. Tell him you want to work for him and, eventually, buy his pharmacy. This may be the best way to get started on your own, and it's being done all the time.

NARD is trying to put pharmacists who are interested in owning their own stores together with people who want to sell. The idea is to help pharmacists gradually work their way into ownership by buying a percentage of their pharmacies each year.

Another way to become an owner is to buy a franchise operation, some of which can be financed with only a modest down payment. One more option is to make an arrangement with a local supermarket that wants to put in a drugstore.

If you do become an independent owner, it is safe to predict that you will soon feel pressure from larger operations. Our little town of 48,000 has a Phar-Mor, two Krogers, a Hooks, three Reliables (all with pharmacies), and four independents. A Walmart and two other chains are on the way. The increased competition promises to be very interesting. In order to meet it, we intend to expand our involvement in home health care and IV services. The big chains are going after prescription business, and we believe we'll find our niche in the service market.

Over the years, I have found that when competition heats up, our business levels off for a while, but then it goes back up again. Even in the face of that, and despite the recession, we showed nearly an 18 percent increase in revenues last year. I attribute that to the thorough training we give our employees and to the fact that we have a large number of profit centers in the store.

Efficiency. That's what independent pharmacy owners have to strive for. Cost consciousness in health care is creating a whole new ball game, and, today, efficiency is the absolute key to success, if not to survival itself. We're where the independent grocers were 20 or so years ago. Then, their own viability was in question. Everybody wondered how they'd compete against the supermarkets. But small grocers have managed to survive. They've done it by learning to run their stores more intelligently. Pharmacists have to do the same.

The need for efficiency was brought home to me 12 or 15 years ago when inflation was bouncing between 15 and 20 percent. I watched a couple of local businesses go under. I knew they could have made it if they'd been able to track their operations better. That's when I computerized my business. Suddenly, we were able to update our prices automatically by simply inserting a disk. If a product's cost went up by 12 percent, we could incorporate the effect instantly. It made all the difference in our bottom line.

Now we have both our bookkeeping and payroll in the computer. Patient records, profiles, allergies, and drug interactions – it's all in there. When we fill a prescription today, the computer subtracts it from inventory, shows every other medication that the patient is taking, and alerts us to any possible problems. It helps us give better service, and it helps us remain competitive. Most important of all, it gives us more time to spend with individual customers.

I've been a member of NARD from its inception, and at the time of this writing I'm president-elect. I consider this position an opportunity to give something back to a profession that has been very good to me.

The work NARD and other professional associations do is tremendously important, and pharmacists entering the profession should become as involved as they can. Without the legislative efforts of these associations, pharmacists would have no protection against damaging state and federal regulations. "Get into politics or get out of pharmacy" is an appropriate motto for the 1990s.

William L. Scharringhausen, PD,
is owner and secretary-treasurer of
Scharringhausen Pharmacy, Inc.,
in Park Ridge, Illinois.
In 1992, he was
president of NARD.

Traditional Independent Pharmacy

Scharringhausen Pharmacy is only 25 feet wide and occupies less than 2,000 square feet. It is a small pharmacy, but it touches the lives of a great number of people in this Chicago suburb.

I work hard to know my customers by name. I grew up with some of them, and many are children of those friends. This is a small community, and people come to us because we have earned their trust. It is my job to see that nothing threatens that relationship.

The tradition is older than I am. My grandfather, George L. Scharringhausen, started our business in 1924 with a simple, two-part philosophy. First, we are dedicated to serving others. Second, we believe in giving something back to the community that provides us with a place to live and work and raise our families. I like to say that what we give back is the rent we pay for the space we occupy.

I learned at an early age that independent pharmacy is a very personal business. Filling prescriptions and taking care of the needs of patients is primary, of course, but to do those things well, you must be able to relate to people. In fact, to thrive in the future, the independent will have to search for new ways to meet customers' needs, new ways to stand apart from the competition. As any independent pharmacist will tell you, the competition today is fierce – particularly from the chains, which can sell prescriptions for less. Mail-order distributors entice customers with their offers. And, often, third-party payers threaten the independent's relationship with patients by reimbursing at a rate that is below the actual wholesale cost.

In my business, it is clear that success depends on building a clientele that wants what my competitors cannot offer: face-to-face, personal service. I must do whatever it takes to give my customers the best possible care – counseling, deliveries, and personal attention. Every business decision I make is made with the welfare of the customer in mind. As a result, people are willing to pay a little bit more for prescriptions from my pharmacy. But my prices always have been competitive – sometimes even lower than the competition's. And as my customers will tell you, there is more to consider than cost when it comes to buying medications.

A Scharringhausen customer benefits from a one-to-one relationship with a professional who keeps up to date with the latest drugs and treatments. I study periodicals, attend seminars and continuing education courses, and meet regularly with pharmaceutical representatives and physicians. I seek knowledge wherever I can find it, and I always am ready to answer a customer's questions. If I don't have the answer, I do my best to get it.

When a customer does business with my pharmacy, he is trading with people who have a personal interest in his welfare. An example of this concern is the Scharringhausen policy that requires two pharmacists to complete a prescription order. One fills the prescription, a second checks it. Another example is our delivery service, which speeds orders to our patients as fast as possible.

To accomplish the dual purpose of educating physicians about new drugs and keeping the Scharringhausen name visible in the marketplace, we publish a newsletter. This publication contains timely health information, brief news items about Scharringhausen Pharmacy, cartoons, and one-line jokes.

We also have tailored our hours to better serve our customers. We are open weekdays from 9 AM until 6 PM and Saturdays from 9 until 5. On Monday evenings we stay open until 8. We have a message line for next-day orders and a 24-hour emergency number. Our telephone is covered by a recorder that will take messages and routine orders. If the call is an emergency, the recording directs the caller to our answering service, which can reach the person on call (usually me) by pager.

We get calls at all hours from people with earaches, toothaches, urinary tract infections ... you name it. Often someone from the hospital emergency room calls with a prescription because the hospital does not fill emergency prescriptions. I've been out early and late on Sundays, Christmas Day, Easter – all the holidays. I've even been called to fill a prescription during Christmas Eve dinner.

Community involvement has been something my family has always taken seriously and enjoyed. Even a partial list of posts held by Scharringhausens is long, but it is good evidence of our commitment to giving something back to our community. My grandfather and father contributed in different ways than I have. My grandfather preferred to limit his activities to Park Ridge. Dad worked in community organizations as well, but devoted more time to groups outside the area. He was involved with NARD and other national pharmacy organizations. He also served as president of the state pharmacy association and was governor of the Illinois-Eastern Iowa District of Kiwanis.

As for my own interests, I am a past president of the Park Ridge Kiwanis, and I stay heavily involved in NARD. In 1982, I was elected to fifth vice president of NARD, and in 1991-1992 I served as the association's president. I have served in many leadership positions in local and state organizations. I remain active as a committee member and usher at the Park Ridge Community Church.

Serving others and doing my share in the community may help my business, but such participation also is personally fulfilling. In fact, the really satisfying part about my life is the contact I have with people. I can safely say that had I not been my own boss, I would never have had the time to devote to all these worthwhile activities.

I have friends and neighbors in other professions whose income is greater than mine, but I wouldn't trade the experiences I've had in my work just for income. For instance, a bigger income couldn't replace the fun I had filming a Medic Alert public service announcement in Charlotte. More income couldn't replace the great time I've had traveling the country representing NARD. And, more money couldn't replace the feeling I got when I received the Alumnus of the Year award from the University of Wisconsin. When I graduated from pharmacy school in 1956, I had no idea any of these things would happen, but the more I get involved and the more people I meet, the richer my life becomes. That is how I find the time and energy to stay as involved as I do. And that is what is good about a profession that offers a reason to get involved.

I am thankful that my mentors were men who knew that there are personal rewards, apart from income, to be derived from owning a pharmacy. My father worked a full shift in our pharmacy the day he died at the age of 84. At 86, my mother still helps out in the pharmacy, usually after playing a round of golf. My wife helps too, and my sister, who also is a pharmacist, covers for me when I need to travel. There is something good about an environment that inspires me and gives me the energy to continue working to improve it.

I have worked in the pharmacy since I was five years old. When I was in high school, I often worked more than 40 hours a week. I started with the simple jobs, taking out the trash and dusting the shelves. When I mastered one task, I learned another. I got to know what merchandise we sold, and when an order came in I was able to stock the shelves. It wasn't long until I learned about wholesale cost and its relationship to selling price, which merchandise moves, and which doesn't, and how best to display what you have to sell. By the time I was in high school, I was delivering regularly, and my father and grandfather had me working in an apprenticeship program.

It still is exciting to be able to work at something that is part of my own vision and to do whatever is required to see it succeed. I've done it all, from filling prescriptions to accounting to repairing the vacuum cleaner. And after more than 68 years, the Scharringhausen name continues on Main Street in Park Ridge.

Joe Smith, PD,
owns The Medicine Shoppe
in Falls Church, Virginia.

Apothecary Practice

Each time I unlock the door to my store, I'm reminded of what I enjoy most about owning my own community pharmacy. There is an excitement, an adrenalin rush that comes when I cross the threshold and prepare to meet the challenge of providing my customers with the best service possible.

I start my day by entering the store as if I were a customer. Of course I have to turn off the alarm, open the register, and organize the bench, but I try to see what customers might see. Walking in their shoes for a few minutes helps me serve them better in two ways: First, it prompts me to make sure that everything I need to operate is in place; and second, it reminds me that the customer is my real employer.

As every successful independent pharmacist knows, working and communicating with the customer is the most important part of the job. A store can be full of medicines, bottles, bags, and staples, but if pharmacists aren't really ready to listen and respond to customers as people, the business won't last long.

When I have a patient in my store, he is my highest priority. Seventy-five percent of my day is spent in patient care of some kind, usually preparing a prescription or answering questions. The trick for me – and this is where the challenge comes in – is to stay on top of the logistics of running the business without sacrificing any time with the customers. This isn't always easy.

In a small pharmacy, finding the pharmacist is no problem. He or she is visible and accessible – or should be. Customers do not hesitate to tell this professional details about their lives, illnesses, or even about the weather as their prescriptions are being filled. They probably have no idea of the myriad mental checks that must be performed to make sure they are served properly.

Helping patients requires much more than what pharmacists have long called "counting, pouring, licking, and sticking." First, I review their prescription for accuracy and completeness. All legal requirements must be met – the patient's name and address, doctor's name, and so forth, must be correct. Next, I cross-check for drug interactions using a computer database and the patient profile. Then, I select the appropriate drug, or the appropriately priced drug if a patient has requested a generic substitute. Finally, I enter the data necessary to keep my computer records current, then I print the label and proofread it for mistakes.

It is vital to the customer's welfare that I focus on these steps when I fill prescriptions. And, as I have already mentioned, it is vital to my business that I remain attentive to them as people while I help them. It also is vital to my business to keep up with the many management tasks that have to be accomplished. Sometimes this is quite a juggling act. For example, I spend part of every day on administrative work – the duties that are important to the financial success of my store. I do my own bookkeeping, prepare the deposits, and do the accounting and payroll. Usually, I do these chores in the morning because that is when I function best. But I have to be flexible, because someone might call with a question, or a patient might walk in the door.

Part of my day is dedicated to continuing education. I educate myself by keeping up to date with journals or literature from pharmaceutical companies. I teach my patients about their medications. I teach my staff. And, often, doctors phone in with questions about new or existing drugs. They call me or my staff because we keep up with the new drugs, can get them a quick answer, and we are friendly about sharing our knowledge.

I spend part of each week buying pharmaceutical and health care products for my store. Buying the right product at the right price in the right quantities requires a lot of decision making.

To be successful as a self-employed pharmacist, you have to be a generalist in many ways. You need to draw on everything you know. When I tell students what course of study is required to survive in a small enterprise, I advise them to work on their weaknesses. If you are weak in business, do what you can to enhance your skills – cover the basics, go to seminars, read books on management. If you aren't a great speaker, join speaking groups, join a debate team, study the humanities. The broader your knowledge, the better you will be able to communicate with the customer.

In my business, I have to wear many hats, so I'm constantly working on my weak areas. That's part of the attraction of self-employment. My secret way of meeting this challenge, if there is a secret, is to stay humble. I work to appreciate the little things that are a part of my job, and I avoid getting overly impressed with what I've accomplished. Pharmacy as a profession is always changing, always developing. As a result, continuing education requires constant attention. I work hard to stay current with the latest advances, and I am always working to improve my relationship with customers. The rest of the time I spend filling the holes that need filling, writing checks, and doing paperwork.

Looking back at how I got my own pharmacy, I can easily make a case for destiny. You might even say pharmacy was in my blood.

To begin with, I had two uncles who were pharmacists. One died early and I never met him, but I used to visit the other uncle during the summer from the time I was about 10 years old. He had a small, full-line pharmacy, and I have strong memories of how personable he was. Most of all, I remember how much I liked being in his store.

Not surprisingly, when I was old enough to go to work I found a job in a pharmacy in Weeping Water, my hometown in Nebraska. I attended high school in Lincoln and went to work for "Doc" and Mary Mayo in their small mom-and-pop store.

I continued working part time for them all the way through college. They took me into their family, and it was probably my experience with them that built the foundation for my career. They showed me how to do many diverse jobs, and as I proved to them I could handle the responsibility, they allowed me to do more. As a result, I learned a little each day about accounting, merchandising, buying, and working with people. Best of all, we were like a family. We did everything together, from eating lunch to going to market. I was very fortunate to have found them. As mentors, they were exceptional.

If I wasn't sure by then that I wanted to be a pharmacist, I believe the welcome I got from the dean of the University of Nebraska College of Pharmacy would have sealed my fate. I visited the university in my junior year of high school. Dean Burt was very receptive, and he encouraged me to come to the University of Nebraska and study pharmacy. Dean (Hoot) Gibson, who was dean during the five years I attended the school, was equally encouraging. He believed that pharmacy was a good career choice, one that offered its graduates a chance to become valued members of the community.

I earned my bachelor of science degree from the University of Nebraska in 1965 and promptly entered the Air Force. For the next four years I added to my pharmacy experience by working part time in a small pharmacy in Columbus, Miss. When I got out of the military, I went to the Washington, DC, area and took a job with a large chain. There, I worked in stores ranging in size from 20,000 to 60,000 square feet, and it would be almost an understatement to say we sold everything. Unfortunately, even though I worked my way up to a district manager's post, it wasn't the right environment for me at the time.

I guess I had always wanted to be in independent pharmacy, and my desire to get back to it began to grow. One day it occurred to me that if I didn't change direction soon, I never would. It was a big step that took a little daring, but I began looking for other opportunities. Most of the ones I found were in two categories: Either the stores were about to go under, and the owners were eager to sell, or they were large, successful, and unaffordable.

Then I learned about the franchise pharmacy Medicine Shoppe. Here was a realistic opportunity to buy my own store. I was able to afford the relatively small down payment, so I was happy to sign the contract. I have never regretted my decision and am as excited about my business as I was when I signed on the dotted line 11 years ago.

My employees also like the environment we have built here. Right now, four people help me – two clerks, one administrative assistant, and a relief pharmacist. Of these four people, one has been with me seven years, another nine years, and another 10 years.

I believe we have created a stable and nurturing environment, and people in a small community like Falls Church appreciate stability. There once was an independent pharmacy down the street. It opened for business 20 years ago and closed for good three years ago. The store had several owners during its life, but the original proprietor made the deepest impression on customers. Long after he sold the pharmacy, his patients continued to patronize the store because they believed they were still trading with him.

Similarly, people come to us because they have confidence in us. They come not because of low prices or hype, but because they want a professional relationship in health care.

My shop is an apothecary, a pharmacy that does up to 90 percent of its business in prescriptions. A larger store might have beauty aids, cards, maybe a cosmetics section, more front-end merchandise. Our market and our purpose are more narrowly defined. Everything in my store is oriented to health, even our book section. I'm open nine hours each day on weekdays and half the day on Saturday, but my customers want to be able to call me up any time and say, "Joe, I know this may be a dumb question, but I don't know the answer, and I was wondering if you could help me." They call because they know that I'll do whatever research is necessary and give them the best answer I can. If I do my job right, their experience with pharmacist Joe Smith will be a good one, and they will pass the word that we truly care about our patients.

Dennis L. Ludwig, BS,
owns Ludwig Pharmacy and
Extended Care Pharmacy
in Boulder, Colorado.

The Long-term Care Pharmacist

There's been much talk about independent pharmacies being unable to compete with chain drugstores. On the contrary, it is possible to compete on all levels by offering high-quality care and innovative services. Even more important, we find special market niches. In other words, we must find a need and then take care of it. That's the key to success.

My niche is long-term care pharmacy. My corporation provides consulting and vending services to seven long-term care facilities in the Boulder/Denver area. Some are acute care institutions, both small and large. Others are residential care facilities – basically, apartment complexes whose residents require less nursing supervision than nursing home patients. In total, we service about 500 beds. I have a full-time staff of seven extended care specialists, and up to 19 people work for me at any one time.

We started providing long-term care services 15 years ago, right after I bought my retail pharmacy in Boulder. The practice had been handling the needs of a few patients in a local nursing home, so we took over their care. When I talked to staff members, they told me the company that was serving the other patients wasn't paying attention to details, and it wasn't providing all the services the facility needed. Soon, I began getting more and more of their patients, and our business grew from there.

Demographics show that the percentage of elderly people in our population is growing faster than any other age group. Older people take more medications than younger folks do and they have special drug-related needs. This gives pharmacists an opportunity to provide a vitally important service.

In long-term care, the pharmacist coordinates therapy with the nurses every day. The nurses describe their problems and challenge the pharmacist to come up with solutions. Once they agree on a solution, it usually must be approved by physicians who tend to appreciate the pharmacist's expertise.

When working as long-term care consultants, pharmacists attend meetings of the quality assurance and pharmacy committees. They confer with the facility's staff to make sure the medications patients are receiving are appropriate. They also review lab results in order to monitor therapy and recommend adjustments to prescribed drug regimens. Ensuring the patients' health is the pharmacist's primary goal.

Each month, consultant pharmacists review all patient charts and recommend changes in therapy where needed. They also make sure that each patient's drug therapy is in compliance with federal regulations. The pharmacist ensures that drugs are administered correctly, checks to see that accurate records are kept, and makes certain that a variety of other federal requirements are met.

Recent government regulations mandate that long-term care facilities document attempts at dosage reductions of drugs that sedate residents. This has forced physicians, consultants, and vendors to sharpen their focus on using medications properly.

This outside attention to drug therapy makes the pharmacist's role in long-term care that much more important. Indeed, over the past four years this intense scrutiny has considerably increased the pharmacy consultant's responsibilities. Today, one of the biggest challenges in this setting is keeping up with the constant changes in regulations and their interpretation. Every change must be communicated to the facility's staff.

It is easy to become personally involved with long-term care patients. The pharmacist talks to staff nurses two or three times every day about certain patients, especially those on complicated regimens. For example, monitoring the pain of terminally ill patients can be time-consuming, because their need for analgesia may change almost hourly. The pharmacist has to monitor those patients and recommend appropriate therapy.

Long-term care patients don't always realize or appreciate the pharmacist's efforts, so gratitude is not often part of the job. However, the staff and physicians do recognize the importance of the pharmacist's role in long-term care.

A constant opportunity to use so much of my knowledge and education is what I like best about working in long-term care. There is a great deal of satisfaction associated with having my suggestions accepted and with being able to feel responsible for the improved health of my patients.

These days, I spend only about one third of my time out in the field – I learned a long time ago that I can't do everything myself. Instead, my staff members are assigned to distribution or consulting duties, usually at a single facility. Occasionally, I rotate duties and assignments in order to give my staff some variety. However, there is something to be said for allowing pharmacists to establish relationships with one client facility. In fact, some of my staff would prefer staying in one place. The trick for me as a manager is to know when things need to be shaken up a bit and when to step back and let things continue as they have been.

Often our business growth comes from client employees who transfer to institutions we don't yet do business with. If the staffers consider their experience with us to have been positive, they'll remember and call us when they need help.

On the other hand, reputation alone won't ensure the success of a business. You just can't rest on your laurels. As I said before, you have to find new market needs and then find a way to fill them. Because those needs vary from time to time, pharmacists simply cannot avoid change – I think change is our profession's hallmark.

I have found that local, state, and national professional organizations are excellent sources for the new ideas that keep my business vital. Through networking I learn what professionals in other areas are doing. Pharmacists I meet at conventions often become my close friends. They are happy to share all of their insights with me about what has and what hasn't worked in their businesses. I save a lot of time and money when a fellow pharmacist will tells me the pitfalls he has encountered and show me how to avoid making the same mistakes.

The majority of my time is spent in my pharmacy, for which another pharmacist and I are responsible. The store is located in a strip mall in a residential area. Walk-in business is good and growing. Because we are located directly across from the university, many of our customers are college students and adults who come to town for continuing education seminars.

On the retail side, chain drugstores are our main competitors. To answer their competition, we provide many extra services, such as those for diabetes patients, hypertensive patients, and patients who require home care products. Many of our patients come back to us because they appreciate the time and effort we put into counseling. That is one of our strongest points, and I think we do it better than most other pharmacies.

If you are interested in owning your own pharmacy, I recommend that you get involved in professional organizations as soon as possible. Pharmacy school will not prepare you fully for the business end of owning a pharmacy. NARD has management programs that will enable you to concentrate on financial management, personnel management, and time management, and these programs can teach you such practical skills as how to talk to a banker.

Work in as many different settings as possible before making a final career choice. Use those early jobs as learning experiences to find out what you do and do not enjoy.

When I first got out of college I worked for a chain. It was a beneficial experience because I learned that I didn't want to work for a chain. I decided that if I was going to work hard anyway, I might as well be working for myself.

Independent pharmacy provides me with continual challenges. I am my own boss, and I can practice pharmacy the way I want. The long-term care part of my practice gives me the opportunity to use the skills I learned in school, and it challenges me to keep on learning. The rewards I get are limited only by my own ambition, my own drive, my own determination.

Carl Emswiller, RPh,
owns Emswiller Pharmacy
in Leesburg, Virginia,
and is president of the
American College of Apothecaries.

The Office-based Pharmacist

The office-based pharmacist subscribes to a philosophy that emphasizes the practitioner and not the place. I believe the future of the profession lies in office-based pharmacy, but before that vision can come true, physicians and patients will need a great deal of education.

While a student in pharmacy school, I worked in a drugstore at night in order to gain the required hours of practical experience. One night, the pharmacist I worked with was rudely reprimanded by a customer because the beer that was delivered to him wasn't cold and the cigarettes were the wrong brand. At that instant I knew I wasn't meant to spend the rest of my life worrying about such details. I love working with patients, and I love knowing about medications. I knew at that moment that I should practice in a setting where the emphasis was on patient care.

Working with me at that pharmacy was a young man who told me I talked about pharmacy the same way his brother did. He said I just had to meet him. His brother turned out to be Eugene V. White, the founding father of office-based pharmacy. I went to work for White in 1962, thinking I'd be there only a year or two. I stayed for six years.

In 1968, I bought a pharmacy in Leesburg, Va., planning to convert it into an office-based practice. With the brashness of youth, I thought I could accomplish this in a year or two. Unfortunately, I underestimated the amount of public relations and education that was needed to explain – both to physicians and patients – what pharmacists could do for them.

For example, under Mr. White, I had worked with patient medication profiles. But when I came to Leesburg, no one even understood the term. Consequently, it was hard convincing people that I wasn't there just to sell products. Far from it – I was going to get involved in explaining how their medications worked. To do that, I would keep careful records and forge a professional relationship with patients that was certain to improve the results of their drug therapy. Even more difficult was introducing my services to physicians without making them believe I wanted to take responsibility away from them.

Over the years, I gradually changed the store's traditional image. I closed the fountain and stopped selling tobacco products, fully prepared to switch to an office practice. But in 1974, several physicians urged me to move into their new medical building. The advantages of being in such close proximity to physicians' offices were obvious and so strong that I made a clean break and started my practice in their location. I've been here ever since, and I've accomplished much of what I set out to do.

When patients step through my door, they know this pharmacy is different. The receptionist's desk is prominently placed. Our waiting area is furnished with comfortable chairs, a couch, a display case, and closed cabinets. No merchandise is on display because I believe its absence reinforces the air of professionalism I want to present.

Our services are what really set us apart from most pharmacies. For example, we have a nurse who monitors blood pressures and assesses blood glucose levels. Computerized medication profiles are standard in our operation, but we also maintain written notes. We use a color-coded insert on the patient's chart to call attention to a particular problem we've noted or to advice we've given. Thus, if I'm not in, my associate will see this code and know there's something he should follow up on. Patients appreciate our careful record keeping because it lets them know we make an extra effort on their behalf.

We also hold brown-bag events when we encourage patients to bring their medications to us for evaluation. We go through all the drugs together and learn exactly what prescriptions they are taking. It's a good way to spot potential problems.

Our consultation room is a comfortable area where we sit and talk with patients in complete privacy. This helps convey our professionalism, and it lets patients know we are dedicated to making sure their therapies are optimal for their conditions.

What I'm describing is service – the basis of every office-based pharmacist's success. All of our time is devoted to the patient. From the receptionist to the nurse to my associate to me, everything we do is designed to serve our patients because they are the single focus of our professional lives.

There is no doubt that we are filling a void in health care. Consider the constraints that physicians work under. They're rushed and often overworked. They examine patients, evaluate lab results, consider many other factors, make a diagnosis, and then they are expected to select the appropriate drug for the patient's condition. It's understandable that they might not remember to tell the patient that the medication should be taken before meals or after meals, or to watch for side effects, or to take it with this and not that. And sometimes they may even forget to tell the patient what the medication is for. Usually, the patient walks out too intimidated to ask. We are an extension of a process the physician initiated. He made a diagnosis, he selected a medication, and now it's our job to help the patient get the best possible benefits from the medication.

In addition to their other responsibilities, physicians are expected to be knowledgeable about every new drug that comes to market. Frankly, I don't believe this is possible. The technology is developing too fast, particularly in this age of specialization. All of this presents a golden opportunity for pharmacists to demonstrate that we are the drug experts.

I don't think all physicians understand the implications of office-based pharmacy. Remember that I started in the profession during the 1960s, when the American Pharmaceutical Association code of ethics said pharmacists shouldn't discuss medications with patients – that was the doctor's job. Well, now I'm doing just the opposite. I tell patients whatever they need to know in order to get the maximum effectiveness from their prescribed medications.

Paradoxically, the upside of office-based pharmacy is also its downside. It is the practitioner and not the place or its location that makes for success. If you're the owner, patients miss you if you are away. And if you've sold yourself properly, you will have created a trust that can be binding.

For example, I get many calls on weekends from patients who can't reach their physician and want me to tell them what to do about their medications. This illustrates how patients come to depend upon the pharmacist as much as they depend upon their physicians. I'm fortunate to have an associate who does a great job and whom my patients trust. But a problem for most pharmacists in this practice is the need to be available around the clock.

Educating physicians about the office-based pharmacist's expanding role probably is a never-ending process. Even so, I have made definite progress. Now, it is not uncommon for physicians to call me and say they have a patient with a problem that is not responding to the drug they prescribed. They want us to suggest an alternative. Our increasing role in pharmacotherapy is the strongest indicator of our potential influence.

I believe the concept of office-based pharmacy will continue to evolve. And someday in the future, patients will make appointments with their pharmacists. Fees for services will be common, and pharmacists will unite in group practices. More and more practitioners will have advanced clinical knowledge that will thrust them into deeper involvement with pharmacotherapy.

The best thing about working in an office-based pharmacy is that no matter what you're doing now, you can always do more. The challenge never ends. I tell students that they don't have to settle for working for a chain. They don't have to settle for working in a hospital. In fact, they shouldn't settle for anything. They should seek a career instead of a job. There will always be graduating pharmacists who are content to work for someone else, and that's as it should be. But for the person who wants to get out and do things as an individual – to be innovative and move things forward, to find a need and fill it – it's a great life.

R. Gene Graves, PD,
is CEO of I Care of Arkansas,
I Care Health Services, and
Professional Family Medical Center
Pharmacy in Little Rock, Arkansas.

Home IV Care

When I started my home infusion business 10 years ago, the handwriting was on the wall. I had spent several years as a director of hospital pharmacy and knew that the days of confining a patient for 24 hours in order to deliver two hours of therapy were coming to a close. Even then, it seemed to me that if you could accomplish the same results in the patient's home for half the cost, it would be foolish not to. The patient might even be able to go back to work. The insurance company would like it, the employer would like it, and the patient would be happier, too.

Whenever there is a crisis, a seed of business opportunity presents itself to people who are innovative and willing to take a little risk. The truth is that America is in the middle of a health care crisis because of escalating costs and the fact that some 37 million U.S. citizens have no access to care. Today, many people can't even pay their insurance deductibles, let alone a hospital bill. As an alternative to hospitalization, home care – especially home IV care – looked like an opportunity to provide top-quality, cost-effective patient care.

Today, I own the home infusion business as well as a durable medical equipment and respiratory supplies company. In addition, I operate a long-term care pharmacy service and a retail pharmacy in a family medicine center.

My newest business is a franchise-like operation that teaches pharmacists, nurses, and other health professionals from 30 states how to start their own home infusion practices. They come to Little Rock for a week-long training session on running a successful home-IV business.

After they leave Arkansas, we remain available to them through our toll-free telephone number. If they have a problem, they can call us day or night for advice. We also help them secure contracts to establish their businesses.

All across the country, home infusion is one of the fastest-growing segments of the health care industry. I Care of Arkansas, my home infusion business, has four facilities and provides service throughout the state. It does $12 million worth of business annually and is growing by 30 to 40 percent each year. But believe me, it wasn't easy getting here.

We've had to be pioneers in reimbursement policy. When I started my business, no insurance company knew much about this alternative to hospitalization. I met with a number of insurance executives to show them that we offered a safe alternative to hospitalization and could save them a lot of money. Eventually, they decided we were right.

We sold physicians on our concept, but insurance companies wouldn't pay for their role in managing the home therapy, even though they had to hold counseling sessions and review progress reports. Third-party payers would only pay the physicians to see patients in the hospital.

Finally, we were able to convince Blue Cross-Blue Shield of Arkansas that the policy was ridiculous, and they agreed to begin reimbursing physicians for managing patients at home. This still is not as widely accepted as I would like, but we are in a much better position than we were 10 years ago.

Medicare, on the other hand, will pay only the cost of drugs used in home infusion therapy if a patient is using an infusion pump. For a number of years before Medicare started paying we gave the drugs away. Medicare's policy is still that it will not pay for pharmaceuticals. Needless to say, we are working hard to get expanded coverage.

Despite payment restrictions, we take Medicare patients on a case-by-case basis. Some can pay their own expenses, but each year we deliver significant amounts of care without compensation. Last year, for example, we provided $500,000 in charity care, partly because I believe we have an obligation to the community. In the beginning, another reason for underwriting patient care was to accustom physicians to having their patients receive therapy at home instead of in the hospital. When we deliver our services without charging, word gets around and it builds community loyalty.

Our sales staff calls on physicians, and I write a monthly newspaper column that reaches 50,000 elderly people across the state. I also speak to various public organizations. If I've learned anything in this business, it's that I can't sit back and wait for opportunity to present itself. The days of complacency in independent pharmacy – or anywhere else, for that matter – are over.

We aren't in competition just with other drugstores. Our competitors include the large corporations that are getting into home care. How do we stay in the game against them? Through personal service. In fact, a big percentage of our patients came to us because they felt they weren't being treated well by companies that tried to provide care in Arkansas from their headquarters in Chicago. Because we're on the scene, all of my businesses are able to give a great deal of personal support to the family and patient alike.

We have four full-service home infusion support centers and six satellite offices, each staffed with a pharmacist and a nurse. We train the family and patient to administer their own drugs in a process that starts while the patient is still hospitalized. We deliver the equipment and supplies to the home before discharge, and the nurse makes regular follow-up visits. We are on call every minute, every day.

Any patient we train could go into a hospital and operate infusion pumps with skillful aseptic technique. And after we train family members, they can perform as well as any hospital employee. In fact, they'll be better motivated. And because they don't have enough medical knowledge to exercise independent judgment, they will do exactly as they're told. In fact, we get nervous when our patients go back into the hospital because the biggest problem we have is with nosocomial infections.

People are demanding more of a role in their own therapy. When they don't get what they want, they may very well change doctors. And when two patients are being treated for the same problem, but one of them is being cared for at home while the other is sent to the hospital, word spreads quickly in the community.

Most sick people don't want to be in the hospital if there is a safe, valid alternative. I believe pharmacists can provide that alternative better than any other professionals in health care.

The practice of pharmacy has always been competitive. Even as store employees, pharmacists had to run more business-like operations than anyone else in health care. The business side of medicine is a fact of life. To remain competitive you must give good service.

A few years ago, I opened a pharmacy in a family practice medical clinic where the physicians were trying to become more competitive. They were getting involved with HMOs and preferred provider organizations. And they began keeping the clinic open seven days a week.

They noticed that when they referred patients, they seldom saw them again. So they brought specialists into their own practice. These physicians decided to provide everything from specialized care to medical equipment. We built our pharmacy in part of their large waiting area, and we do patient counseling right there. We offer home diagnostic aids and teach newly diagnosed diabetes patients to measure their glucose levels.

I never set out to accomplish particular goals in pharmacy. But I like to think of myself as someone who never had blinders on. There are plenty of opportunities for everyone, and it only takes time and energy – and a little nerve, perhaps – to capitalize on them.

People ask students, "What do you want to do for the rest of your life?" The best advice I can give young pharmacists is not to have such long-range concerns, but to cultivate a positive attitude and an appetite for challenge. The world of pharmacy is getting bigger every day, and you don't need a specialized degree to be successful in it.

My responsibilities – especially in management – are endlessly challenging. They also are capable of producing great stress. However, when things get tough, I remember one of my earliest cases.

I had gone to the hospital to teach a 70-year-old man to administer an IV to his terminally ill wife. When she was discharged, I went home with them and got the woman started on her therapy. As I left their house, the old man wept as he shook my hand over and over and over, thanking me for helping his wife come home to die. I cried all the way back to the office. Even today, that memory brings me to tears. It is the most rewarding experience I have ever had as a pharmacist.

Allison Holden, BS,
owns an independent retail pharmacy in
Mulberry, Indiana.

The Small-town Pharmacist

Make orangeade ... change the battery in a little old lady's watch: Some of the things I learned in my first job had absolutely nothing to do with pharmacy. Yet they are basic skills for a small-town pharmacist. A woman once asked me what she should do to make her gander eat. That stumped me until I realized she was talking about a bird. Instantly, the saying "What's good for the goose is good for the gander" popped into my mind, and I was able to give her good advice – I suggested she take her gander to the vet.

Those early lessons were among my most important because they drove home the fact that customer relationships form the cornerstone of independent retail pharmacy. I'll never forget those lessons because I know they are my lifeline to success in business and a career I enjoy.

I graduated from the University of North Carolina, where I completed rotations in various settings. One was a chain pharmacy, and for those few weeks I felt isolated from customers. Only once did a customer approach me with a question. "Please ask anything," I encouraged him. I was desperate for human contact.

Today I don't lack for interaction. In fact, my customers have become my friends, and my store has become an informal meeting place. Every morning, a group of older people gather here to drink coffee and chat. They are such serious socializers that they even take attendance. I love the fact that my business is central to their lives.

When I entered pharmacy school I had never set foot behind a pharmacy counter. I followed an unusual career path for a pharmacist. No one in my family was remotely involved in the profession, but my father had encouraged me to take math and science classes in college. When it came time for me to declare my major, I compared what I'd already taken with the requirements for various majors. Pharmacy was the obvious choice.

Not until the end of my first year, when I got a summer job at the local pharmacy, did I get a real insight into the business. Fortunately, I could not have found a better place to work. The pharmacist who hired me had been named the state's Pharmacist of the Year, and working for him I saw a professional who loved his work and had the respect of his patients. After that summer, I knew I belonged in retail pharmacy.

After graduating with a BS in 1987, I went to work for a small chain pharmacy in North Carolina. Although I was pretty sure chains weren't intimate enough for me, this one operated on the philosophy of a small, independent store. And because I wanted to move to a city – I'd grown up in a small town – I decided to give it a try. In 1988, I married another pharmacist and we bought a pharmacy, in Mulberry, Ind., population 1,000. So much for big cities.

From the beginning, we had our work cut out for us – from marketing and advertising to renovation and store design. The previous owner had allowed the store to deteriorate, and Mulberry's residents had become accustomed to driving to another town about 10 miles away for their pharmacy needs. Wooing those customers back has been my priority.

We cleaned the store from top to bottom and discarded items that had been on the shelves for decades. Then we restocked, adding hardware, gifts, cosmetics, and snacks to increase traffic. We filled prescriptions as quickly as possible, usually within minutes. Some patients said that before we came on the scene even same-day service seemed quick to them.

After spending a few months getting the pharmacy in Mulberry on its feet, we bought a second store in nearby Delphi. Now we have "his and hers" pharmacies: I run the one in Mulberry, my husband runs the one in Delphi.

I try to appeal to all our customer segments. Elderly customers appreciate our free home delivery, and the teenagers who drop in after school like our snacks and gift items. If we can get people to come in for the first time, I feel confident I can get them to come back.

We are happy to file insurance claims for customers, and we have a payment plan for people who can't afford to pay the full amount at once. Many of my customers are poor, and this is an important service.

My husband and I do our own billing. We figure our own taxes and payroll. Not surprisingly, we also handle purchasing. All of these economies help keep our prices competitive. We can't always match the larger chains – and we don't really try. But we do regularly beat the prices of a nearby smaller chain. In my opinion, the main thing we have to do is make sure our customers know we're not taking financial advantage of them just because we happen to be convenient.

The people of Mulberry are learning to stop here instead of driving 10 miles for items they need. In the four years since we came here, we've managed to increase our customer base substantially, and our sales have grown almost 25 percent every year.

At first, business picked up because people were curious about the new store and pleased with the modernization. It's been sustained because I've earned my customers' trust. That was no small task. For the most part, Mulberry's people thought a pharmacist should be male. Consequently, everyone used to ask for my husband, even though I was just as able to help them. Besides, I was fairly young and they weren't sure I knew what I was doing. When a customer asked for Tom, I simply had to say, "I can help you." Sometimes I got downright stubborn. But it paid off: Finally, customers stopped asking for Tom and started turning to me. And now they have learned to trust me. They know they can confide in me.

Pharmacists provide vital services, and never more so than in a small town. In general, patients don't find us as intimidating as doctors. We have more time and we're more approachable.

I enjoy having people come to me for advice about all sorts of problems. That's part of the job I bargained for when I became a pharmacist. One woman came in with shingles. She was in a lot of pain and didn't know what to do. I suggested a relatively simple treatment that worked for her. Now I have a happy and loyal customer. I'm happy too when I can give advice that saves my customers money and worry. People in Mulberry can't afford a $45 visit to the doctor for every ache or pain.

In addition to my efforts in the pharmacy, I feel I should contribute to the community at large as well. We participate in a poison-prevention program, and we sponsor an annual brown-bag day to monitor the medications our older citizens use.

Life as a pharmacist in Mulberry isn't perfect; there are a few persistent headaches. One is dealing with third-party insurers. Another – and this one can be heart-rending – is collections. Because I own my business, people who write bad checks are robbing me. On the other hand, I know my clientele, and I know many of them need medicine they simply don't have the money to pay for. I've learned that I cannot turn away a customer who has a sick baby, whether she has the money to pay or not. So sometimes I get stuck. It goes with the territory.

As a student, I took a course on over-the-counter drugs that has been useful here in Mulberry. To a large extent, that's because this is a low-income area and folks here tend to try an OTC product before spending money and time on a physician's visit. In addition to courses like this, I would urge students interested in retail pharmacy to take as many business courses as they can. You'll hear it again and again, and you better believe it: Skills in accounting, computer operation, and taxes for small businesses will prove indispensable. So will management training.

I would caution pharmacy students thinking about life in a small-town pharmacy to abandon the almighty dollar as the sole reason for choosing this area of the profession. For those who work hard – and smart – independent retail pharmacy can produce significant financial rewards, but that's not what it's all about. And it's hard work. When I worked in a chain, I had every other weekend off. Now, I hardly know what a weekend is. I'm always on call.

In addition to the time I spend in the store, I spend 15 hours each month as a consultant pharmacist in an area nursing home. This activity is optional, but I enjoy it so much that I completed a year-long certification course at Purdue. Because of the flexibility, the consultancy complements my retail practice and provides additional intellectual stimulation.

Of all the attributes a small-town pharmacist needs, good common sense and communication skills head the list. Professionals in this setting need to be outgoing and caring. I can't imagine a shy person enjoying working in a small retail pharmacy. Never forget that you're dealing with sick people. Some of them are dying. In time, you will learn the right things to say to those people and their families. In small communities, you're dispensing friendship as much as drugs. I know that's true, because my patients have given me the highest vote of confidence I can get in Indiana: They say they'll make a Hoosier of me yet.

Jim Vincent, BS,
owns Shop-All, a two-store
food and pharmacy operation
in Yuma and Holyoke, Colorado.

Independent Pharmacy in a Grocery Store

I can still remember that day in 1959. I was talking to a friend who managed the local Safeway in Yuma, Colo., and he told me the grocery chain was putting in a drugstore of sorts: it would offer headache remedies and laxatives and toothpaste and the like. I asked my friend why his store was branching out. To my way of thinking, a drugstore should sell drugs, and a food store should sell food, and I told him as much. He replied that the entire chain was moving in the same direction.

In fact, such combinations were beginning to pop up in various parts of the country. I knew that people entered food stores seven times for every one time they entered a drugstore, and a basic retail principle is that traffic sells product. Clearly, the idea made good business sense. That was the beginning of one-stop shopping.

It occurred to me that if Safeway sold both food and drugs under one roof, it could be a real threat to the independent drugstore, including my own practice, which I'd started after attending the University of Colorado on the GI bill.

I could see the writing on the wall. And I also knew I couldn't fight city hall – or Safeway, for that matter.

There were three similar stores in Denver, so I went up to look them over, to see how the concept worked in practice. It looked so good that I decided to take a gamble on the future. I went home and built Shop-All, which, at the time, was a pretty good-sized food store and drugstore. Of course, it doesn't compare to today's superstores, but in rural Colorado, it was an innovation.

My gamble paid off, and Shop-All has been good to me all these years. During the more than 30 years I've been in independent pharmacy, I've never looked back. A year after I opened for business, the Safeway I had considered such a threat left town.

I've enlarged and remodeled my store three times and now have 15,000 square feet. Five years after I opened my first store, I opened a second one in Holyoke, Colorado. Furthermore, I believe I could have opened successful stores in rural America from Canada to the Mexican border. Rural areas are frequently underserved by their drugstores as well as their grocery stores.

Today in Yuma there's another independent drugstore and another food store, but Shop-All is the only combination store. The union of the two operations increases traffic, makes it possible to give better service in both areas, and provides a tremendous break in my operating expenses. Our

73

physical costs, such as electricity and repairs, and the "soft" administrative costs can be held down because many of the same employees work both sides of the business. And because customers are so concerned with price, I'm eager to pass those savings along. Without the two operations under one roof, my prices might have to go up as much as 10 percent.

As a past president of NARD I can say that independent pharmacy will give you a tremendous degree of freedom. It will allow you to move around within the business structure, it will give you unlimited potential for financial growth, and it will require you to take no orders from headquarters. With all that, of course, comes a serious responsibility: You have to be innovative on your own.

Although I was something of a pioneer in my business, I know that most people just getting started aren't very likely to go out and start a new pharmacy. What I'd recommend for students who are interested in a niche like mine is to minor in business. From management and accounting to advertising, promotion, and buying, squeeze in as many business courses as possible. To succeed as an independent, it's necessary to be interested in many areas beyond pharmacy.

However, although my work is largely business-oriented, I still take continuing education classes in various aspects of pharmacy so I can advise customers appropriately. I also attend state and national conventions and read professional publications. My roots are in pharmacy, and I never want to stray too far from those roots.

Recently I had a customer ask me where he could find the matches. In someone else's store, the customer would simply be directed to the matches. But this was *my* store, and I knew the man. It was my privilege to pry, so I asked him if he was still smoking. He said he was, so I gave him a good-natured lecture on why he needed to quit. We talked a little bit about how he could break his habit, and we discussed the possibility of using nicotine patches. I walked away knowing that I had planted an idea in his head, also hoping he would make an appointment with his personal physician.

Good customers must be treated as treasures. They're the most valuable assets you have. The key to survival is to understand what your customers want and give it to them. From service to price to the store's appearance, you have to offer the very best you can.

For me, one of the most enriching things about my business is the knowledge that people depend on me. There's a warmth and a wealth in that. They'll come and tell me about their aches and pains. I'll commiserate, and they'll leave feeling better than when they came in. Especially in a rural area, customers need a health professional who is *available*, and more and more often it's the pharmacist who fills that role. That's what I've learned living in Yuma. My customers are my friends: I spend a few minutes chatting with them when they come in, catching up on their lives and sharing mine. I play golf with them on Saturdays, and I volunteer for community events. Independent pharmacy will give you an entree to the community. It will also give you personal access to people every day. This may be more apparent in a rural setting, but the same principle holds in a suburban or urban area.

To be successful in this job, you need a particular personality – hard-working, outgoing, friendly, and giving. Not only do you have to give a great deal of yourself, but you also have to believe that's the best part of life. An introverted person or a person who doesn't care about people would kill this business. Consequently, in this setting more than almost any other, you hire the person before you hire the license. When I interview a prospective employee, I look for someone who will be able to transfer his or her ebullience to a customer. I look for someone with a strong work ethic – someone who wants to go to work, not just someone who needs a job. I always check references.

A common problem in this kind of business is handling employees and managing personnel relations. Frequently one employee will feel that another is getting more or is being treated better, and you have to sit them down and smooth their feathers. Old-fashioned as it may sound, the store has to be one big happy family. If it's not, you've got a problem.

I've been lucky. I have a tremendous market share and virtually no competition. But I'll tell you one thing: If my business volume placed this town's other drugstore and other food store in danger of going under, I'd feel compelled to help them out. If you knock out all your competition it scares customers off and they'll resist coming in to trade with you. A better business move is to ensure a competitor's success. It will help you sleep at night. As a businessperson in a small town, my first responsibility is to help the town, which includes competitors as well as my customers.

I received an award once, and someone said that a person has a charge in life to leave something better because he was there. That is what I've always tried to do, and independent pharmacy lets me do it.

Ronald L. Ziegler
is president and chief executive officer of the
National Association of Chain Drug Stores in
Alexandria, Virginia.

Opportunities in Chain Pharmacy

Today's chain operation has renewed its focus on the pharmacy as the heart of the chain drugstore. What does this mean for the pharmacy student? It means abundant career opportunities in a wide variety of areas utilizing both professional and managerial skills. Both behind and beyond the counter, opportunities for pharmacy graduates abound.

To serve the health care needs and demands of the consumer, the contemporary chain pharmacist must be prepared to assume the role of drug use counselor. In order to meet that challenge, most chains are redesigning their pharmacies, making the pharmacist more accessible to the patient. Some stores are even adding special counseling rooms. In a recent survey conducted for the National Association of Chain Drug Stores, 64 percent of customers indicated that, compared with five years ago, the pharmacist is now more accessible and more willing to offer counseling on prescription and nonprescription medications. This, and the increased concern it demonstrates for the patient's well-being, has been well noted by the public. The pharmacist continues to be the best goodwill ambassador for any drugstore.

By revamping their pharmacy format and placing greater reliance on technology and ancillary personnel, chain drugstores ensure that patients receive high-quality service from a professional they can trust and respect. Technical support personnel perform some of the more perfunctory tasks, and this enables the pharmacist to spend more time talking with patients about their medications. In addition, computers are being used to increase the pharmacist's access to information by providing data about drug interactions and storing patient profiles.

In response to patients' demand for information, the chain drugstore pharmacist is becoming a public relations specialist. Because pharmacies have become the most convenient source of information about prescription and over-the-counter drugs and preventive health care, chain pharmacy companies are designing creative programs to supply this information.

A career with a drugstore chain need not be limited to practice within the store. Indeed, for students who would like to combine their professional talents with the challenge of the fast-paced retail business, numerous management positions are within reach. Many chains now offer management training programs and specialized education support that can help pharmacists chart a path that leads from the pharmacy counter to one of several career tracks in management at the store, district, regional, and even corporate level.

Reliance on computerization in the pharmacy profession has created additional opportunities for system development and maintenance. Beyond the need for pharmacists to manage the day-to-day use of computer systems, managers also are needed to develop training procedures and to keep abreast of the rapid evolution of electronic data processing.

Chain pharmacies operate under a plethora of local, state, and national laws and regulations. Patient counseling, activities performed by ancillary pharmacy personnel, and packaging safety are just a few of the issues that are regulated. For that reason, government affairs specialists monitor legislation and regulations and serve as representatives of the chain corporation and the patients it serves.

Because nearly half of all medications dispensed are covered by third-party insurers, chain stores employ reimbursement program administrators to follow changes in these plans and implement them throughout the company's operation. Third-party administrators also market programs to HMOs, PPOs, and other managed care systems.

For students whose interest lies in marketing, the chain environment provides challenging opportunities in inventory management, product movement, and merchandising through the use of buyers and marketing managers. Pharmacists who enter this area are concerned with the acquisition and promotion of products and services needed to meet consumer demand.

Pharmacists in professional affairs and pharmacy operations are charged with monitoring developments in the practice of pharmacy and incorporating these changes into the chain operation. Their responsibilities put them in close contact with colleges of pharmacy, pharmacy associations, boards of pharmacy, and related organizations. These professionals must identify new opportunities for community involvement, plan and implement health-related programs, and develop staffing patterns. Moreover, they participate in designing the layout of pharmacy departments and in selecting and purchasing pharmacy equipment.

All of these career possibilities can be found in traditional chain pharmacy practice. Even more are developing as chains branch out into such innovative areas as freestanding wellness centers that address the needs of home care patients. Many chains are beginning to provide consultant services to long-term care facilities, in which pharmacists provide in-service training and counseling on medication regimens, while still performing their traditional drug distribution duties. Through these activities, chain pharmacists make a significant contribution in this rapidly developing arena.

Many chain corporations have begun selling and servicing durable medical equipment, sickroom supplies, respiratory and physical therapy products, health maintenance products (including diagnostic and testing equipment), and ostomy supplies. Marketing and maintaining these products require a pharmacist's expertise.

As of this writing, chain drugstores employ 54 percent of all pharmacy graduates, and the number grows every year. These companies offer career opportunities in every phase and type of pharmacy practice. Students who pursue a career in chain pharmacy have made an important decision: They have elected to practice pharmacy in one of this profession's most challenging, service-oriented settings. In this setting, they have the freedom to follow multiple career paths as they develop their potential and realize their strengths. Those who choose chain pharmacy will find endless opportunities for professional growth and satisfaction.

Deborah Lane, BS, RPh,
is a retail pharmacist who works
for Eckerd Drugs in Gainesville, Georgia.
Currently, she is president of the
Georgia State Board of Pharmacy.

Staff Pharmacy in a Large Chain Drugstore

I have been a retail pharmacist for 17 years, and I've worked in a chain outlet for the last six and a half. I can say without reservation that my work has consistently brought me challenges, rewards, and happiness.

I work in my hometown of Gainesville, Ga., a growing community of about 100,000 people. Practicing in my hometown has several advantages. For example, I've grown up with many of my patients. They are my friends and neighbors, and I know their families and children. I also know many of the area physicians. Practicing here is a tremendous responsibility, but sometimes it feels like a gift. Each day, I am able to help people I've known all my life. Usually it's in small ways, but I know I'm contributing, making the quality of their lives better. It gives me a special feeling.

The store I work in is large and fast-paced. We are open from 8 AM until midnight. Midday and early evenings are very busy, especially on Mondays and Fridays. Despite these patterns, no two days are alike. Much of my time is spent filling prescriptions. In fact, we fill between 300 and 400 prescriptions each day. While we have technicians to help with the packaging, labeling, billing, and other paperwork, it's still up to the pharmacist to do the actual counting, measuring, pouring, and, when necessary, compounding.

Pharmacists at my store have close contact with area physicians and, over time, we've built close rapport with them. They are not reluctant to ask our advice about particular drugs, potential conflicts in therapy, or treatment modifications. In the same way, we often call them to suggest therapy alterations, or to ask questions about billing. If we're concerned that a patient is doctor hopping, we don't hesitate to mention this to the physicians. These interactions are part of a continuing process of establishing professional respect. I know of many retail pharmacists who complain that physicians are pejorative or don't take them seriously, but we don't have that problem. I believe the reason we don't is that we are sure of ourselves and our abilities, and we evaluate circumstances carefully before initiating contact. Moreover, the fact that we are cordial and diplomatic throughout all correspondences works in our favor.

Another communication-intensive component of retail pharmacy is counseling patients on the proper use of therapy. Now, this activity is mandated, but in the years I've been with Eckerd, we have always taken time to perform this service. Doing it well can be a challenge, but I believe it increases patient compliance and results in better outcomes. Counseling also is important because it is an acknowledgement of the cognitive services pharmacists provide. Most chains have continuing education programs to help their pharmacists maintain their counseling skills. These programs emphasize the value of such communication tools as active listening and open-ended questions, demonstrative techniques that enable the pharmacist to determine what patients have learned in the counseling session, and role-playing exercises that show pharmacists how to sharpen their counseling skills.

Even with training and years of practical experience, impediments to counseling crop up regularly. One of the most frustrating is that, in a retail setting, pharmacists often do not know the conditions for which medications have been prescribed. And for the most part, little or no information is available about the patient's medical history. Pharmacists may ask for this information, but the patient does not have to reveal anything. In such cases, or when patients have sketchy recall about their histories, counseling becomes difficult. Legally, pharmacists are required only to make a "reasonable effort" in finding out about the patient's history and the therapy's current use. Still, it's difficult to leave it at that because most professionals want to serve their patients to the best of their abilities.

The busy environment in most chain pharmacies has a built-in impediment to effective counseling: time. If a patient comes in at the busiest hour of the day, when the phones are ringing, the pharmacist is alone behind the counter, and, say, the computers just went down, counseling is tough to do. In those trying circumstances, the temptation is to hand over the prescription and say, "Take so many of these pills this many times a day until the bottle is empty," and move along to the next order – especially if other anxious patients are waiting. Nevertheless, patients must have the right information, and the pharmacist has to make sure it is understood. At times, the pharmacist may not be able to go beyond the reasonable effort in determining the reason behind the prescription or the patient's history. This frustrates me because I know I could do more, given more time and, perhaps, some privacy with the patient.

A benefit of working in a busy environment is that each day it puts the pharmacist in contact with many different patients and a broad range of needs. This is perfect for me because I enjoy problem solving and dealing with people. The reason I am here instead of a robot or a technician is that I have the skills and knowledge that can help patients and physicians find the best solutions for problems in drug treatment. It is this challenge that keeps my practice fresh.

Contact with patients is important because much of retail practice involves one form or another of public relations. I must sell myself as a professional who can be trusted, I must sell the value of pharmacy itself, and I must sell the benefits of using this particular store. Most of this is accomplished through good communication with the patients – understanding what they need and helping them understand what I can provide.

I've found that the key to good pharmacist-patient rapport lies in never losing sight of the patient's needs and perspective. To make sure this happens, it's important to be a good listener and a good observer of people. If patients aren't feeling well, it's important to be sympathetic to their condition. Some patients want to talk about their ailment, but others just want to pick up their prescription and leave as quickly as possible. With many of my older customers, the communication between us is just as important as the medications they use.

It's important to remember that patients and customers don't just appear magically in the store. I often make presentations on pharmacy in local schools, from kindergarten to junior colleges. I talk about pharmacy as a career, discuss how consumers should approach their relationships with pharmacists, and address various health care issues. I make similar presentations at adult day care centers. These activities have great value to the community and are an effective form of marketing for Eckerd. Traditionally, retail pharmacists have been respected and trusted members of the community. Our special knowledge is a responsibility to be shared. And because of how our practices are structured, we are probably the most accessible of all health care professionals.

I believe my responsibilities should extend into the professional community. As a result, I have actively participated in associations for most of my career. Several years after I began practicing, I rejuvenated the local pharmacy association, which had sort of faded away. Later, I became involved with the state association. Both experiences have been rewarding. Associating with colleagues provides more than an opportunity to swap war stories. Through these activities I've learned how others have redesigned their pharmacies to cope with busy periods. I've learned better approaches to counseling and how to improve my interaction with physicians. Our meetings address such issues as third-party billing, managed care, the difficulties currently being faced by independents, and the impairment of professionals.

In 1988, through my work in the state association, I was appointed by the governor of Georgia to the state board of pharmacy. I am now president of the board and will finish out my term in the fall of 1993. During my tenure, I have worked with the disciplinary process and have been involved with licensing and impairment issues. The latter has been the most distressing because the problem is becoming increasingly visible. Many impaired pharmacists get into rehabilitation and are able to stay clean and get their licenses back, but it's painful to witness.

Another duty of the state board is to issue the state licensing exam. I enjoy this because it has kept me in touch with young pharmacists who are just getting their feet wet. Not only am I impressed with how well prepared most of today's students are, I also have been surprised to discover how many women are entering the profession. In 1975, when I graduated from the University of Georgia's College of Pharmacy, there were only 19 women in a class of 150. Now the admission classes are nearly 70 percent female.

Some of the benefits I enjoy are specific to a chain practice and can't be found in other retail settings. One is the flexibility of career paths in large operations. Also, chain pharmacists tend to have less contact with billing-based paperwork, most of which is handled by corporate headquarters. In essence, the chain pharmacist just has to verify the patient's coverage plan and use the computer to see what is covered. Other details – billing, collecting, and chasing down delinquent payments – are left to the corporation. That frees pharmacists to deal solely with pharmacy.

Working for a chain, pharmacists can work as consultants in nursing homes or serve in ambulatory surgical centers and other similar freestanding facilities. Moreover, there are plenty of opportunities to go beyond the hands-on component of pharmacy and undertake the responsibilities of managing a single store, multiple stores, or an entire district. Corporate positions in purchasing, marketing, contracts, policy making, management, or other administrative duties also are open to the chain pharmacist. Generally, chains also offer more scheduling flexibility than other practice settings. In fact, as a mother of two small children, I can testify that this is an ideal job because it meshes almost perfectly with family obligations. There is a great deal of latitude in setting work hours, including part-time, full-time, and extended-time options. My partners and I take advantage of the latter, and we work two extended-hour shifts and one regular shift. We have changed our schedule somewhat to help with patient counseling. We overlap more now. So, it might be more accurate to say we have "extended-hour shifts." This usually gives us three days on and four days off each week. Yet one more advantage of working for a chain is that starting salaries tend to be higher, too. In this state, the average retail pharmacist starts at between $40,000 and $42,000, but chain-based pharmacists generally are paid at the higher end of the scale. Salaries increase significantly when pharmacists get into local and corporate management.

For all the advantages, there are frustrations in this type of practice. For example, despite the flexibility of scheduling, our pharmacies are open nights, weekends, and holidays, and just about everyone has to take a turn working these hours. Very few retail pharmacists work Monday-through-Friday schedules. In addition, the workplace can be stressful at times because this is one of the few professions where a practitioner simply cannot afford to make mistakes. Another factor to consider is that retail pharmacists are working in businesses, which can be difficult at times. Our patients do not make appointments, they just walk into our stores – and sometimes they do so all at once.

Third-party reimbursement can be a difficult issue. Because every plan is different, I often feel as though I spend most of my time poring through the computer files to find out whether an individual is covered, whether the drug is covered, whether the patient has used up his pharmacy benefit, and what if any copayment is involved. Each patient must be billed on-line, which is no problem until the computers go down. When this happens – and it does happen – billing and the third-party verification become a nightmare.

Even though starting salaries are excellent, a pharmacist has to move into management or consulting to earn much more than cost-of-living pay increases. This can be frustrating for pharmacists who are perfectly happy behind the counter and have no desire to enter into these other areas.

Nevertheless, the positive features of chain pharmacy far outweigh the negatives. And in terms of opportunities for personal and professional growth, career advancement, remuneration, and daily challenges, I can't believe there's a better environment for a retail pharmacist.

Charles F. Monahan Jr., BS,
is president of the
Monahan Pharmacy, Inc.,
in Worcester, Massachusetts.

Home Care in a Chain Setting

Twenty years ago, everyone went to a drugstore to buy toothpaste and shampoo. Today, things have changed and over half of patent medicines and health and beauty aids are purchased in food stores. Only 20 percent of those items are bought in pharmacies.

That is why I expanded my small chain operation into home health care, which I believe is the future of pharmacy. When a patient goes into the hospital, cost containment is the name of the game. The cataract patient, for example, doesn't even stay overnight after an operation. These in-and-out patients need home health care services. They need beds, wheelchairs, dressings, and other supplies. Meeting those needs helps us compete against the giants of the industry.

We're not a medicine shop, but we're very close to that type of professional pharmacy. We don't sell a lot of the sundries we used to sell, and we've proved that it isn't necessary to stock those items in order to achieve high volume. Twenty-six years ago, we started with three employees. Now, we have 82. In that quarter century, we have expanded from one store to four.

We've remodeled the main pharmacy at least half a dozen times since we moved to its current location 18 years ago. Recently we took the main store, which had been approximately 5,000 square feet, and squeezed it into 1,000 square feet. Today, we're doing the same volume we used to do, but we're doing it in 20 percent of the space.

Our retail pharmacy is completely walled off from the rest of the business, which occupies 9,000 square feet. Half of that space serves as a showroom where customers can see wheelchairs, canes, and crutches. They also can talk to our nurse or pharmacist. We have certified professionals on staff to make sure braces and supports fit properly. We spend about half an hour training patients to use equipment they buy.

We have contracts with many HMOs and nursing agencies, and we are the preferred provider for an area hospice and for a number of health plans. For these clients, we supply durable medical equipment, oxygen, pain medications, prescription drugs, and home infusion therapy.

Most of our competitors are national companies whose gross annual sales range from $680 million down to about $6 million. Moreover, many nonpharmacy companies, including oxygen companies and certain equipment manufacturers, have gone into home care. We're able to withstand their competition because the home care services we offer belong in pharmacy. As chief executive, I spend my efforts establishing – and maintaining – the company's strategic direction. In successfully positioning this company in the marketplace, I've drawn on every experience I've ever had in pharmacy.

I became interested in pharmacy as a business and a profession when I worked during high school as a soda jerk in a local drugstore. While at Massachusetts College of Pharmacy, I held as many as four different part-time pharmacy jobs.

After graduating with a BS in pharmacy in 1962, I spent a year as a hospital pharmacist, working 40 hours a week for $80. In those days, retail pharmacists earned the big money – $100 a week. To make ends meet, I also worked part time in a retail store.

I enjoyed the technical challenge of the hospital pharmacy. There I learned compounding and new drug therapies, and I later put that experience to work in my business. As I said, I don't believe I ever wasted an experience.

I also adopted some of the philosophies of a pharmacist for whom I worked part time. He didn't sell cigarettes, greeting cards, or chocolates. The pharmacists who worked for him wore shirts and ties with white jackets. Classical music played in the background. And the pharmacy was exquisitely clean. Working for this man set me on a nontraditional course in the profession. As a result, I wasn't afraid to try new things. That was fortunate for me, because many pharmacies that didn't change ultimately went out of business. In time, I went to work for a small chain, which paid a better-than-average salary. After a year, I bought one of the company's smallest stores.

In those days all the pharmacies in Worcester (the second largest city in New England) referred customers who wanted a simple item like a cane to a single medical supply dealer. As soon as I got settled in my new store, I got rid of the soda fountain, the television tube tester, and the cosmetics. And as fast as I could, I started to carry wheelchairs, crutches, and canes. Little by little the acorn grew and, now, durable medical equipment is responsible for 60 percent of my business.

Even when I first started, I could see that the pharmacy business was in transition. There were 2,400 independently owned pharmacies in Massachusetts. There were no chains. By the end of the 1980s, there were approximately 900 chains and 300 independents in the state. Today, the chain operations hire 72 percent of pharmacy school graduates.

After opening my business, one of the first things I did was to join the Worcester County Pharmaceutical Association. With a group of recent pharmacy school graduates we rejuvenated the association, which was at a low ebb. Eventually I served as president.

Participating in professional organizations has been a big factor in the success of my business. Close contact with other pharmacists has made it possible to keep up with new ideas in the profession. As a result, I was able to implement a vision for my company by telling my own pharmacists about the trends I was spotting. In addition, I believe I was helping strengthen my profession.

In time, I served on the board of directors for the Massachusetts State Pharmaceutical Association. I also spent 10 years on the Board of Registration and Pharmacy, where we introduced legislation, made new rules and regulations, and coordinated efforts with the Department of Public Health.

For the four years I served as executive director of the pharmacy board, I was fortunate to be able to turn my businesses over to some very good managers. In addition, my wife is active in the business and shared some of my responsibilities. One of my sons, a registered pharmacist, runs our home infusion service. Another son, who is not a pharmacist, is active in our medical equipment business.

Although I am now back in charge of the business, I remain heavily involved as chairman of the board of trustees for the Massachusetts College of Pharmacy. In that capacity, I am spearheading the college's $20 million fundraising drive to build new buildings.

I also serve on the government affairs committee for the National Association of Chain Drug Stores (NACDS). This association gives me an opportunity to exchange ideas with colleagues from national chains with thousands of stores. It's a good place to find out about regulations, new laws, cost containment – to learn what's really going on in the profession.

People who want to run their own businesses still can find good opportunities in pharmacy, especially with the increasing need for home health care. A good place to start may be to buy a small-scale operation, say a home infusion franchise. Some of these are one-person operations. The parent company shows franchisees how to run their own businesses, and these folks seem to do well working for themselves.

But before you set out on your own, make sure you have learned something from every pharmacy-related experience you have. In any internship or externship, go beyond the professional aspects of pharmacy and learn how the business is run. Ask how much merchandise is on the shelf and learn what the payroll is. Find out what margin of profit the store needs to make on prescriptions. If you keep your curiosity alive and keep up with new trends in the profession, you will find as I have that you're in for a long and rewarding career.

Mark B. Dodge, BS, RPh,
is pharmacy manager at Eckerd Drugs,
in Clearwater, Florida.

The Chain Pharmacist as a Consultant

Many chain drugstore pharmacists spend most of their time filling prescriptions, counseling patients, managing inventories, and handling the paperwork associated with reimbursements. All of this certainly keeps them busy, but after a few years the challenge of their work may diminish. When that happens, some pharmacists decide to step away from their behind-the-counter duties and begin pursuing management careers. Others have no desire to become managers, preferring to seek new challenges that emphasize cognitive services without eliminating the hands-on component of a retail environment – and without diminishing the benefits associated with chain operations. Often, these pharmacists turn their attention to consulting services in order to exercise their cognitive and clinical skills. In addition to opening the door to new professional growth, consulting affords opportunities to work with different therapies and new modes of patient interaction and even to establish a foundation for future entrepreneurial activities.

Basically, three types of facilities employ chain pharmacists as consultants: ambulatory surgical centers, nursing homes, and adult care living facilities (ACLF). The pharmacist's responsibilities in these environments vary according to the client's needs. Some may contract with the drugstore simply to have prescriptions filled and to have medications and other supplies delivered. Others want the chain to provide a pharmacist who is able to offer a range of cognitive services, including site visits and interaction with staff and patients. Not infrequently, the client wants an arrangement that covers all these responsibilities.

Currently, I am charged with providing consulting services in a local ambulatory surgery center. Here in Florida, as is true in many states, these freestanding centers are bound by law to have a consultant pharmacist monitor the handling and use of medications – to conduct periodic reviews of drug inventories and medication-related documentation. These reviews serve as checks and balances to prevent shortages and to make sure providers in the facilities are complying with state and federal laws.

Ambulatory surgery centers must keep a running inventory of all controlled substances that are prescribed, administered, or dispensed to patients. Consequently, I visit my clients each month, generally on weekends, and compare their paperwork with current inventories as well as prescription and disposal records. In the end, I create documentation that verifies my findings.

This process is straightforward but demands attention to detail and is quite time-consuming. I must be thoroughly familiar with all the procedures and protocols that govern the use of every drug used. Moreover, I must determine whether medications have been dispensed according to state laws and the regulations set by the center's P&T committee. For example, one of my client centers requires multidose packaging used in an OR to indicate the date the package was opened: If the contents have not been used within 30 days of that date, the product has to be discarded. Part of my job is to identify the package and verify its contents, or note that the drug was disposed of properly. I also have to make sure that every prescription has a corresponding physician's order.

Because few surgical centers have centralized pharmacies, pharmacists usually have to perform monitoring comparisons in operating rooms, endoscopy suites, post-op areas, and the pharmacies where post-op prescriptions are dispensed. A busy surgical center may serve 15 patients each day, so it's easy to see that performing a 30-day review can be quite time-consuming.

Among other duties, the consultant pharmacist must serve actively on clients' pharmacy and therapeutics committees. In order to do this effectively, the pharmacist is required to maintain comprehensive knowledge about products on the formulary, to know the protocols and uses of these agents, and to review new products that may be considered for inclusion in the formulary.

In nursing homes, which also are required by law to hire consultants, the pharmacist's responsibilities are more extensive and clinical in nature. In these institutions, pharmacists not only serve as a double check for prescription medications, they also are expected to use their drug information skills to suggest changes in therapy and in the way medications are administered. The nursing home consultant has access to patients' histories and charts, a tremendous advantage that is uncommon in the retail setting. This full access enables the pharmacist to contribute on equal footing with physicians and nurses.

Often, a nursing home will have a drugstore prepare medications in a unit-dose form. In such cases, a great deal of the consultant's responsibility can be discharged in the drugstore as the pharmacist goes over each patient's chart and compares entries with the medications prescribed. The pharmacist makes sure lab values are correct for the medications being used. He or she must evaluate dosages with consideration for the patient's condition and search for drug-drug or other possible interactions. At the same time, it is necessary to look for protocol conflicts that, left unresolved, could reduce the efficacy of patient care and lead to a citation from a state inspector. Naturally, any recommendations for changes in therapy are made to the patient's physician. This requirement alone can test the pharmacist's communication skills, because nursing home patients are treated by many different physicians.

The consultant pharmacist who works for a chain may have to go on-site and follow the nurse on a medication run to see how therapies are being administered. This is valuable interaction because it creates an opportunity to interact with nurses and patients. During visits to a client, the pharmacist can discuss alternative dosing strategies, demonstrate how a new product is to be administered, or ask patients about medications they receive.

The newest type of institution to seek the expertise of consultant pharmacists is the adult care living facility. Patients in ACLFs do not need the level of care provided by a nursing home, but they may require help with cooking, bathing, and dressing. They also may need help taking their medications correctly and on time, and ACLF facilities maintain centralized pharmacies and staff nurses who help with this. Nevertheless, patients are expected to be able to take medications on their own, and they have the right to refuse to take them.

As in a nursing home, the consultant pharmacist in an ACLF has access to patients' charts, checks medications for appropriateness and dosage, and tries to avert interaction problems. On the other hand, there is little or no patient contact in adult care facilities and, at least in Florida, the law doesn't mandate a role for consultant pharmacists. Even so, most ACLFs do hire consultants for legal and insurance purposes. Besides, consultants help eliminate dispensing errors, boost quality of care, and reduce operating costs.

I came to work at Eckerd Drugs in Clearwater in 1981 – after I graduated from the Massachusetts College of Pharmacy. This store is fairly busy, and we often fill 200 or more prescriptions a day. I enjoy life in a chain operation, but after nearly a decade behind the counter I was beginning to look for new challenges in the retail environment. Consulting appealed to me because I knew it placed a strong emphasis on decision making and cognitive services without diminishing the importance of hands-on work with medications. In Florida, as in many other states, a pharmacist must get a separate license to practice as a consultant. For me, the process required 12 hours of seminars and courses, followed by an exam.

While the state consulting license process does demand specialized study, it does not require the pharmacist to have prior experience in a consulting practice. As a result, I knew I had the skills to provide the services clients needed, but I was not completely confident that I could walk into a facility and start working. The feeling was similar to the one I had after graduating from pharmacy school: I had plenty of knowledge but little experience in a real-life practice. Just in the nick of time, a friend who owned a local independent pharmacy gave me a call.

He had been providing consultant services for two ACLFs and a small retirement community but decided he needed to devote more time to his retail business. He knew that I had recently been licensed and was hoping for some consulting experience. He asked if I'd like him to show me the ropes with the understanding that I eventually would take over his clients. He introduced me around and let me shadow him for a few months until

I became familiar with the needs of his clients. In addition to my other duties at Eckerd, I've been providing consulting services ever since.

Some chains have programs that allow experienced staffers to learn how to function as consultants. Pharmacists begin by dispensing and are eased gradually into cognitive services. Depending on the chain and the environment, experienced pharmacists may be able to limit their practice activities to the provision of consultant services.

Consulting can be a very rewarding entrepreneurial activity for pharmacists who are considering a career move. In fact, an established consultant can make $70,000 to $80,000 per year. Apart from the special licensing requirement, work in this field calls for significant continuing education. For example, to maintain a license in Florida, the consultant must earn credit for 12 hours of continuing education each year in addition to the 15 hours required for the general pharmacy license.

Trends in health care will ensure the growing need for consultant pharmacists. America's geriatric population will increase steadily over the next 20 years and will cause long-term care operations to proliferate. Moreover, advances in medical science will enable people to live longer. At the same time, ambulatory surgery facilities will become more widespread. And last but not least, managed care will become more prevalent. This system embraces pharmacists' cognitive skills and will increase the demand for their services.

The rewards are great in consulting. In the retail environment, most of a pharmacist's satisfaction lies in the precision of filling prescriptions and the satisfaction associated with counseling and helping patients. Consultant work offers an added dimension of complex decision making and problem solving. It places a stronger emphasis on drug information, and it yields the pleasure of peer acknowledgement that comes with working on a team with physicians and nurses. All in all, consulting is an excellent option for pharmacists who want to diversify their practices and sharpen their clinical skills in a chain environment.

*Albert F. Lockamy, Jr., RPh, BS,
manages pharmacy operations for a Revco store
in Raleigh, North Carolina.*

Store-level Management

I've spent much of my career trying to overcome the stereotype that I'm "just" a chain pharmacist. Historically, there has been a perception that chain pharmacists are not as caring and don't know their customers the way the folks at the corner drugstore do.

That perception is completely untrue. I have never thought of myself as being just a chain pharmacist. I am a practicing community pharmacist who counsels patients and provides pharmaceutical services to institutions outside of the store setting.

Gone are the days when pharmacists work high in the sky, elevated behind a barrier that isolated them from their customers. I know most of the customers who come to this store, and I want to know them all. In many chains, management encourages its pharmacists to get acquainted with customers because personal relationships keep them coming back.

As a pharmacist-manager, I am responsible for pharmacy operations. I also assist the store manager in the day-to-day operation of a 10,000-square-foot drugstore in a regional chain of 1,700 stores. Keeping pharmacy inventory, scheduling sales associates and technicians, handling payroll, and dealing with vendors are all part of my job.

But my most important responsibility is counseling patients, particularly now that more and more drugs are being sold over the counter. Also, over the next several years some of the top-name prescription drugs will be going off patent and will be sold over the counter as well. As that happens, there will be an increasing need to educate patients about how to take these medications properly.

In addition to counseling patients about over-the-counter drugs, federal legislation now requires pharmacists to talk with each patient before handing over a prescription. This is a far cry from the way things were when I graduated from pharmacy school in 1964. We were taught not to intervene in the doctor-patient relationship. When a customer asked about a prescription, the pharmacist was supposed to ask, "What did your doctor say it was for?"

Personally, I have always thought the interaction between pharmacist and patient is extremely important. In fact, I consider pharmacists to be the gatekeepers of health care for their communities, regardless of whether they own independent stores – as I once did – or work for a chain.

It is surprising how many people don't have a family physician. And especially during hard economic times, patients often come to pharmacists first when health problems arise. Usually, this is because pharmacists are so accessible. People expect pharmacists to be knowledgeable about the significance of histories and conditions and to be able to help them make reasonable decisions about how to handle different problems. As the public becomes more health conscious and price conscious, it's obvious that more demands will be placed on pharmacists.

There have been times when I've had to redirect people with serious health problems. Once, in fact, I actually had to tell a person, "You need to see a doctor *now*. If you don't have one, I can either call a clinic or an emergency room for you." Another man came in complaining about terrible heartburn. When I asked him to describe his symptoms, he told me that his left arm was completely numb. He began turning pale in front of me, so I dialed 911. He was having a heart attack.

On a less dramatic scale there are many situations where I can be helpful by making sure people are buying OTC drugs for the right reasons. For example, during an epidemic of chicken pox in our county many customers came in wondering whether they should put hydrocortisone cream on their children's rashes. I cautioned them against it because the worst thing they could do is to use cortisone for a viral infection.

The importance of patient counseling becomes even more apparent if one considers that, after drug abuse, noncompliance probably is the number two drug problem in America. If we can't teach people that they must take an antibiotic for a full course, most of the prescription is likely to sit on a shelf for a couple of years. Then, not only is there a risk of creating a drug-resistant organism, the next time the patient gets sick, he may take the leftover medication, which will either have deteriorated or may not be appropriate for the new illness. Such unnecessary drug misadventures add to the cost of health care.

The older a patient gets, the more likely the occurrence of such scenarios. Many elderly people regularly take four or five medications, and this can be both confusing and expensive. As a consequence, they may decide to stop one medication, reasoning they'll feel just as good. But, almost inevitably, as they start eliminating drugs, their health problems get progressively worse. I believe situations like this could be avoided if physicians and pharmacists were to share common data. In that way the pharmacist would be able to monitor therapeutic outcomes and provide effective pharmaceutical care.

At Revco, we enter detailed patient profiles in our computer system. Every time we fill a prescription, our software reviews and analyzes the patient's medication history and alerts us to any incompatibilities, contraindications, or allergies. The system will freeze if we fail to enter appropriate information, which often must be obtained by calling the prescribing physician. There's no doubt that the pharmacist can be an important factor in the overall health of a community.

One of the greatest satisfactions in my job comes from knowing that the medication and advice I give will help patients. I think that if patients believe in the drugs they use, they are more likely to get better. If I can help them understand the hows and the whys of their prescriptions, and if I encourage them to comply with their physician's orders, I'm making a big contribution to their therapy.

Retail pharmacy is the wrong field for a person who doesn't enjoy people. If you prefer to work alone without interruptions, and if you don't communicate easily, consider instead a career that will let you work in a laboratory or in some other setting removed from the demands of questioning customers.

In my store, we handle approximately 1,200 prescriptions each week. That's a lot of volume, but our pharmacists have technicians to help dispense the drugs. We also have sales associates to finish the transactions, although if we want more time to interact with patients, we may elect to ring up the sales ourselves.

Revco's management structure allows the pharmacist-manager the opportunity to oversee pharmacy operations. In my case, this means I supervise several employees, including the assistant pharmacy manager, sales associates, and technicians. I'm also responsible for our professional displays. I enjoy my management duties because they require my involvement in store operations, in solving a broad range of problems, and in implementing long-range policies. As a chain manager, I like the challenges of the business side of pharmacy.

For the successful manager, advancement in a chain will come naturally as the company expands and opens new stores. Store-level managers are promoted from the ranks of pharmacists who are assistant managers. New district managers are found among the chain's pharmacy managers. The opportunities for promotion are sure to decrease as a pharmacist climbs the management ladder, but most of my company's top people are pharmacists. It is comforting to know that somebody up there understands my problems.

Because Revco encourages its pharmacists to earn advanced degrees, a PharmD or MBA may be helpful in a career at this company. Not only will the advanced education reflected in these degrees help pharmacists climb the promotional ladder, but they also have great value in daily business.

My company has encouraged me to become involved in local, state, and national professional organizations, as well as pharmacy governing boards. Because of the leadership positions I have held within these organizations, I have been able to travel and promote my profession. I make it a point to take my family with me on these trips in order to compensate for some of the long hours and irregular schedule that I keep during the week.

As a pharmacist-manager, I have made a commitment to community involvement. For example, in addition to managing the daily operations of this store, I provide pharmaceutical services to a local nursing home, a rest home, and an alcohol dependency center. My company encouraged me to initiate these services after I made it clear that those institutions would be forced to go elsewhere for pharmaceutical care if we did not provide it for them. Every one of those clients came to me and said, "Listen, Al. We need you to help us in our institution." I've found that if I can convince my company that my ideas are profitable and useful in the community, higher management will support me. In fact, other chains are beginning to provide institutional services, and this is a departure from the chain pharmacist's traditional role.

One of my proudest achievements came in helping the University of North Carolina at Chapel Hill establish the nation's first full-time pharmacy rotation program in chemical dependence. This evolved from my work with a local alcohol treatment center and from my academic duties as an associate professor in pharmacy at Chapel Hill.

Jobs are available for retail pharmacists in nearly every chain. One of the best ways to find openings is to attend career days at school or talk to a chain pharmacist where you might like to work. When students ask me about jobs, I always direct them to my district manager.

The best way to prepare for a job like mine is to spend a summer working in a chain. How else could you be sure this career is right for you? If you decide it is, work on developing good communication skills, as well as work accuracy and speed, and the ability to prioritize tasks that need to be accomplished. Get involved in professional associations. This will give you a voice in your future because pharmacy organizations significantly influence legislation and regulations that affect pharmacists.

I decided to become a pharmacist when a high school aptitude test indicated I should choose a scientific career that allowed me work with people. After pharmacy school, I worked in an independent store. A few years later, I ventured out on my own and opened my own store. But competition was tough, and I eventually sold out to another pharmacist in the area. Again, I went back to work for an independent, but I wasn't satisfied there. Finally, someone recommended me for a job here, and I have been with Revco more than 20 years. For all that time as a pharmacist and then store manager, I have felt that I was able to make a difference in my community and my profession. When I started out, I could have stayed behind the pharmacy counter and still had a satisfying life. But I wanted to do something more for my profession. I wanted to make a contribution. The chain pharmacy environment has allowed me to do that.

That old saying is true: You get out of life only what you put in.

Mark Brackett, BS,
is a pharmacy district manager
for Kinney Drugs
in Gouverneur, New York.

District-level Management

I started with Kinney Drugs as a stock boy when I was 16 years old. I was already interested in pharmacy because an uncle I admired was a pharmacist. Through his example, I saw pharmacy as a way to become a respected businessman as well as a medical professional, with an opportunity to help people. I have always found the business side of pharmacy appealing, especially because of my interest in management.

I worked for this company throughout pharmacy school and was hired as a full-time pharmacist following graduation. I have just completed my twenty-second year with Kinney. After working as a staff pharmacist for about six months, I became an assistant manager. This position gave me the opportunity to devote a great deal of time and effort to pursuing my management goals. My bosses allowed me to set my pace for advancement, and this attitude still holds true in our company.

Before long, I was managing my own store. I was given ample opportunity to attend management courses and seminars. Two years later, I was given the added responsibility of developing a long-term care center to serve several facilities. From there I went on to become director of nursing home services for the entire company. Then, in 1985 I was assigned to my current position as pharmacy district manager and director of Kinney's long-term care services. Sometimes I feel that I have held most of the positions in the company. In my current role, I am responsible for 12 of my company's 36 pharmacies in New York and Vermont.

Through the years I have found the most important aspect of management is encouraging people to develop, because they are the ones who make a business successful. I derive a great deal of satisfaction from watching the progress of the pharmacists I supervise. I especially enjoy being a part of the professional growth of students I have hired.

My days are seldom predictable. Generally, I catch up on messages and details to start the day. Some of my time is spent scheduling staff vacations and coverage, corresponding with people we are thinking of hiring, communicating with interns, and working with nursing homes. It seems as though nearly every day I talk with one organization or another about ways our pharmacists can work with them on public interest issues. One of the more popular activities is making presentations to senior citizen groups. Our company is not inclined to sit around meeting rooms too much, and I am thankful for this. Our attitude is that we should listen to our front-line people and react as best we can. One of the projects I headed was a task force on recruitment and retention of pharmacists in our chain. Twelve pharmacists from the field met with us monthly for two years.

They told us their feelings about our company, and we listened carefully and worked to make appropriate changes.

After I finish my daily tasks, I visit some of the stores in my district. When I go into a store, I first observe the general atmosphere. Then, on a casual basis, I try to bring the pharmacy staff up to date on corporate information, including the chain's figures and where that particular store fits in. We talk about sales figures, profit or loss, gross profit percentages, inventory control, payroll, and expenses. Because Kinney Drugs is owned by its employees, I usually have very alert listeners for these discussions. And because our employees enjoy profit sharing on a per-store basis, they have added incentive to know how the location is doing and learn what can be done to improve profits.

Next, I listen to any concerns of the pharmacy staff and address them as best I can at that time, with follow-up as necessary. Supervisors lose credibility unless they are responsive to the needs and questions of those under them. Many times, employees share ideas with me that can make their jobs easier or result in greater efficiency. I pass these ideas on to other stores in the chain. I frequently see my ideas and those of the people I supervise come to fruition. That is very rewarding.

As a supervisor, I know the importance of communication, especially in the face of the changes that are coming so rapidly in our profession. Consequently, when a project keeps me out of the stores for an extended period, or if I feel there is some confusion over certain subjects, I call the pharmacists in for a luncheon meeting. During a two- to three-hour lunch, I listen to the concerns of the group and try to clear up any confusion. The exchange of ideas and renewed enthusiasm that result make it well worth the time and the cost of the lunch.

As changes take place in the profession, the role of the retail pharmacist is being transformed dramatically. As we leave behind the dispensing function and begin accepting responsibility for cost-effective drug therapy, change is inevitable. The pharmacist of tomorrow will be more deeply involved than ever before in managing drug therapies and providing appropriate information to the patient.

In recognition of these changes, I have been spending a lot of time working to develop a program that will give on-the-job training to pharmacy technicians. These technicians can perform the routine tasks of counting and pouring and can do most of the data entry. However, a pharmacist still must check the information for accuracy. As technicians take over noncognitive aspects of dispensing, the pharmacist will be able to spend more time counseling patients on the proper use of medications.

Our company has adopted a program to educate and equip our pharmacists with the counseling skills that will enable them to meet the needs of our customers. Most of the session involves interactive learning in a workshop setting. In addition to ensuring that we conform to federal pharmacy regulations, this program usually brings out the best in our pharmacists.

Apart from my duties as district manager, I direct Kinney's long-term care services for nursing homes, intermediate care facilities, and prisons. We provide pharmacy services for those institutions as well as the actual medications that are packaged in forms that work best for each facility. We generate computer printouts of physician order forms, medication and administration records, and other information that can help ensure cost-effective therapy. Moreover, we conduct drug regimen reviews and serve as pharmacy consultants. This is a very popular activity for our retail pharmacists, because working as a consultant is so dramatically different from retail pharmacy. Pharmacists can work at their own pace performing reviews in association with the nursing and medical staff. I often find that pharmacists who work as consultants are rejuvenated in their attitude toward pharmacy.

Some but not all of our store managers are pharmacists. We don't require them to accept this dual responsibility. However, many pharmacists find rewards in the added responsibility, both financially and from the standpoint of career satisfaction.

In this company, there is ample opportunity for pharmacists to become senior managers. In fact, our president and our senior vice president both are pharmacists. Because pharmacy is the backbone of our business, it is only natural to have so many pharmacists in the upper management of the company.

There is a great deal of discussion today about advanced pharmacy degrees. In my opinion, experience is more valuable in a retail setting than advanced degrees. In fact, practical courses in communication, finance, business, and psychology are likely to be more useful in advancing a career in the chain setting. With my company's help, I have completed many workshops and seminars on those topics.

Pharmacists pursuing rewarding careers as managers in retail pharmacy should learn every job in the store. Although the pharmacist may not be doing these jobs on a regular basis, it is important at least to know how they should be done. Above all, as a student and as a young pharmacist you must build a strong base of knowledge about all aspects of your profession.

The best preparation for a career in retail pharmacy is an internship. My company provides many of these, and some years we have an intern in almost every store. This has proved to be beneficial because we hire many of our interns after they graduate. For that reason, I make it a point to pay close attention to individual interns to learn whether they may be compatible with our organization. I try to shift them around among several stores so they can learn different perspectives about people and settings. With all of the staff, I stress the importance of working together for a smooth-running operation. Often, I try to involve the interns in some of the basic personnel issues. Above all, I emphasize the need for quality pharmacy care and for treating each patient as an individual.

Keeping in tune with the business and the profession is extremely important for managers. As part of this process, I subscribe to many professional and business journals. And I belong to the local chapter of our state pharmaceutical society. This exposure allows me to follow issues as they develop in other parts of the nation, and it helps me prepare for changes in the business.

It takes a great deal of dedication and hard work to advance in pharmacy management. Often, the necessary management skills have to be developed outside the regular work schedule. For instance, one of our manager trainees once reported to the warehouse at 5 AM on his day off so he could ride with the freight truck on a 12-hour run. I'm certain that was a tiring day, but now, 11 years later, he understands the trucking part of this business better than most people do. If a pharmacist has the required dedication, the door is always open for advancement in chain pharmacy. Speaking for myself, I can't imagine a more interesting career.

Region-level Management

A. William LaRose, BS,
is a pharmacy region manager
for CVS Peoples in
Montvale, New Jersey.

Community practice appealed to me from the start. My work always put me in contact with different types of people and, now, it gives me the challenge of running a business. Joining a drugstore chain early in my career made it possible for me to broaden my horizons in both of those areas.

My interest in pharmacy can be traced to my junior year in high school. I was strong in science and had good interpersonal skills, and a career-preference test suggested I consider a career in pharmacy. Add to that the fact that my family lived across the street from a pharmacist, who encouraged me to go in that direction, and I was launched at an early age.

As a student at the Philadelphia College of Pharmacy and Science, I spent three years working part time for an independent pharmacy. I learned about customer service, was able to talk with physicians, and filled prescriptions under the guidance of the owner. This reinforced my inclination toward community practice.

After graduation in 1977, I moved back to Binghamton, NY, and went to work as a graduate intern for an independent pharmacy until I received my pharmacy license.

Through the county pharmaceutical association, I met several CVS pharmacists who liked their jobs because they felt as if they were running their own businesses. The company believed that even though pharmacists worked for a large corporation, they could make their own professional decisions under the philosophy "If this were your business, what would you do?" Naturally, I was intrigued by this. CVS also had an excellent reputation in the community. When I heard there were job openings, I put in an application. I've been with CVS now for 15 years.

My first three years were spent working as a pharmacist in several Binghamton stores. Usually I was teamed up with another pharmacist and two or three pharmacy technicians. The technicians operated the cash register and answered telephones. At that time we didn't have computers so they also performed such clerical functions as typing prescription labels. With their help, the pharmacists were free to concentrate on filling prescriptions and counseling patients.

It was an excellent work environment. The pharmacists and the store manager functioned as a team. We didn't report to each other. Unlike pharmacists at some other chains, CVS pharmacists are responsible for just the pharmacy department. The store manager takes care of the front of the store.

Our stores can be described as neighborhood drugstores. As is true in independent pharmacies, prescriptions are the heart of our business. We also carry health and beauty aids, cosmetics, and OTC products for colds, allergies, and first aid.

The stores average 8,500 square feet – larger than most neighborhood stores but much smaller than some of the deep discounters. Typically, we are located in neighborhoods or strip centers. CVS stores that are in malls usually don't have pharmacies because most people don't like to go to a mall to get their prescriptions filled.

I took my first step into field management when I was promoted to pharmacy supervisor and given responsibility for 15 pharmacy departments in my zone. After two years in upstate New York, I accepted a lateral transfer to the New York-New Jersey metropolitan area in 1983. I believed the move would be advantageous for my career because it was to a newer, high-growth market in a metropolitan area.

When I first became a pharmacy supervisor, I had to make some big adjustments. A pharmacist in a store – regardless of volume – fills prescriptions, talks to customers, schedules hours, monitors inventory, and tries to improve customer service. For the most part, every task has been completed at the end of the day.

As a supervisor, I was frustrated in the beginning. At the end of the day, my "to do" list kept growing. I was continually carrying tasks over, trying to keep track of several different things for days.

Another adjustment was in learning to set priorities and deciding where to spend my time. My territory encompassed three different market areas. From my office, I could travel two hours in three different directions before reaching the boundaries. It was difficult to figure out where I was needed and how to be effective once I got there. Depending on the problems I encountered, I might spend two days in one store. Sometimes I had to spend an entire week in a market area, visiting four or five stores.

I tried to use every minute as wisely as possible. While driving, I would plan my store visits. Eventually, I started using a tape recorder to organize my thoughts. I also listened to personal-development cassettes on management techniques.

Through skill development and the ability to achieve profitable results, I was promoted to pharmacy region manager. I oversee 13 pharmacy supervisors and two pharmacy human resource managers who are responsible for staffing, interviewing, recruiting, and coordinating college relations in our region.

Primarily, I am an administrator, responsible for 300 stores in four states. I work with pharmacy supervisors to develop a business plan that results in a profitable business operation without sacrificing customer service. We do have payroll and inventory considerations, but customer service must be our number one priority. If it were allowed to become secondary, our business would quickly cease to grow.

I believe we have an important responsibility to help educate our communities on important health issues. Our pharmacists make presentations to senior citizen groups, schools, and civic organizations. In fact, we have nearly 80 programs to offer on such topics as proper use of medication, drug abuse, and poison prevention. We advertise these programs in pamphlets that are displayed in the pharmacies. We also call and write to let schools and civic organizations know what we offer. Our programs, entitled *Healthwise*, are well received.

As a pharmacy region manager, I divide my time between one day and a half to two days in the office and three days in the field. I'll spend a day with a pharmacy supervisor, visiting stores and talking with managers, pharmacists, and customers.

The added responsibility was difficult at first as I tried to adjust my career to suit my home life. After two or three months, I found a perfect balance by sharpening my time-management skills and setting priorities. I also have the good fortune to have excellent people reporting to me. This allows me to concentrate my time in the field. It also allows me to spend time with my wife and three boys.

I have plenty of responsibility and a great deal of autonomy. In fact, I do feel as if I am in charge of my own business. I enjoy interacting with other people, from supervisors to customers, and working with the advertising, operations, purchasing, and human resource departments in my company.

As great as it is for me, this job isn't for everyone. Someone who wants a community practice with intense patient interaction might be disappointed. Because I have gone into management, I don't see patients very often. Instead, I coach pharmacy supervisors. In turn, they manage pharmacists, who are the ones with constant patient contact. I am somewhat removed from that part of the business.

In addition, the hours I work are long. Twelve-hour days are not uncommon, especially if travel time is included. Still, I devote most weekends to my family. Someone looking for a regular nine-to-five job might find disappointment in my position.

Salary and benefits are generally better in a chain than in an independent pharmacy. Career opportunities also tend to be better because there are more avenues for advancement.

At CVS, the entry point is the staff pharmacy position. We are looking for people who can communicate well and who will cooperate with store managers in a team environment to ensure the entire store functions as a unit. From that level pharmacists can follow several different paths. They can go into field operations, which includes pharmacy supervision. They can go into human resources, becoming human resource managers.

There also are opportunities in corporate pharmacy operations. For example, the managed care department at CVS has several pharmacists that negotiate contracts with HMOs, employer groups, and third-party administrators. In pharmacy purchasing, our pharmacists work with manufacturers and vendors in making decisions about product selection.

Finally, pharmacists in a large chain environment can shape their careers toward corporate management. At CVS, pharmacists hold positions at the vice president and executive vice president levels. There are many opportunities to climb the next rung of the ladder because this is still a growing company.

For those interested in working for a chain pharmacy it is never too soon to start refining interpersonal skills. Throughout one's career, success will hinge on the ability to communicate with patients, supervisors, peers, and subordinates. This is advice I give students when I talk about pharmacy careers.

It's gratifying to dispel some of the myths about working for a chain. When I was in pharmacy school, I heard again and again that chains don't care about individuals and that their pharmacists don't have much support. Some chains may be that way, but they can't all be painted with the same brush. Speaking for myself, I'm glad I chose community practice and went to work for CVS. I encourage any student to follow a similar path.

William G. Thien, BS,
is vice president for health services
for Walgreen Company
in Deerfield, Illinois.

Corporate-level Management

One of my favorite stories about this company started with a phone call from a panicked customer at Chicago's O'Hare airport. He had forgotten to pack his important medication and was just about to board a flight to San Francisco, en route to Hong Kong. There was no way he could leave the country without those pills.

Not knowing what else to do, he ran to a pay phone and called his local pharmacist, who said, "Don't worry, let Walgreen take care of this problem for you."

The pharmacist called Walgreen's district office in San Francisco and arranged to have a store near the airport deliver the prescription to the airline ticket counter. Sure enough, when the man walked off the plane to make his tight connection, he was handed the medication with a note that said, "Please send a check for $3.49 at your convenience – and have a nice trip."

This story illustrates the challenge we face in managing a chain: combining technology with individual creativity to solve problems in patient care without losing sight of the bottom line. Our sophisticated computer network made it easy to transfer the customer's prescription to California. But it was a pharmacist named Steve King who made the story possible. He was the bridge between technology and the patient.

Much of pharmacy's excitement lies in making decisions and solving problems in a health care system that is changing dramatically. Say that as a corporate manager I want to stock a new drug that I believe will benefit our patients. I also believe it will be profitable for my company. The problem is this: How can I achieve distribution in more than 1,700 stores without driving inventory costs through the roof?

Managing such a dilemma takes a lot of cooperation among our purchasing people, our distribution people, the product's manufacturer, and physicians who prescribe the medication.

Finding the right answer is complicated further by the fact that this isn't a black-and-white issue. There may be 100 good answers, but management's job is to find the best one. As is true of many quandaries that confront large chain operations, even approaching the problem requires creative thinking.

Unfortunately, the process of scientific education sometimes conditions students away from this kind of creativity. For five years they are told, "This is the right answer, and that's the wrong one." While this may be good training for the technical aspects of pharmacy, it can limit one's view of the world while moving up the corporate ladder. The demands of business require examination of many possible approaches to a problem, and students who want to become effective managers will have to free themselves from this rigid aspect of their educational experience.

I hear from Walgreen pharmacists all over the country who are devising ways to make technology serve them and their patients better. The ideas they send me aren't always tempered by the realities of cost, but that's fine with me because worrying about cost is my job. It is my responsibility to encourage the free and upward flow of their ideas and to find ways to afford the best of them.

More often than not, this works, and I consider it a vital process. It is extremely important for our people to give us suggestions – including criticism – about the way we operate our stores. As General Patton said, "If we're all thinking the same way, then somebody isn't thinking."

Many factors are causing changes in retail pharmacy. Underlying them all is the question of how we can continue increasing our professional services in a cost-effective manner. In other words, how can we give patients more tomorrow than we're giving them today without having to charge significantly more?

In the search for an answer to that question lies vast opportunity. I can't imagine a more exciting challenge for a young pharmacist. It excites me, too, but today's challenges weren't an issue when I learned to practice pharmacy.

Even so, look how far we've come with computers. Patient profiles, drug interactions, tax documents for customers, instant access to prescription records – these services are almost standard now. Not many years ago they were barely conceivable.

My generation can't even imagine the things technology will allow us to do. We've set a basic standard with computers. Now, it's up to a younger generation to see how far they can advance it. The application of computers in pharmacy has miles to go before we'll have learned what they can really do for us. Robotics, now just becoming a reality, will take us places we've never even dreamed about.

I've tried in my career never to lose the desire for learning. When computers came on the scene, I went to night school to study the history of their technology and to learn how to program them. I said, "Hey, that stuff is going to hit my profession 20 years from now, and I'd better learn something about it." It didn't take 20 years; it took only 10.

The pursuit of education is always admirable and always valuable, but unless it has a practical, functional application, it will never turn you into a problem solver. It may spur you to think of new ideas. But it probably won't teach you to implement those ideas and push them until they become operational. Most of the knowledge I have that's been useful in my career was gained in pharmacy school and in the drugstore.

I've never consciously sought to advance my career. But I have a competitive spirit that makes me want to be the best I can be at whatever

I'm doing at the moment. When I was a pharmacist, I tried to be the best pharmacist there was. As a manager, I've always wanted to excel. Attitude has a lot to do with success, whether it's conscious or not. When people enjoy their work and try to do a superior job, opportunities have a way of creating themselves.

On a pragmatic level, refined communication skills are more responsible than any other factor for success in pharmacy. And they can be learned. I'm not certain that one can be taught to care about patients, to be concerned, but this is also a valuable trait. Who can say which is more important? If you care but are unable to communicate with people, what good can result?

Good judgment – like that exercised by Steve King – is just as vital. This quality is what makes the pharmacist pick up the phone to consult with a physician. An instinct sets off alarms when a patient's prescriptions come from too many different physicians. It's a gift that enables pharmacists to solve problems for people who appear at their counters each day.

Pharmacists interested in becoming corporate managers in chain operations should do whatever is necessary to develop strong economic and business backgrounds. Here, specialty education can be helpful because increasing emphasis is being placed on business in pharmacy. There's no reason to expect this to change, because mixing business with pharmacy usually has positive results. It creates a healthy conflict because it underlines the need to balance professional judgment with good economic decisions.

This combination is unique in retailing. If you own a hardware store, you need only be a good businessman. If you run a chain of shoe stores, there's no reason for you to be an expert on leather or shoelaces. But unless retail pharmacists have parallel talents in business and pharmacy, one of two things is sure to happen: We'll go bankrupt, or we'll be replaced with machinery.

Opportunities in Hospital Pharmacy

Joseph A. Oddis, ScD,
is executive vice president of the
American Society of Hospital Pharmacists.

There has never been as exciting a time as now to begin a career in hospital pharmacy. Not only are well-paying jobs widely available, but the range of positions and job responsibilities in hospitals and other institutional settings presents numerous options. Scan the personnel ads in any monthly issue of the *American Journal of Hospital Pharmacy,* and this will be apparent. Best of all, the pharmacists who fill these positions make real contributions to the well-being of an institution's patients – and of the institution itself.

Once hospital pharmacists were relegated to a basement "drug room," where they had little opportunity for contact with patients or other health professionals. They were seen primarily as materials managers. This picture of hospital practitioners has faded into history. Today, pharmacists are found throughout the hospital's patient care areas, and they are valued both as clinical professionals on the patient's multidisciplinary team and as forces for cost-effective health care.

Now more than ever before, physicians, nurses, and other members of the patient care team rely on America's approximately 40,000 hospital pharmacists for advice on medication selection, administration, and dosage levels. And hospital executives look to pharmacists for help in ensuring appropriate drug use and dosing, minimizing the hospital's liability, and controlling skyrocketing drug costs.

Since the early 1960s, hospital pharmacists have gradually shifted their primary attention from the drug product itself to the quality of drug use and the important health needs of individual patients. Today, hospital pharmacists are strong advocates of the concept of a practice model in which the pharmacist takes increased responsibility for the outcome of a patient's drug therapy.

Pharmacists are increasingly taking a patient-centered approach to the safe, appropriate, and cost-conscious use of drug products. Hospital pharmacists help patients use medications safely and appropriately by performing a number of patient-specific clinical services:

- monitoring drug therapy by reviewing patient charts and providing written or oral follow-up to the prescriber
- monitoring, documenting, reporting, and managing adverse drug reactions
- evaluating the appropriateness of drug use through a structured,

ongoing process
- performing pharmacokinetic consultations to evaluate drug levels in the patient's body
- providing nutritional support consultations

Naturally, hospital pharmacists are encouraged to document their actions in the patient's medical record.

As these pharmaceutical services demonstrate, hospital pharmacists are concerned with the safety and appropriateness of drug therapy. But in today's economic climate, their expertise in ensuring a proper balance between the quality and cost of drug therapy is increasingly important.

In the course of a single day in a hospital pharmacy department, one practitioner might determine the appropriate dosage for a seriously ill oncology patient, another might explain to a new, homeward-bound mother how to administer an oral antibiotic to her baby who has an ear infection, and a third might monitor the efficacy of a postsurgical patient's newly prescribed medications.

In some hospitals today, patients often meet their pharmacists during morning rounds. In addition, the pharmacist may conduct a bedside interview, during which the patient's medication history is recorded. This gives the pharmacist a chance to explain the purpose, dosage schedule, and possible side effects of each medication. It also gives the patient an opportunity to ask questions about the safe use of medications.

When the time for discharge from the hospital arrives, pharmacists in many institutions participate in making sure patients are ready to assume responsibility for their own therapy. The pharmacist supplies valuable information about where to store medication, what to do if a dose is missed, and how safely to combine over-the-counter medications with prescription products.

A wide variety of medications are available today, and new products are constantly being introduced. The hospital pharmacist evaluates new products and recommends medicines the hospital should stock. The factors weighed in making these recommendations include product safety, effectiveness, and cost.

Hospital pharmacists prepare medications and are responsible for making sure they reach the patient in the appropriate form and dose at the correct time. Working under sterile conditions, they compound injectable drugs with fluids that are administered to patients intravenously. They prepare some of the powerful new compounds used to treat patients with cancer. They oversee intravenous nutrition support therapy, which plays a vital role in helping the body combat illness and disease. Hospital pharmacists also supervise the dispensing and distribution of tablets, capsules, liquids, ointments, and all other forms of medication used in the hospital.

Because of their expertise in the use of medications, pharmacists may be asked to serve on hospital-wide committees, including the pharmacy and therapeutics, infection control, quality assurance, and drug-use evaluation committees. By bringing their knowledge to these committees, pharmacists help establish hospital policies that improve the quality of patient care and reduce the threat of risk to the patient.

All hospital pharmacists must have a basic knowledge of pharmacology, therapeutics, and pharmacokinetics. Their jobs also demand very strong written and oral communication skills. Because of the growing need for practitioners with the special skills institutional practice requires, many pharmacy school graduates today enter residency programs for training in specific areas of practice. The American Society of Hospital Pharmacists (ASHP) is the official accrediting body for such programs. Increasingly, many employers indicate a preference for individuals who have completed an accredited residency.

There are three types of ASHP-accredited residencies: a residency in pharmacy practice, an advanced residency in hospital pharmacy administration, and a specialized pharmacy residency. The type of residency selected will depend on whether one's career objective is general clinical practice, hospital pharmacy administration, or a focused area of practice, such as geriatrics, nuclear pharmacy, or psychopharmacy.

Hospital pharmacists enjoy various opportunities for career advancement, which can come either through movement into management responsibilities or through clinical achievements. Skilled professionals in both pharmacy administration and clinical pharmacy will be needed to keep hospital pharmacy departments running efficiently and to provide patients with high-quality, cost-effective drug therapy.

With experience in institutional pharmacy, practitioners have significant opportunities to practice outside the hospital in other organized health care settings, such as managed care, home care, industry, and long-term care programs. And opportunities also exist in such related fields as hospital administration, academia, the pharmaceutical industry, pharmaceutical research, and pharmacy associations.

Hospital pharmacists are making a tremendous difference in America's health care system. In everything from procurement of drug products to direct patient care, these professionals are integral members of the health care team, employing both time-tested and innovative strategies to design, implement, and monitor drug therapy. As a result, hospital patients receive safer, more effective, and more economical health care than has ever before been possible.

Cathy Johnson, BS,
is a staff pharmacist in the neonatology unit
at the University of Cincinnati Hospital.

The Staff Pharmacist

Because my patients can't talk, the contact I have with them is quite different from the contact other hospital pharmacists have with their patients. Another difference is that my patients weigh as little as 500 grams – they are premature babies in our hospital's neonatal unit. This means that direct patient-counseling skills count for little in my job. However, parent-counseling skills are quite important.

Some of the babies in our unit stay as long as nine months, so it's hard not to become attached to them. And when a baby doesn't make it, it's tough. But I have learned to deal with it the same way our nurses do. We realize that the babies we treat here are always the sickest ones. We do everything we can for them, but there are some problems that science just can't solve.

Because I don't have an advanced degree or residency experience, it's unusual that I have been able to specialize in such a clinical area. Most specialty pharmacists in the hospital have PharmD degrees. My opportunity came about five years ago when our hospital hired a neonatal pharmacy practitioner, also a PharmD, to develop services to the neonatal intensive care unit (NICU). The department also decided to open a satellite pharmacy to the NICU at that time, and I volunteered to help develop pharmacy services from the satellite. I had been working in the central pharmacy for about five years and was ready for something different, something that might offer new challenges.

As the first pharmacist to staff the satellite, I was given most of the responsibility for organizing the physical work space. I ordered all of the equipment and drugs and helped develop many of the policies governing pharmacy services from the satellite pharmacy. We expanded drug distribution services to the NICU when two other pharmacists joined the satellite pharmacy staff.

When the neonatal practitioner resigned, the hospital was unable to recruit another one because there just aren't many neonatal pharmacists around. Management asked the NICU pharmacists to assume responsibility for clinical services to the NICU patients. This meant going on daily patient rounds and being directly responsible for patients' drug therapies. My colleagues and I felt a little nervous about this added responsibility, but we agreed to the proposal.

At first, I was apprehensive about going on rounds and asking questions about patients' drug therapies. I read as much as I could about neonatal medical problems and neonatal drug therapy. As I became more knowledgeable, I felt more comfortable handling questions from the physicians and nurses and in bringing up important drug therapy issues on rounds. Challenges abound in neonatology, and I haven't stopped learning since I accepted this position. The physiology of neonates is far different from that of adults, and this has a great impact on the way they handle medications. That learning process continues as more and more information about neonates becomes available.

More than the other staff pharmacists I work with, I like to handle administrative duties. This means that I work closely with the pharmacy manager. Right now we're working to set policies that will govern pharmaceutical care in this hospital. I also have drug distribution and clinical duties. Each month, the other neonatology staff pharmacists and I rotate between those two duties.

When I am handling the drug distribution, I am responsible for all of the unit-dose drug preparation. The nurses prepare most of the standard IV maintenance fluids because we don't have the manpower to handle that task. I supervise a technician who prepares dilutions of drugs for the neonates. I then check the bulk drug dilutions and the individual doses the technician has prepared from those solutions.

Every day, the technician fills a unit-dose cart with a 24-hour supply of medications for the unit. This cart is checked by the pharmacist before delivery. Every hour, I also pick up orders from and make deliveries to the neonatal unit, and then I enter those orders into our profiles. The technician helps prepare new doses from these orders. That accounts for half of a typical day in my life.

Later, I make parenteral nutrition solutions – 10 or so each day. I use a computer program to make the recipe for formulating the TPN solutions from the doctors' orders. The technician draws up the various ingredients and I mix them together. The technician tubes the TPN solution for a syringe or IV pump, and I check to make sure all of the correct pieces of tubing are together. If I'm working the evening shift, I have to handle these duties myself because the technician will have gone off duty.

When it's my turn to handle the clinical assignment, I spend the morning making rounds with physicians, a charge nurse, and, occasionally, a dietitian or an occupational therapist. Respiratory technicians are available at the patients' bedsides, and together we all discuss the status of each baby. We have 50 beds in this unit.

The pharmacy staff keeps a notebook for each patient. In it is detailed information about the baby's day, including a description of the medical problem, the drug therapy being used, what the end-points of therapy might be, and what monitoring parameters are being employed. That notebook is passed to each new shift, and it is updated continually.

In discharging my clinical duties, I monitor each baby's drug therapy by checking serum levels or judging the baby's response to the medication. Then I make sure the baby is not experiencing drug-related problems. To keep the drug distribution pharmacist from being interrupted, I answer the physicians' and nurses' drug information questions.

I love the level of responsibility I am given in this job. Physicians and nurses come to me for advice on drug therapy. I talk to them and, based on my expertise in pharmacokinetics, I give them advice about adjusting doses. I help them choose medications that breastfeeding mothers can take safely and work with them in timing medication administration. Some of our patients have percutaneous venous catheters (PCVC), and because these often provide the only drug access we have in these tiny babies, we must send all medications through the same line. I spend a lot of my time trying to address those kinds of drug delivery problems.

In neonatology, one of the biggest challenges is keeping up with the changes. To do so, the pharmacists in this unit read all the pertinent journals. If we find a particularly important article, we'll make copies and see that it gets to those who need the information. Occasionally, we get together with our counterparts from the children's hospital across the street. We meet to discuss common issues and neonatal problems that we confront in our own institutions.

Because the University of Cincinnati Hospital is a teaching facility, I spend time teaching the medical residents. Every month when a new resident team comes to neonatology, one of our staff pharmacists gives the residents dosing guidelines established in the neonatal drug literature that I summarized on pocket cards a few years ago and continue to update. We teach them how to order TPN solutions. Most of this takes place during daily rounds.

Occasionally, we will work with a pharmacy resident who wants to do a rotation in our satellite. During the rotation, we try to provide this person with an overview of neonatal pharmacy, but that is difficult to do in just one month. Pharmacy students also come through our department now and again, but they do so on an elective basis.

I am collaborating on a couple of research projects related to neonatal drug therapy – but I wouldn't want to do research all the time. In fact, I suppose that the beauty of this job for me is that it allows me to do a little bit of everything, from research to clinical rounds, from drug distribution and teaching to administrative activities.

In developing different treatment protocols for neonatology, I devised several printed forms that make it possible to evaluate, step by step, drug therapy for specific problems suffered by our tiny patients. For example, the seizure form details a decision tree for treating seizure incidents. It summarizes the usual guidelines on what medication to use and what to look for clinically (on an EEG or MRI, or with regard to patient behavior) to determine how long therapy should be continued. It also makes clear what drug interactions might be involved with anticonvulsive medications. These forms are useful as teaching tools as well as for recording the patient's response to a particular drug therapy.

I always knew that I would go into hospital pharmacy or, possibly, some form of industrial pharmacy. I didn't want to work in a drugstore, because I wanted to have a broader range of professional experiences than is possible in a retail store.

I recommend that students who are interested in working in a hospital take at least one course in hospital pharmacy, or do internship or externship rotations in a hospital. My school did not offer a course in hospital pharmacy, but I was able to get a job as a pharmacy intern at a hospital. Students who have never been exposed to the hospital pharmacy environment can be expected to have difficulty weighing the pros and cons of hospital pharmacy as a career.

Those who are interested in hospital pharmacy should spend considerable time looking at several institutions to see what they offer. From one to another there can be a surprising difference in the responsibilities they give staff pharmacists. Usually, institutions that give the technicians responsibility are best, because this frees the pharmacists to take on more challenges. A hospital residency would be an asset to anyone considering a career in hospital pharmacy management.

Wherever young hospital pharmacists end up working, they should never stop lobbying for change – change that can streamline their work or improve patient care. My motto is "Don't be satisfied with the status quo," and I believe that applies in every setting. The pharmacist who takes the initiative in trying to make improvements can always have an impact. Job satisfaction is directly related to one's level of involvement.

My own job satisfaction is very high. In fact, it's so high that, for now at least, I have no interest in seeking a management position. The main reason for this is that I have plenty of challenging projects to work on. Besides, there wouldn't be any monetary incentive for me to go into management because of the salary level I have reached after 10 years.

The only complaint I have about my job is the fact that retail pharmacy pays so much more than hospital pharmacy, at least here in the Midwest. And really, that's not much of a complaint because I still make a pretty good living.

Even better, I am doing work I like. I enjoy my responsibilities, and I really feel as though I'm making a difference here. I know that my colleagues – pharmacists, doctors, and nurses alike – count on me and respect my knowledge and skills.

That's a good feeling to have.

John E. Murphy, BS, PharmD,
is professor and head of the department
of pharmacy practice at the
University of Arizona College of Pharmacy.
He is a fellow of the American College
of Clinical Pharmacy.

Clinical Pharmacokinetics

I came to pharmacy rather late in college. I had been majoring in chemistry, but my interest in it had begun to wane. I started thinking about pharmacy because my grandfather had been a pharmacist. I was only an average student until about halfway through pharmacy school when a professor took me under his wing. He told me that I ought to be concerned about doing a good job in all aspects of my career, and he showed me that doing a good job is important. It is fair to say that he converted me from an average student willing to accept mediocre results in my work to a dedicated pharmacy student. I saw the burning bush, you might say, with the aid of this mentor.

My career has been quite fulfilling. It has enabled me to pursue a challenging variety of activities. It also has given me the opportunity to conduct research, to teach both pharmacy students and practicing pharmacists, to be active in pharmacy organizations and to write articles for publication. All in all, I believe I have been of service to my colleagues and to my profession.

In 1976, only some seven percent of U.S. hospitals provided pharmacokinetics services on a daily basis. At that time, the idea of determining dosages by measuring drug concentrations in a patient's blood was still somewhat revolutionary. Within a decade and a half, that figure had climbed to 40 percent. In a recent survey I conducted in Georgia, nearly 74 percent of responding hospitals had established or intended to establish a pharmacokinetics service. This is becoming such an established field that within the foreseeable future almost every hospital will need pharmacists who can provide pharmacokinetic consultations.

For 10 years, I worked as a clinical pharmacokineticist for a private practice that had a contract with a 500-bed hospital in Atlanta. During that time, I was also on the faculty of Mercer University Southern School of Pharmacy. Since then, I have been an academic administrator at the University of Arizona College of Pharmacy. In those roles, I have witnessed – and participated in – the tremendous growth of this specialty.

Pharmacokinetics is a mathematical depiction of how drugs move through the body. It describes the rates of their absorption, distribution, and elimination. In clinical pharmacokinetics, these mathematical principles are applied in managing the drug therapies for individual patients.

In a hospital setting, pharmacokinetics services can have significant influence on the quality and cost effectiveness of patient care. Well-designed programs that monitor therapy and identify patients who should be reviewed can alert physicians to potentially toxic or subtherapeutic drug concentrations and can serve as a precise guide to patient care.

For example, consider the patient who is receiving a drug to control his asthma. He may be taking an oral dose of the agent two or three times a day. The starting dosage will be based on his size, degree of disease, and other related factors. After the drug has been used for a period of time, concentrations of the drug in the patient's blood can be measured at prescribed times. When the results begin falling within the therapeutic range, the patient's response is evaluated. One response, the ideal one, would be an absence of symptoms of asthma. Another response could be a lessening of symptoms. Yet another might be the development of drug side effects. Balancing the patient's response and the measured concentration against the desired concentration makes it possible to adjust the dose as needed.

This evaluation of the patient's response may take place daily until the patient is stabilized. After that, monitoring can be performed at longer intervals if the patient continues doing well.

Knowing when the blood was drawn relative to when the dose was given is critical in pharmacokinetics. If blood is drawn just after a drug has been administered, the concentration will be at its highest. If the concentration is measured right before the next dose is due, it will be at its lowest. Unless I know when the blood was drawn, my assessment of the therapy may be completely skewed. For that reason, a system for ensuring accurate timing of drug-concentration measurement is essential. Otherwise, the value of pharmacokinetic monitoring can be considerably diminished.

At our hospital, the pharmacokineticists arranged the timing of all drug-concentration measurements. That required us to have a close alliance with the nurses who administered the drug and the phlebotomists who actually drew the blood.

Our service monitored every baby in the hospital's neonatology unit. Many were having seizures, respiratory difficulties, or infections. To make certain their doses were adjusted properly, the neonatologist was eager for us to be involved with every baby whose therapy could be monitored by serum concentration.

Clinical pharmacokinetics services began to evolve in the mid-1970s in a very small number of U.S. hospitals. The progress of pharmacokinetics as a science and patient care practice depended on the development of instruments capable of measuring very small quantities of drugs in the bloodstream. In the beginning, only highly educated research scientists could use the delicate measuring devices, but now lab technicians routinely run up to 25 samples simultaneously.

Even this scenario is changing. Today, the technology of pharmacokinetics is so accessible that this once rarified science can be used for patient care in a community pharmacy. A patient comes in, gets a finger prick, and the pharmacist can quickly determine the concentration of certain drugs in the bloodstream. The pharmacist can then determine how the patient is doing and decide whether the dosage needs to be adjusted. Consultation with the patient's physician can save a trip back to the physician's office for dose changes.

No matter how accessible the technology may be, most pharmacokinetics specialists still must develop effective working relationships with nurses, doctors, lab technicians, pathologists, and computer technicians. In fact, I believe that one of the most appealing features of my job as a clinical pharmacokineticist was the chance it gave me to interact with so many different people in the hospital. I considered myself their link to the patient.

Pharmacokinetics is attaining stability as a practice specialty, even as it continues to evolve. Now, many pharmacists are hired straight out of school to work in pharmacokinetics services. And because 40 percent of U.S. hospitals have such services, job opportunities exist today that simply were not there 15 years ago. This means 60 percent of hospitals don't provide pharmacokinetics services, but this lack represents opportunity for the trailblazers among us. Surely, this field will continue to grow.

What are the attributes of a successful pharmacokineticist? First and foremost is a powerful interest in top-quality patient care. A talent for mathematics also is high on the list. And not far below that are well-developed skills for getting along with people.

In my opinion, pharmacokinetics should be an underpinning for all pharmacy students, no matter where they plan to practice. The knowledge is sure to be utilized.

The application of pharmacokinetics principles in setting dosages will take on increasing importance with the development of expensive biotechnology-derived drugs. In fact, as pressure to save money mounts, the value of pharmacokinetics will be revealed more fully than ever before. At the same time, the already significant rewards of practicing in this field are certain to increase.

Allan Ellsworth, PharmD, BCPS,
is associate professor of pharmacy
and family medicine at the
University of Washington, Seattle.

The Primary Care Pharmacist

I became immersed in family medicine pharmacy in a group practice when the University of Iowa College of Pharmacy sent me to practice in a little farming community of 1,000 people in northeast Iowa. There was no permanent physician in town, so in addition to dispensing drugs and counseling patients when the physician wasn't around, I ended up riding with the ambulance, watching unexpected home deliveries, and taking care of heart attacks during transport to the "big city."

I took that first job right after completing my PharmD degree because I wanted some first-hand primary care experience before considering an academic career. As harrowing as those days were, I now realize that they were invaluable preparation for the position I now hold at the University of Washington.

I feel fortunate to be a member of two excellent faculties: the department of pharmacy and the department of family medicine at the University of Washington. These departments have been leaders in family medicine pharmacy group practice since early in the history of this specialty. Ten years ago, there were few pharmacists working in family medicine training programs. Today, 60 percent of the family practice residencies in this country have a clinical pharmacist on the faculty.

Family medicine is a recognized medical specialty, as is cardiology, gastroenterology, or infectious disease. Family physicians are skilled in dealing with common medical problems experienced by a broad range of patients – literally from cradle to grave. Because of the breadth of the specialty pharmacists can contribute significantly to the continuing education of physicians and to the provision of pharmaceutical care to ambulatory patients. I try to instill this excitement for primary care practice in my students.

About 50 percent of my job involves patient care. Teaching, research, and administrative duties consume the rest of my time. Typical days for me are not nine to five. An hour in the office before work is my most productive time, and I frequently carry work home. Morning report starts at eight o'clock. During this meeting, the on-call family medicine resident describes his emergency room visits, phone calls from patients, and any hospital admissions. This session is meant to serve as a reporting and teaching conference for residents, physicians, and pharmacists. This is followed by hospital rounds.

A couple of days a week, I conduct my own pharmacy clinic where patients are scheduled to see me specifically. These patients usually have medication-related problems. For those who are having difficulty complying with their prescribed regimen, I try to develop helpful alternatives. I might spend time monitoring and adjusting a hypertensive patient's drug regimen. Or I might help diabetic patients understand their disease and teach ambulatory blood glucose monitoring or insulin injection techniques. I have a special interest in helping people who are trying to quit smoking. Also, I handle the clinic's anticoagulation patients, telephone calls regarding prescription refills, and drug-related questions from our patients and outside pharmacies.

Refill questions and problems land on the pharmacy desk along with the patient's chart. I review the chart, question the patient, review the physician's treatment plan, and decide whether to issue a refill. Washington state allows pharmacists prescriptive authority under protocol, and the result is a fair amount of autonomy.

In addition to my patient care duties, I have teaching responsibilities. Three days each week, we have attending rounds – teaching conferences for the family medicine residents, PharmD candidates, and pharmacy undergraduates. About once a week, I have lecture responsibilities somewhere on campus, at the nursing school, pharmacy school, physician's assistant program or medical school.

The University of Washington is well known for its research. I am currently involved in a number of research projects involving treatments for common medical problems. In the past, I've conducted research with antibiotics, antihypertensive agents, and yeast vaginitis.

Additionally, I have had the opportunity to conduct research on Mt. Rainier on pharmacologic prevention of acute mountain sickness. During summer climbing seasons, climbers participate in clinical trials, in which some are given active medications and some placebo. Because of Mt. Rainier's elevation – 14,000 feet – more than half of the climbers develop acute mountain sickness, making it an excellent field laboratory. I couldn't ask for a better job.

It's easy for me to name the biggest challenge I face in my job: finding time to get everything done. Besides my responsibilities for patient care, teaching, and research, I am on call with a volunteer mountain rescue team. I just don't say no very well. In fact, I enjoy getting mixed up with about anything I'm asked to do.

Patient care is my strong point. I like people. And they are more than willing to show me their gratitude for going to bat for them and helping them through the system.

One of my patients is 84 years old and suffers from chronic anxiety. Before our clinic took over his care, he was constantly in the hospital because he took overdoses of his medication in an unsuccessful attempt to control his anxiety. Now, I make it a point to see him one or two times a week in order to regulate his medication. It's gratifying to know that I am helping to keep him out of the hospital. I don't know whether he appreciates my efforts on his behalf, but I certainly appreciate the challenge he has posed for me over the past six years.

Occasionally he fails to show up for his appointment. When that happens, I hop in the car and go out to his house. Once he had fallen and was unable to get up. I've been there a number of times. In fact, it's not unusual for physicians or pharmacists from our clinic to make home visits. For example, a lady came into the clinic for an appointment with me but forgot her pills. She didn't have a car, so I sent a student home on the bus with her. The student was able to take care of her medication problem right there at her home.

There's no doubt that patients appreciate it when we go that extra mile for them. Some simply offer a heartfelt "Thanks for helping me." Other patients bring flowers, candy, or pies.

It's the reward of feeling needed and appreciated that makes up for whatever salary differences might exist between an academic career and private enterprise. The freedom, the variety, the challenges I enjoy, and the appreciation I get more than compensate for the salary differences.

I enjoy a very positive working relationship with the physicians here. When they come in with questions, they respect my answers and follow my recommendations. They know that I will tell them if I don't know the answer to something. Consequently, the physicians here are usually up for whatever I propose. That kind of trust carries with it a lot of responsibility. For me, that's great because I believe that a job without responsibility isn't a job for me.

In any job, the first couple of years are the most important in establishing that sort of trust. I truly believe that there's no limit to what you can accomplish in a job if you just go ahead and take responsibility. I've found that people will let you take on whatever you're good at and whatever you're confident that you can do.

Another axiom for success is "If you want to do more, learn more." I'm still learning and growing, and I hope I never stop. Last year, for example, I passed a specialty board certification exam in pharmacotherapy. I believe that problems arise for pharmacists who allow themselves to be stereotyped in roles that have become stagnant. This is destructive for the individual and for the profession.

In this day and age, to be able to function in a family practice-pharmacist group practice in an academic setting requires an advanced degree or advanced training. There are many pharmacists who have been in private practice for 10 or 15 years without advanced training. They've been in a nurturing environment where they've had a chance to learn while working. Students simply don't get enough training in pharmacy school to provide complex pharmaceutical care.

For pharmacists, the family medicine pharmacy group practice area is relatively small compared with other fields in our profession. However, if one widens the category a bit and includes ambulatory care or primary care, then this field is growing tremendously.

In the future it's going to be even bigger, with lots of opportunity. You see, we've essentially filled all of the hospitals with clinical pharmacists. Yet, only five percent of hospital patients take their medicines there. The other 95 percent take their medications as outpatients. So, who helps them? The people on the outside, the ambulatory care pharmacists like me. There is no doubt that outpatients deserve services that are just as sophisticated as those provided to hospitalized patients.

For pharmacy students who are interested in family practice or ambulatory care, I recommend that you get the most out of your education. Don't let any preconceived ideas or role models influence you. Choose what you want to do, aim high, and go for it.

If you choose family practice, you will be blessed with many rewards. I certainly have been. My patients appreciate me. The students I teach enjoy their learning experiences. The family physicians respect me. Perhaps best of all, I am given the freedom to be involved with many different things. Patient care is a constant in my life, but I can work hard on a research grant, write a paper, then shift back to teaching. And when research can involve mountain climbing it's tough to complain.

Cindy J. Wordell, PharmD,
is assistant director of pharmacy in
the department of pharmacy at
Thomas Jefferson University Hospital in
Philadelphia, Pennsylvania.

The Drug Information Specialist

I discovered at an early age that I wanted to be a pharmacist. I liked science and I was interested in medicine. So when my mother saw an ad for information on a career in pharmacy, she sent for the brochure and gave it to me. It looked exciting. In addition, a friend of my family's was a local pharmacist, so I imagined I would work in a store like his.

Things didn't work out that way, and the work I do as a drug information specialist bears little relation to activities in a retail pharmacy.

As an assistant director of pharmacy at this 727-bed, nonprofit university hospital, I have a number of responsibilities. I hold an adjunct academic appointment that gives me an opportunity to teach drug information to undergraduate and doctor of pharmacy students. Until recently, I also coordinated an elective course on drug information. Even though I no longer do this, I still lecture on this subject in a similar course.

Beyond my academic duties, I have major responsibilities to the hospital. For example, I'm responsible for the revision and publication of the formulary, a pocket-sized 200-page book that outlines all of our medication-related policies and procedures. The formulary is used by our medical staff when physicians need information on anything from medication prescribing to drug administration. It lists every drug, with doses, that the pharmacy and therapeutics (P&T) committee has approved for use at Thomas Jefferson University Hospital. The committee is responsible for making sure that there are adequate data on safety and efficacy for every drug selected for use in the hospital. The formulary book also contains a great deal of other useful prescribing information, including clinical tables. We publish a new edition each year.

As a drug information specialist, I am responsible for coordinating the monthly meeting of the P&T committee, of which the director of pharmacy and I are members. We evaluate new agents, comparing them with similar drugs that are available. Last year, we assessed 45 agents.

Finally, the P&T committee conducts a periodic review of medical staff policies on drug usage, developing new policies or revising old ones. Since this committee meets 10 times a year, much of my effort is concentrated on coordination.

To stay informed about new drugs, I scan the major medical journals, and I use the word *scan* deliberately. In the course of a day, I'll go through two or three journals to see if there is something of importance I should know about. Articles on new drugs are certain to catch my attention.

Another important resource for me is the pharmaceutical sales representative. This person is invaluable for the information he can give me about new products. He is a bountiful source of pertinent articles and bibliographies.

I haven't even mentioned our telephone responsibilities. We answer approximately 300 drug information questions a month. Almost a third of the questions come from outside our institution. A small number of these are from consumers, and the rest are from area pharmacists or physicians.

Drug information specialists are not found only in hospitals. They can be found in industry and in various community settings. Every pharmaceutical company has a drug information department, and these offer interesting career options, too.

What I like most about my work in drug information is that every day I learn something new. In fact, my job is a continuous learning process. Even though drug information is considered a specialty, and within it I have my own area that I particularly enjoy, I have to maintain a broad base of knowledge about pharmaceutical agents. Comparatively speaking, a cardiology specialist will concentrate mainly on cardiology drugs. He doesn't have to review antibiotic agents with the same detail because they are outside his specialty. Not so with drug information specialists – they must keep up with nearly every development in pharmacology.

For all the challenge and excitement I experience in my job, there are frustrations, too. One of these is found in dealing with institutional politics. When we develop a recommendation it is not at all uncommon for someone to feel he should be an exception to the new rule. Consequently, a lot of discussion takes place, and a considerable amount of lobbying goes on before final decisions are made and approved.

Often, someone will call to say that his interest is not being represented. I find that taking a measured approach is the best way to avert such problems. This means I must invest a good deal of time working behind the scenes to make sure every interested individual has been contacted before final recommendations are made. Ultimately, this helps to avoid future conflicts.

It is said that successful drug information specialists have certain personality traits. In particular, it is not the perfect job for people who want instant change, because that just doesn't happen. Instead, you have to be willing to sit back and negotiate – to take the slower path. In the end, the desired objective will be accomplished, but this approach requires a level head.

Many students don't think of drug information as being clinically oriented. They tend to consider it an activity that is performed at a desk in an office, not on the hospital floor where the patients are. I look at it this way: When we get a call from the physician, he's calling us because we have valuable information that he must have. We take the request, make an evaluation based on the literature and patient-specific information, come up with an answer, and give it to the physician as quickly as possible. Most of the time, that information is going to be used directly in caring for a patient. Often, we must speak with the patient or review the medical chart. In my opinion, our responsibilities are just as clinical as those of the person who's rounding with the medical team.

There was some serendipity involved in my becoming a drug information specialist. In my third year of pharmacy school, students were required by the state board to register internship hours in a pharmacy before licensure. I intended to accomplish this in a local pharmacy where I was actually working. However, the pharmacist could register hours for only two students, and I was the third. Fortunately for me, there was a small Catholic hospital in the city that allowed the nun who ran the pharmacy to have one summer student each year. I initially worked two days a week for her to register my hours and then worked full time during the summer. When I started working there, I realized that I really enjoy hospital pharmacy. Still, it wasn't until my fourth year in pharmacy school that I knew I no longer wanted to work in a community pharmacy after graduation. Soon after that, I decided to serve a hospital residency.

The direction in which drug information is heading keeps me keenly interested in my work. We're in the middle of a rapid growth in biotechnology. As a result, drug information specialists are more and more often consulted for our understanding of pharmaceutical products and for our ability to develop institutional guidelines that make sure these agents are used appropriately. Helping the medical staff understand and use the increasing number of drugs is going to make the role of the drug information specialist even more important.

The other trend to be aware of in drug information is that cost containment is a growing issue. That bodes well for pharmacists who practice this specialty in hospitals, because drug control has placed our skills in great demand. We're the people who are called upon to evaluate drug products, and we play a major role in ensuring high-quality and cost-effective patient care.

Vicki S. Crane, BS, MBA, FASHP, RPh, is associate director of pharmacy services at Parkland Memorial Hospital in Dallas.

The Pharmacist in Administration

It took several years for me to find my niche in pharmacy. But what began as a patchwork of trial-and-error experiments with jobs has finally proved to be invaluable background for a rewarding career.

At first, I thought I wanted to earn a PhD in pharmacology. I pursued this for a year before realizing that I really didn't want to be around rats and labs for the rest of my life.

Then I tried retail pharmacy. But my employer and I disagreed over the value of patient counseling. His philosophy was that pharmacy involved little more than licking, sticking, and pouring. I soon decided I didn't want to do that either.

Still, I knew I wasn't a failure just because I didn't like my first two jobs. That's the wonderful thing about being young and adventurous: It's okay to try different things in the quest for your place in the world.

My husband was in graduate school, so it was important that I limit my search to one geographical area. I continued to sample careers. I worked full time at a hospital. I spent time as a pharmacy dispensing lab instructor at the pharmacy school, and I tried working as a nursing home consultant. I also worked part time for a community pharmacy that offered patient counseling services. In the end, this experience gave me a very broad practice base that serves me well, especially now that the line between institutional pharmacy and community pharmacy is blurring.

People go into management for various reasons, but my ambition was to improve patient care. I was primarily a clinician before I went into management, and I think I was a good one. But I wanted to have more impact on the patient care delivery system. At the staff level, I knew I would only be in control of myself. As a manager, I thought I could have a more significant impact by directing a group of effective individuals who had responsibility for pharmaceutical care.

A good pharmacy manager does whatever it takes to help the front-line practitioner take care of patients. I see my job as a vehicle for making sure staff pharmacists get the resources they need to do a good job. I lobby for pay raises, procure equipment, and see that the squeaky wheels on carts get fixed. In a way, I live vicariously through my staff's achievements.

Before I got my MBA, I had gone up the ladder at Presbyterian Hospital in Dallas, from supervisor to assistant director to associate director. Then, in the mid-1980s, the financial management of pharmacy became more important, both in staffing patterns and skill levels. Drug budgets skyrocketed, and I began to feel the need for more expertise in finance. I deliberately chose an MBA over an MS in pharmacy administration because I felt that I needed to strengthen my financial management acumen if I expected to compete on a level playing field with other administrators.

Professors at the University of Dallas believed as I do that above all else, students should learn how to apply academic information. So, during my master's work, I tried to combine class projects with my job. When I was assigned to do a five-year financial plan for a hospital, I asked a Presbyterian Hospital vice president (I had kept my job there) if he wanted me to develop a financial plan for one of our satellite hospitals. The hospital was flexible enough to let me go to graduate school, but at the same time, it benefited from my participation in the program.

After I graduated in 1989, I decided I wanted to work in a university or academic medical center. Typically, the main mission of a community hospital is patient care – and rightly so. But a university medical center also has teaching and research missions. I was eager to get back into an atmosphere where all three goals were in the mission statement. Also, I think that university medical centers tend to be more creative and willing to try new ways of doing things, and this tends to give pharmacists greater responsibility on the patient care team.

Some people might say I made a lateral move from associate director at Presbyterian to associate director of pharmacy services at Parkland Memorial Hospital in Dallas. I don't see it that way. The titles may be the same, but my responsibilities and the contributions I make to patient care are much broader at Parkland.

At Parkland I wanted to implement pharmacy programs in accord with the new pharmaceutical care model, in which pharmacists focus directly on patient care, assessing the appropriateness of drug therapy.

When I first came here, departmental goals were set by only a few people. That soon changed, and the staff now has more say about policies and procedures. However, as beneficial as this has been, it really is not a very efficient way of accomplishing things. In my opinion, self-governance models yield better decisions but take longer. In such models, managers must exercise a great deal of patience and perform a lot of coaching.

At Parkland, I am in charge of inpatient pharmacy, and I manage about 110 full-time employees. I report to the director of pharmacy. The inpatient care division is divided into four service areas. The first of these is decentralized pharmacy services, which deploys teams of pharmacists and technicians to provide specialized patient care. Sterile products services makes its formulations available throughout the hospital. Central pharmacy services offers logistical support to patient care teams. Finally, we have clinical support services, which provides clinical support for these teams.

I work 10- to 12-hour days, and when I'm not in meetings, I am teaching or trying to solve problems. My two most important management skills involve delegating and coordinating. In everything I do, I try to keep the department's mission statement and goals in mind. A major part of my job is to move people toward those goals.

Beyond my duties in the hospital, I expend a lot of energy keeping up with what other hospital pharmacies are doing. I'm a great advocate of copying – with the permission of those I'm copying, of course. For example, some of my colleagues at other institutions are helping us restructure our inpatient department. In particular, I'm drawing on the experience of friends at the University of Utah and the Henry Ford Hospital in Detroit, both of which recently reorganized their pharmacy departments. I visited them and asked them to talk to me about the details of making such large changes – the mistakes as well as the successes. My restructuring won't turn out exactly like theirs, but by following their lead, I hope to avoid some pitfalls.

My biggest challenge as a manager is getting people in my department to work together and to appreciate each other's viewpoints. Inpatient pharmacy is a multidisciplinary department with a large number of pharmacists and support personnel. There is not much homogeneity here: Our pharmacists are managers and clinicians, baccalaureates and PharmDs. Some pharmacy employees are 18 years old, others are 60, and they represent all races. What I hope we have in common is a desire to make sure Parkland's patients receive top-quality, consistent drug therapy, 24 hours a day.

To achieve this, I make certain that people who work with me know that they are working toward the same goal, no matter what their job. The person who makes IV deliveries is no less important than the clinical specialist. If the IV is delivered to the wrong room, everything the clinical specialist and the IV pharmacist have done will be wasted. Left on their own, people become very territorial and myopic. It is my job to give them a vision of our mission and to involve them in as much responsibility as possible.

I believe that asking a lot of questions is the best way to keep communication channels open. Before I take any important action, I try to have every pertinent fact, and I make an effort to keep everyone informed. Even then, I proceed one step at a time. In my opinion, too many managers make the mistake of not basing their assumptions on a reality check. Intelligent questioning is the only way to avoid that trap. In management as in day-to-day pharmacy, communication is hard work.

Training pharmacists to become managers is difficult. But it can be just as difficult to teach pharmacists to be clinicians. The problem is that we learn in school to function one way. Then, once we start practicing, we are expected to function in a different way. When most pharmacists finish school, their technical skills usually are very good. They probably know a great deal about drug therapy, but nothing at all about managing support personnel. As a consequence, they may order these employees around as though they are robots or let them run wild. By the same token, inexperienced pharmacists may not know how to approach a physician who has just written a 10-fold overdose. I once heard a young pharmacist say to a physician, "What are you trying to do, kill this patient?" Not surprisingly, the physician didn't respond well to that criticism.

I train managers by first letting them observe me doing a particular task. Then I have them perform a number of tasks under supervision. I make certain my assignments are straightforward projects that incorporate plenty of checkpoints along the way. This strategy makes it possible for trainees to succeed in stages. In this way the frustration of failure can be avoided, while their confidence is slowly being built. Gradually, the checkpoints are spaced farther and farther apart. In the end, all I require is that they report back to me when the project has been completed.

For students interested in going into management, I recommend first gaining a couple of years of experience at a staff level or even working part time during pharmacy school. I think it is necessary to be under the authority of others before it's possible to exercise authority properly. If such a background is topped off with a master's degree, the pharmacist will be well along toward developing managerial competence. Some people elect to go directly for their master's degree, but those who do often are not effective as managers because they have never had an opportunity to apply their academic knowledge. They may eventually find success, but it will take them some time to get up to speed.

Pharmacy's rewards can be found in countless fields at every professional level. I know this because I've experienced many of them. But I have come to realize that, for me at least, the greatest pleasure lies in making it possible for others to do their best. If, as a manager, I am able to help other pharmacists perform more effectively, I can still have a significant impact on patient care. In a way, that gives me professional satisfaction at both ends of the spectrum.

*Pete Suresky, PharmD,
is a clinical pharmacist for oncology/bone
marrow transplantation in the
department of pharmacy services at
Northside Hospital, Atlanta.*

The Oncology Pharmacist

Physicians often ask pharmacists for drug information pertaining to the incidence of adverse effects following drug administration. Pharmacists have several references they can utilize to answer a physician's request. It's a skill that comes with experience, and it is essential in helping design effective anticancer therapies. It also makes it possible to avert – or at least diminish – the toxic reactions that can occur when potent chemotherapy agents are combined.

Refining this skill and applying it successfully is a great source of satisfaction. But for pharmacists who seek the extraordinary rewards that come from meeting difficult challenges, I can't think of a better career.

The bone marrow transplant program at my hospital is relatively small. Nevertheless, the work we do is revolutionary, and its importance is unquestioned. Some of our patients couldn't survive with conventional anticancer treatment. And while we won't know whether transplantation has cured their disease, many have responded positively. Knowing that my expertise had something to do with that is gratifying.

We're learning that patients with many forms of cancer can benefit from marrow transplantation. The procedure is now reserved for treating leukemias and lymphomas; however, it may soon become a therapeutic standard for such tumors as breast and ovarian cancer.

The oncology patients I work with are among the sickest in the hospital. There is no denying that it can be difficult to work in a setting where there are sick patients who may be going through at least some degree of suffering. Toughest of all is working with young cancer patients who should have their whole lives ahead of them. I am always available when patients want me to explain the medications they will be using and the side effects they may expect.

My choosing to be a clinical pharmacist in oncology occurred in a roundabout way. As an undergraduate, I was a chemistry major at Bucknell University. After graduation, I decided to go to graduate school at Emory University and enrolled in the department of pharmacology. That took me south to Atlanta, where I spent three years at Emory.

During those years, I realized that my interests had begun to focus on clinical pharmacy rather than research. After completing a master's degree at Emory, I enrolled in pharmacy school at Mercer University. After four years, with a good bit of help from my earlier graduate training, I graduated with a PharmD.

I went on to complete two residencies. The first was in general clinical pharmacy practice at the Medical College of Virginia Hospitals, at Richmond, in 1985. At that time, pharmacy residencies were just starting to become popular. I had a great experience there. Although I knew I enjoyed clinical pharmacy, I lacked a specific goal until I went through an oncology rotation at the end of that year.

After completing the first residency, I left Virginia and returned to Atlanta. There I did a second residency in hematology/oncology at Emory University Hospital, working with cancer patients. That experience left me feeing quite sure that clinical pharmacy with a specialty in oncology practice would be the area I would choose.

If there's a moral in my story, it's that students should keep an open mind about their options. Don't imagine that just because you seem to be headed in one direction, your life won't veer off in another that's even more rewarding.

I usually get to work by 7:30 AM. My first task is to prepare drug therapy profiles on patients in the oncology ward and bone marrow unit. I make sure that everything prescribed is appropriately dosed. At the same time, I check the IV fluids to make sure the bags are timed correctly. Naturally, I monitor for drug interactions and adverse reactions. I don't round with any particular physician, as some clinical pharmacy specialists do, but I make sure I'm available during physicians' rounds, which take place from 8 to 10 AM.

At about 10 I deal with any special issues or problems that come up. For example, I just compiled a drug compatibility reference chart that tells the nurses and pharmacists at a glance which drugs can be given together intravenously, and which ones cannot. Often I use this time to do a drug usage evaluation. In fact, I just finished evaluating an agent used to control nausea and vomiting in chemotherapy patients.

At 11:30 AM, I cover the lunch shift for our staff pharmacist, who actually dispenses the drugs. Some clinical pharmacists would resist doing that, but I'm eager to have the chance to do some staffing. It gives me an opportunity to keep in touch with day-to-day problems of some of the patients. When nurses bring orders down, I enter them into the computer and fill the prescriptions with the help of a technician.

After lunch, I do a number of things that fall into my rather broad job description. For instance, my supervisor may have a special project for me to work on for the pharmacy and therapeutics committee. If not, I may go downstairs and work with our drug information service. Among other things, I answer therapy-related questions that are phoned in.

Occasionally, I participate in cardiopulmonary resuscitation events in the bone marrow unit. These "codes" are announced over the public address system, and I go to make sure that if patients need any medications that are not readily available they will have them at a moment's notice. Sometimes this means I have to race back to the pharmacy, but our emergency carts are always stocked with 95 percent of necessary medications.

While middle-of-the-night phone calls are not routine, they aren't a rarity, either. Recently, we had a patient whose nausea and vomiting were intractable. None of the drugs we had given him had worked. So around midnight, the physician decided to try a new agent in a high dose, and he wanted me to advise him if that was safe. Fortunately, I had some references at home and, before long, was able to call back and assure him that it was safe. I described the restrictions and told the nurse how often the drug could be given and what side effects to expect. I didn't mind being awakened, because the patient was so sick from chemotherapy that his life was in danger. Everyone knew it was a true emergency.

Sometimes, information on the drugs we use is incomplete or inaccessible. Consequently, especially if the patient is being given multiple agents, it's up to the pharmacist to help the physician fine tune the regimen for maximum safety and efficacy. At such times we take whatever objective clinical data are available and weigh this information against our clinical judgment and experience. This is where oncology pharmacists (or any well-trained pharmacists for that matter) come into their own.

My experience in this field has enabled me to do tasks quicker and more efficiently. As specialized as this field may be, it is important to have a wide base of pharmacotherapeutic knowledge. This is so because there are situations in which general pharmacy or medical questions arise in cancer patients. When they do, it isn't enough to be the expert in oncology. I have always felt that basic skills in clinical pharmacy practice are the foundation for any specialty area.

One of the most important things to do when you're in pharmacy school is to ask the appropriate expert or advisor about areas in which you think you might have an interest. Use that as a springboard. Then, when you have your rotations, don't be afraid to ask for information about general and specialized areas. From that, you should get an idea of what area of pharmacy practice you might enter.

Anyone interested in oncology pharmacy should consider a residency. Many pharmacists decide not to do so because they are eager to begin their careers. However, if you have a serious interest in becoming an oncology pharmacist, there's no better way to gain exposure to the field.

In oncology practice, there is no shortage of opportunity. Hospitals represent an important career path, and because patients there are sicker, they present a great many challenges to the pharmacist. But as the trend to outpatient care continues, career options in this field will expand dramatically as specialists are needed to ensure top-quality chemotherapy outside the institution. Wherever the activities of oncology pharmacy practitioners are performed, their impact will be profound.

Victor Lampasona, PharmD,
is associate director for clinical and
education programs at
Emory University Hospital in Atlanta.

The Infectious Disease Pharmacist

The field of infectious disease is expanding rapidly because organisms that cause infections are way ahead of the antibiotics that are being created to kill them. It's just nature. Almost as soon as we develop infection-fighting agents, the causative bacteria begin developing resistant strains.

The compound penicillin G was considered a miracle drug when it became available in 1944. It saved the lives of countless soldiers during World War II. Now there are dozens of penicillin-related antibiotics, and together they can't kill all the infection-producing organisms that exist today. The process continues and holds significant opportunity for pharmacists interested in antibiotic pharmacotherapy.

And that's just one of the opportunities that exist today in the growing field of infection control.

The number of patients who have AIDS is increasing dramatically. And it will continue to do so. Already, we are alarmed by the growing range of individuals who are HIV positive. From the most desperate of indigents to the most famous achievers, this disease is ravaging society. And we still haven't seen the whole iceberg – only the tip. There are going to be great opportunities for pharmacists to work in the medical management of this disease state. There also will be increasing opportunities for pharmacists in the general management of other complicated infections.

At Emory University Hospital, most of our patients have been transferred in from other hospitals where they have not been doing well or because they require a specialized medical procedure. They come here for specialized support. Many come with hospital-acquired infections, because they have been so compromised by surgical procedures or medical therapy. Many have been in intensive care for a number of days and have developed an infectious process. Their infections must be treated with drugs that are extremely potent, but the potency has to be balanced against their toxicity. These patients often are debilitated and may have other problems that compromise the disposition of therapy.

Infectious disease pharmacy is a very focused field. Consequently, the training students have received by the time they finish their pharmacy degree probably will not be adequate for the vast majority of practice circumstances. This means that students who want to be on the cutting edge of infectious disease should seriously consider pursuing a postdoctoral clinical residency. And subsequent to that, perhaps an additional year or two in a fellowship.

I earned my bachelor's degree in pharmacy from St. John's University, New York City, in 1978. Then, in 1980, I received my doctor of pharmacy degree at the Medical University of South Carolina (MUSC).

As I began working toward my PharmD, I started to develop a keen interest in pharmacokinetics, especially as it related to antibiotic therapy. At that time in pharmaceutical drug product development, a number of new anti-infection agents were being introduced, and I could see that there would be an important role for pharmacists who were equipped to help select the most appropriate therapeutic modalities.

In those days, pharmacy training in infectious diseases and pharmacokinetics was not common. But MUSC had a strong pharmacokinetic training program. I remained there after I completed my studies and did a residency in clinical pharmacokinetics, with a strong emphasis on antimicrobial therapy. In 1982, I went to work at Emory University as a pharmacokinetics specialist.

Soon after I came here, we developed a pharmacokinetic dosing program for antibiotic therapy. My work placed me in close contact with patient populations that were supported by Emory's infectious disease medical subspecialists. Naturally, I was drawn toward these clinicians, and I have retained very close ties with them as a collegial member at the hospital.

In 1986, I was promoted to associate director in charge of clinical and education programs. By then, my practice had evolved to the point that it was focused equally on infectious disease and pharmacokinetics. I've been fortunate enough to recruit a number of clinical specialists who work under my administrative direction, and I hired another pharmacist whose efforts are concentrated on pharmacokinetics. As a result, for the last four years I've been focusing almost exclusively on the infectious disease process.

This evolution of interest has taken me from the clinical arena, where I worked directly with patients on a routine basis, to the management arena, where my days are more likely to be spent directing subordinates or training them.

We have a pharmacy residency program that was established in 1983. Individuals with PharmDs come to gain experience in various areas of clinical practice. Those in my area spend most of their time working with me or the other clinical specialists who report to me. I still keep my hand in research by investigating certain areas of infectious disease and pharmacokinetics.

In the past, I worked alternate months on the infectious disease service. Nowadays, on an average day I come in early and, beginning at 8 AM, go on morning rounds with the infectious disease consult team. On the team with me are attending physicians, regular medical residents, and fellows who have finished their residencies and are subspecializing in infectious disease. We meet again in the afternoon and make rounds on patients who are new consultations. Such a day may not end before 6 PM or 8 PM.

The remainder of the day is spent working on current research projects or developing new ones. I also attend monthly meetings of several committees I serve on in the hospital and medical school. Among these are the committee that establishes guidelines for antibiotic use in the hospital and the medical school committee that is responsible for evaluating prospective research projects.

Currently, my administrative tasks comprise up to 70 percent of my responsibilities. I still meet several times each week with pharmacy students and the infectious disease pharmacy resident to discuss pertinent topics and to go over new literature and specific patient problems. Now, much of my time is spent directing pharmacy residents in infectious disease or developing new research protocols for investigation at Emory.

In our research, we evaluate the disposition of antibiotics in selected patient populations, such as those who have renal failure. Also in this institution we work extensively with microbial surveillance. We look at the types of microorganisms that are thought to be causing infections in various areas of the hospital, and we try to make certain we are providing drugs that are most appropriate for managing them. In the process, data collection and report writing are ever-present chores.

We spend considerable time on pharmacokinetic studies for new agents that are not on the market yet, as well as agents that have just become available. We want to know how effective they are in very specific patient populations. This is an important part of an infectious disease pharmacist's professional life, and it is particularly interesting now. New and extremely exciting drugs are slated for approval in the 1990s, and students who enter this field in the next two to three years will surely participate in the process of evaluating and selecting these drugs.

As these new agents are introduced, many of the older ones will remain in the formulary. Consequently, a physician who in the mid-1980s might have had 15 drugs to choose among will now have to select from as many as 50 or more agents. Many of these are quite similar, having only subtle differences. An infectious disease physician can understand those subtleties, but a general practitioner may have a very difficult time differentiating among them. This proliferation will lead to an expansion of pharmacy's sphere of influence, especially in infectious disease. The result will be a great opportunity for pharmacy students who develop expertise in this area. Tomorrow's infectious disease specialist will have an important role to fill in educating the entire medical community about these very complex and sometimes difficult-to-understand drugs.

Lawrence J. Cohen, PharmD, FASHP, is associate professor of pharmacy, psychiatry, and behavioral sciences at the University of Oklahoma and director of pharmaceutical services for the Oklahoma Department of Mental Health and Substance Abuse Services in Oklahoma City.

The Psychopharmacist

Psychopharmacy is one of the most rewarding specialties in pharmacy. This is true because practitioners in this field have considerable clinical input and a dramatic impact on patient care and outcome. Often, the results of our efforts are quickly apparent. Our work is exciting and encompasses multiple disciplines.

My decision to become a psychopharmacist was a natural consequence of my interest in animal behavior. At the University of California at Los Angeles (UCLA), I majored in biology, with special interest in animal behavior, and psychology.

I was drawn to pharmacy rather than medicine because my friends in medical school told me they didn't use much of the chemistry we had learned. The subject had fascinated me while I was an undergraduate, and I simply hated to think that all my previous education would come to naught. There was no doubt that I would use chemistry when I enrolled in the PharmD program at the University of Southern California (USC). A couple of carbon atoms here or there can make a big difference in the pharmacologic property of a compound and may even change its purpose. I did a post-PharmD residency in psychopharmacy at the USC-L.A. County Medical Center.

For as long as I've been interested in pharmacy, I have been drawn to clinical care. In fact, I worked at the UCLA hospital and clinics as an undergraduate and as a pharmacy student. I started as a nurse's aide and went on to other positions such as EKG technician. For a long time, I was the EKG lab supervisor on Friday nights and weekends, and this experience helped me learn how to interact with patients. During the summers, I worked as a graduate student intern at Atascadero State Hospital, which is a four-hour drive north of Los Angeles. My experience there with Dr. Fred Raleigh, the director of pharmacy, further influenced my decision to dedicate my efforts to psychopharmacy practice.

After residency training, I embarked on an interesting trek. I made it a point to move every few years to a different, more challenging position. The resulting diversity of work taught me that people raised and trained in the same place may never realize how many opportunities are waiting for them over the horizon. Many of the opportunities I've had came to me because I took a chance and moved.

My first job was director of clinical pharmacy services for the Kern County Department of Mental Health. The department was headquartered in Bakersfield, and it was my responsibility to go out a couple of days each week to coordinate programs at clinics all over the county.

I reported to the director of mental health, a psychiatrist who felt strongly about the need to have a PharmD in my position. I was expected to monitor drug therapy, recommend modifications to treatment, and educate patients in the use of their medications.

The director gave me great latitude, and I was able to help create a position that was tailored to my professional interests. One of my first steps was to develop a referral pharmacy system to fill prescriptions. For two years, I ran a medication clinic for outpatients, and I monitored the therapy of patients who were making the transition from inpatient to outpatient status. Setting up these programs was a great challenge because the department hadn't had anything like them before.

In the next two years, the scope of my duties broadened, and I eventually became responsible for medical services. In addition to managing the clinics and coordinating medical staff activities, I was given great latitude in selecting employees. Fortunately, I had the full support of the director.

In time, I married and relocated to San Francisco. There, I found a job on the faculty at the University of California at San Francisco. I was a preceptor for pharmacy students and residents and, although UCSF had no psychopharmacy residency program, we did have students who rotated through the Langley Porter Psychiatric Hospital.

I also taught students how to use psychiatric drugs clinically and how to determine when their use is appropriate. That was a difficult task because the students were with us for such a short time. Clerkships typically lasted four or six weeks.

I have a lot of praise for UCSF's program. Pharmacists were stationed on the wards rather than in a central location. If patients experienced any complications, pharmacists were only 20 steps away. This arrangement maximized positive outcomes and patient care, especially for neurosurgery and neurology patients, my primary practice area at the time.

After about two years at UCSF, I realized I missed having more contact with psychiatric patients. I had been doing some psychopharmacy consulting and liaison services for UCSF's medical staff, but I wanted even more involvement.

I moved to Napa State Hospital, a 1,200-bed psychiatric hospital that had been established in the 1850s. I rejuvenated Napa's clerkship, and the hospital credentialed me as psychopharmacy consultant. In California, that credential traditionally had been granted only to psychiatrists.

During my stay at Napa some of my time was spent performing distribution services, an experience that emphasized for me the importance of distribution in patient care, and I was later able to apply this experience to the hospital's clinical review process. Another benefit of my work was that it prompted me to be involved in forming a statewide advisory committee that generated guidelines for all psychotropic drugs. Years later, I still keep up to date on what the committee is doing.

My next job was in Maryland, where I was director of pharmacy at

Spring Grove Hospital Center, a 650-bed state psychiatric hospital outside Baltimore and one of the oldest psychiatric hospitals in the United States. The reason I took the job was because it would enable me to combine clinical work with teaching and administrative duties. I also oversaw the distribution and expansion of unit-dose pharmacy services and participated in the development of mental health pharmacy services.

As the only person in the hospital with clinical pharmacy training, I did a lot of consults and coordinated investigational drug studies there. In addition, I taught at the University of Maryland. To gain more clinical experience, I worked one day a week at the nearby Perry Point Veterans Administration Medical Center. There, I helped develop guidelines for using psychotropic drugs.

After working at Spring Grove for two years, the University of Oklahoma made me an offer I couldn't refuse: a position as associate professor of pharmacy, psychiatry, and behavioral science. It's a remarkable job.

I teach psychopharmacology in the medical school and to psychiatry residents. I coordinate a psychopharmacy program for the College of Pharmacy. Together with a psychiatrist on the faculty, I provide consultations on drug therapy. At the moment, we're developing a training program for psychiatry residents at one of our state hospitals.

As director of pharmacy services for the Oklahoma Department of Mental Health and Substance Abuse Services, I oversee pharmacy services for state hospitals and community mental hospitals. I answer their questions and develop guidelines for drug therapy. In addition, I work hard to foster research in the department. I chair several committees, including the statewide pharmacy and therapeutics committee.

What I enjoy most about my job is that every single day offers different challenges. I am never bored. Today, for example, someone in the state legislature might call, asking what programs could be eliminated as part of a drive to cut $2 million out of the mental health budget. Tomorrow, a worried physician might contact me to find out whether his patient's seizure might have been drug induced.

I am involved in program development at every department level. I write a newsletter, I interact with the media, and I am serving as an expert for the College of Pharmacy as a faculty member at the geriatric education center. Moreover, I am on the physicians advisory board of the Oklahoma Nursing Home Association. More than in any other job I've had, variety characterizes my life in Oklahoma.

Typically, I work some 50 to 55 hours each week – up to 60 at crunch time. I feel that I am fairly compensated for a pharmacist, but I earn less than other professionals I know. In fact, if I were in it for the money, I might be asking myself what I am doing here. But for me, the challenges in my job make up for what may be missing financially.

As I said earlier, a pharmacist with a PharmD will enter this field more easily than one who has a bachelor's degree. Residency training also is becoming more important because it strengthens pharmacists' clinical skills and gives them practical hands-on experience judging patients' conditions. After years of experience, I'm sure that someone who has no doctoral degree could function well in psychopharmacy, but it would take a great deal of time to develop the same level of expertise.

The demand for pharmacists in this field is so great that it will take a long time to fill the need. And more positions are opening every day in clinics and HMOs. As for students right out of school, many might consider my job to be more administrative than they would like. But I worked my way here by creating a new position I wanted every time I made a move. Graduates with drive, imagination, and a sense of adventure can surely follow a similar path.

Bruce M. Schechter, PharmD,
is director of scientific communications for
ADIS International in Langhorne, Pennsylvania.
He also is a clinical assistant professor of
pharmacy at the Philadelphia College of
Pharmacy and Science.

The Geriatrics Pharmacist

People today are living longer than ever before. They're also living healthier. In fact, the over-65 population represents about 13 percent of the overall U.S. population, and these people consume 25 to 30 percent of our health care resources. In the 21st century, the elderly will represent some 25 percent of the population, and they will likely consume over half of all health care resources.

Simply because of that, every health care professional will have to be a geriatrician to some degree, unless they specialize in obstetrics or pediatrics. For the most part, the very difficult patients and the very complex and problematic patients will need to be referred to the geriatrics specialist.

The demographics of our growing elderly population are so vast that there will never be enough specifically trained geriatrics specialists to care for all the old people. There will just be too many of them. The goal in geriatrics is to help people maintain their active, ambulatory lifestyles and to reduce their use of institutional resources.

People over the age of 65 are the most heterogeneous of all subpopulations. That's the important thing to remember. The older we get, the more different we become from each other. This is true because people age at different rates. Just because overall liver function deteriorates over time, one can't predict on the basis of age alone how a person is going to metabolize a drug. Aging is a very individual process.

The conventional stereotype of aging depicts a person who retires and begins slowly to deteriorate. Soon, he experiences chronic disease and begins taking multiple medications. On the other hand, people who age "successfully" do so without age-related decline. The retiree who remains virtually free of chronic diseases, doesn't take a lot of medication, and remains able to lead an active, healthy life is considered by most to have aged successfully.

We actually place the elderly in three groupings. Those between 65 and 74 years are the so-called young-old. The middle-old are between 75 and 84. The old-old people – those over 85 years of age – are this country's fastest-growing subpopulation. Generally speaking, they also are the sickest. As a group, not surprisingly, they consume the most medications (over-the-counter as well as prescription drugs). Of the three groups, this is the one we know the least about in terms of age-related changes in drug distribution. In my opinion, one of the most rewarding aspects of geriatrics is maximizing the clinical benefit of medications these people must use.

In my first class each year, I ask students to describe old people in one word. The most common responses are "frail," "dependent," "sick," "demented," "grumpy," "recalcitrant." All of these adjectives reflect negative images of what it means to be old. It indicates that too many of us still view old age as an abnormality and not as an extension of our own lives. I take it as a personal mission to dispel that ageist prejudice because I believe it can be very damaging.

My pharmacy career began while I was still in high school. I worked in a community pharmacy in New York City, not far from Yankee Stadium. I worked my way up from delivery boy to stock boy, and, finally, to more technical responsibilities. After high school I knew I wanted to practice in the profession, so I enrolled in pharmacy school.

Even at that early stage, I had decided that I didn't want to work again in a retail pharmacy. I went into pharmacy school knowing that I wanted to come out as a hospital pharmacist. After earning a BS degree, I completed a residency in hospital pharmacy and practiced for three years before returning to school to complete the doctor of pharmacy program.

For the last four and a half years, I've served on the faculty of the Philadelphia College of Pharmacy and Science (PCPS). Before that, I was at Purdue University. Until recently, I was primarily a geriatrics clinical practitioner. In June of 1992, I became director of scientific communications at ADIS International, an international drug information publishing company.

Geriatrics pharmacy has offered me tremendous rewards because it has been my passport to an extremely broad range of professional activities. I have delivered direct patient care in the hospital setting. I've done the same in long-term care facilities. In addition, I helped establish the Geriatric Pharmacy Institute, a large educational and training institute at PCPS. Through that experience, I was able to communicate the importance of geriatric care to literally thousands of practitioners who, even though 75 percent of the people they serve are elderly, never truly understood their patients' special needs.

Generally speaking, today's health care practitioners are not adequately trained to address the unique changes that occur with the aging process. We are travelling in uncharted territory, and we know too little about what happens with drugs in old people because we haven't studied them adequately. We do know that with regard to the disposition of drugs and their pharmacology, aging is not merely an extension of earlier periods of life. People age at different rates and with different effects. It is clear now that the impact of aging on drug action is determined not only by the aging process, but also by such individual factors as lifestyle, disease states, and general health status throughout a patient's life.

As we developed the Geriatric Pharmacy Institute, I became involved in coordinating educational programs in geriatrics. At the same time, we initiated some very interesting publishing programs. We published newsletters and journals on geriatric topics. At national professional meetings, we conducted symposia. As the institute grew, it became apparent to us that we could do even more. Consequently, in addition to my clinical and teaching duties I developed a whole range of new skills. Before long, I was attracted to my new company, which publishes a variety of international journals, including one entitled *Drugs and Aging*.

Geriatrics pharmacy is a multidisciplinary field. Our patients' needs vary so widely that serving them properly requires input from physicians, nurses, social workers, and pharmacists – all of whom should be specialists in geriatric care. In some cases, because of the incidence of psychiatric illnesses, particularly depression and dementia, the skills of a geriatrics psychiatrist may be needed.

Not only must pharmacists specializing in geriatrics possess good interviewing skills, they also must be skilled at overcoming the barriers that can impede communication with elderly patients. These barriers can be dreadfully high at times, and never more so than in cases of demented patients who simply cannot be interviewed. With such patients, the family often holds the key to understanding. Hearing loss, poor vision, and illiteracy are other problems that may complicate the relationship between the pharmacist and the elderly patient. Yet, they must be overcome if proper care is to be given these patients.

The specialist in geriatrics has no shortage of practice options. Some work in geriatrics specialty clinics, others in long-term care facilities. Some have consultant pharmacy practices, and some work in industry and academia. But the greatest opportunity in this specialty lies in the community, where most of our over-65 population resides. In fact, it may develop that pharmacists who work in geriatrics will have their greatest impact in neighborhood community pharmacies.

In our society, old people are considered disposable, while other cultures respect their wisdom and life experience and place them at the center of the family. In those societies, the elderly are cared for by their families until they die. We still have much to learn.

Even when one is accustomed, as I am, to working with the elderly, it is easy to forget that their lives have been rich in experiences and knowledge. That realization first came to me in a nursing home when I was interviewing a patient. I introduced myself as a pharmacist, and he replied, "Oh, that's very interesting." And he went on to describe his lengthy career as a chemist for a pharmaceutical manufacturer. He mentioned that he had worked on the discovery of some of the most important drug receptors found during the 20th century. I found myself looking at this gentleman, realizing that I had forgotten some of my own lessons. I had assumed he was ignorant of his therapy when, in fact, he could have been one of my professors in his younger days. This underscores the need for pharmacists to become good communicators and, most important, life-long learners.

Robert J. Kuhn, PharmD,
is associate professor of pharmacy and
assistant director for pediatrics pharmacy at the
University of Kentucky, Lexington.

The Pediatrics Pharmacist

I go to too many funerals for kids. But when I attend a service and the parents say, "Thank you for everything you've done for my child," that makes up for all the anguish that goes with my job.

The heartaches associated with treating very sick children are tolerable because I know that if I, along with the physicians and nurses, were not around to help care for them, more children would be in Lexington Cemetery right now.

I am able to have that kind of impact because of the clinical service I provide to the pediatric and neonatal units of the University of Kentucky Medical Center. I round with physicians and make specific recommendations on drug therapy. I also monitor the therapy and help develop protocols for patient care. In working with nurses, I make sure they know the latest techniques of drug administration, and I help identify and solve problems relative to drug distribution in pediatrics.

Of course, clinical service is only one part of my job. As an associate professor, I teach both undergraduate and doctoral students in the therapeutics and pharmacology sequence of the college of pharmacy. I also help teach medical students and staff members in pediatrics and other subspecialties. I provide in-service training for the college of nursing and the division of pediatric nursing. I serve as preceptor for students in both neonatal and pediatric rotations, and I supervise the training of pediatrics residents and general clinical residents.

Although it's not an everyday responsibility, research is a significant component of my professional life. My investigational activities center mainly on cystic fibrosis, drug delivery, and new types of dialysis. Even so, I've had at least some involvement with some of the pulmonary surfactant trials. Our department played a small role in developing this drug, which now saves 5,000 lives a year. That's pretty exciting.

I enjoy every aspect of my job, but my clinical involvement is the primary source of my career satisfaction. Perhaps that's because there is no such thing as a typical pediatric patient. Similarly, there is no such thing as a standard pediatric dose. Our patients range in age from one minute old to 17 or 18 years. They may weigh as little as two pounds, or as much as 150.

As a result, pediatrics pharmacists are confronted with a variety of technical challenges. For example, how do you give a tiny infant a proper dose of antibiotic? And how do you do it accurately in a manner that can be reproduced? It's no small challenge to administer two milligrams of a drug, but in an 80-mg dose, 2 mg may be lost in tubing. If that tiny amount is the prescribed dose, a patient may be in big trouble if I am not very careful.

I work in an area of pediatrics where there are many information gaps. Often, I have to rely on the knowledge I have and the expertise I've developed over time in shaping recommendations for drug therapy and dosing. In my department, we have such great rapport with physicians that 90 percent of our pharmacists' recommendations are followed. I can't afford to mess that up, so I apply my skills with the greatest of care.

I especially like working in this setting because I like kids and find it exciting to see them respond so quickly to disease or to changes in therapy. Children – especially premature babies – will go downhill very quickly unless they are given the correct therapy. A baby that weighs only 800 grams either gets better or it dies.

My interest in pediatrics pharmacy began when I went to my first cystic fibrosis camp in 1978. The children there were taking many medications, thousands of dollars' worth each year. That summer it became clear to me that pharmacists knew less about the disease than other health care professionals. Too often they just said, "That will be $64.95. See you next week."

At the camp, I learned how children with chronic disease have to struggle with regimens that call for 20 different pills each day, and this in addition to aerosol treatments and IV antibiotics. In such dire circumstances, it's simply not enough to say, "Take this medication four times a day and everything will be fine."

I decided then that this disease was too serious and these kids were too important to be treated that way by pharmacists. That and the experience of working one on one with camp patients helped me decide to be a clinical pharmacist in pediatrics. I wanted to devote myself to making a difference in the lives of such children. When I came to Kentucky, I promised myself that I would try to ensure that no student at the University of Kentucky College of Pharmacy would leave without an understanding of cystic fibrosis and an awareness of the effect of chronic illness on children. I believe I have kept that vow.

A survey I recently conducted with my Ohio State University mentor shows that the average undergraduate pharmacy curriculum offers only three and a half hours of pediatrics. In a five- or six-year program, that just isn't enough. At Kentucky, we changed our curriculum to make sure all pharmacy students get at least a general exposure to the subject, and now we require about 12 hours of didactic work in pediatrics.

Students seem to enjoy this part of the curriculum. Some develop the same passion I have for pediatrics. This specialty has really caught on during the last few years. Nevertheless, there aren't more than 50 or 60 pediatrics specialists in the entire country.

No matter how deeply budgets are cut in other areas of education, I think there will always be teaching opportunities for clinical pharmacists of any subspecialty. Moreover, the trend toward expanding pharmacy education into problem-based learning is going to revolutionize pharmacy schools. As a result, it will take six years of training to become a pharmacist. Consequently, most people will get a PharmD degree, because spending six years to earn a bachelor's degree won't sound like much of a bargain. Naturally, this elevated level of education will increase the need for faculty members.

Outside of academia, there are three jobs for every pharmacist in pediatrics training. Children's hospitals, large medical centers, and even some community hospitals are looking for pharmacists to fill pediatric positions. And that circumstance is sure to continue because this society will not significantly reduce the resources we invest in the care of sick children. Pediatrics pharmacy will always be a sector of opportunity.

The clinical pharmacist who will do best in pediatrics is the person who can integrate a great deal of general knowledge with the limited amount of information that is specific to pediatric drug therapy. If you're the kind of person who needs 15 studies to document the appropriateness of therapy, you'll be paralyzed in this setting. There can't be more than a handful of therapies we employ that are supported by that many studies. For other therapies we rely on limited information or we extrapolate from data gained from adult patients.

Pediatrics pharmacists also need pretty big hearts, even if they are wrapped in cast iron. The question that I am asked most often is, "How can you deal with a three-year-old who is dying of cancer? Or a five-year-old who has been run over by a truck? Or a kid who has been burned to a crisp?" My answer is that nothing can be allowed to impede the care of sick children. As painful as it can be at times, I just work as hard as I can to make certain their drug therapy is effective.

In the future, more pediatrics pharmacists will be found in community hospitals because more and more therapy is going to be provided in a decentralized area. There's no longer any reason to fly a child 400 miles to receive chemotherapy. Today's technology is such that nurses and pharmacists can deliver that therapy in a local 200-bed hospital for a lot less money. Also, more and more ill children are being seen as outpatients, and they must rely on outpatient and community pharmacies.

Pediatrics pharmacists are having to face the liability associated with drug-induced diseases in children. The fact is that when errors are made in drug therapy, pediatric patients may die. So, the pharmacist who fails to check pediatric doses, who fails to understand what's different about pediatric patients, runs the risk of not protecting this needful population. So if you believe as I do that there is nothing more important than the care of a sick child, you realize that pediatrics pharmacists have to pay attention to detail in a way that other pharmacists may not. We must cross every t and dot every i. We must double check doses and titration. With adults, it doesn't much matter whether the patient weighs 130 or 190 pounds.

With children, the difference between 1.5 kilos and 1.9 kilos can be critically important.

The biggest professional reward I have is the satisfaction that comes with knowing my job is important, that I can make a difference. That's why I fight for compassionate use of drugs. That's why I get involved with clinical research; it enables me to give investigational agents to my patients. My life has a single focus: to make my patients better.

I am well paid, but I could earn more in other areas of pharmacy. Clinical faculty members don't get paid as much as we would if we worked in industry – at least at first. Nevertheless, there may be more upward salary mobility here than in traditional pharmacy practices. I work for rewards other than money, and the most important of these is the chance I have to help children and to teach our residents how to help them. That's what gets me out of bed in the morning.

*David L. Laven, NPh, CRPh, FASHP,
FAPPM-APhA, is director of the nuclear
pharmacy program at the VA Medical Center
in Bay Pines, Florida.*

The Nuclear Pharmacist

Nuclear pharmacy is an innovative specialty that can change quickly with scientific advances. It also is a relatively new professional option for pharmacists.

Although biologists were using radioactive tracer techniques in the 1920s, the use of radioactive materials did not begin until the 1950s. During the 1960s, nuclear medicine became a medical specialty, and within 10 years nearly half of all U.S. hospitals had some type of nuclear medicine department. Now, the Joint Commission on Accreditation of Healthcare Organizations requires that every accredited hospital have access to nuclear medicine facilities. Yet despite the proliferation of opportunities in this field, nuclear pharmacy is given little mention in most pharmacy schools. As a result, its practitioners form a small but vocal group, most of whose members work actively to advance the profession.

Serendipity brought me into nuclear pharmacy. I had been studying psychology at Wayne State University in Detroit during the mid-1970s – a time when it was difficult to get into medical school. After my third unsuccessful try, the assistant dean of the medical school suggested that I abandon my ambition to be a radiologist and consider a career in pharmacy instead. I had never even thought of that, but I liked the idea. I applied and was accepted.

I started pharmacy school at the University of New Mexico in 1977. At 25, I was no youngster, and I was starting my third undergraduate program. The university gave me a year's credit for my BA from Michigan's Albion College and for the courses I had taken after graduating from there. Continuing my interest in radiology, I specialized in nuclear pharmacy at New Mexico.

In my final year, I petitioned to combine a curricular track in radiopharmacy (as it was often called back then) with another geared towards hospital pharmacy. The college granted my request. The program's reputation was so good that I received numerous job offers during that year. In fact, for me, the biggest career problem I faced was deciding where I wanted to live. I accepted an offer to join a commercial nuclear pharmacy chain in Miami as assistant manager. The title may sound exalted, but our pharmacy was just a two-person operation.

Even though many hospitals have their own nuclear medicine departments, most rely on commercial, centralized nuclear pharmacy operations for the radiopharmaceuticals needed for a wide range of diagnostic procedures. These outside pharmacies, which serve a number of institutions in most major U.S. cities, can take advantage of economies of scale that simply aren't available to a single hospital. Moreover, commercial nuclear pharmacies relieve hospitals of the sometimes onerous responsibilities of preparing the radiopharmaceutical agents, controlling their quality, and disposing of waste material – not to mention record-keeping functions. I enjoyed my work, but I missed having closer interaction with patients and the medical staff. As it was, client hospitals would merely telephone their orders to us. We then worked to fill these orders and deliver them in a timely manner, 24 hours a day, seven days a week.

After I had been there for three years, it appeared that my company would close its Miami facility. I wanted to find a more secure and challenging position, so I left to take a job as a staff pharmacist in a small 200-bed community hospital. However, within a year I was back working for the competitor of my first employer. Soon after that the two nuclear pharmacy companies merged, and South Florida suddenly had a glut of nuclear pharmacists, even though there was a shortage in the rest of the country.

Because I was not in a position to accept a job in another part of the country, I sought refuge as a staff pharmacist in a South Florida rehabilitation hospital. I soon found that long-term care was not my cup of tea. Compared with nuclear pharmacy, it was too slow-paced. I don't know how many times I rotated inventory on the shelves, but it eventually became too many for me.

Fortunately, that's when I received a call from the Veterans Administration hospital. The chief of nuclear medicine at the VA Medical Center in Bay Pines, Fla., believed that having a nuclear pharmacist on board would be less expensive than contracting with one of several commercial nuclear pharmacies that had been serving him before.

I became director of the center's nuclear pharmacy program, which has no staff. I am affiliated with the center's nuclear medicine program, not with the pharmacy department. However, the VA does classify me as a pharmacist, and this entitles me to some special benefits. Even so, I sometimes feel like a leaf on a limb. I would like closer ties with the pharmacy, but I enjoy what I am doing. It's a trade-off.

In the seven years I have been here, I have saved the center $750,000 overall. During that time, I spent $900,000 on radiopharmaceuticals, with wastage less than $20,000. Our rate of product utilization averages nearly 98 percent, and inventory turns over between 50 and 70 times a year. This is especially striking in comparison with an average retail pharmacy, which will turn its inventory only four or five times a year. Since my arrival in 1985, our patient load has averaged increases upwards of 15 percent per year, and the cost of the tests we perform has increased as much as 30 percent. At the same time, my annual radiopharmaceutical budget has gone up a mere four to six percent (with no increase at all for three successive years). So it's not surprising that I'm having trouble staying within the budget.

I start the day at about 7 AM. When I arrive, I already have a good idea of what the work load will be, because tests are scheduled 24 hours in advance. Immediately, I'm off to the races. As I begin the compounding for that day, I have to take into account when patients are scheduled because radioactive drugs decay quickly. I have to make sure the dosage is right for a patient who is to be given the drug at 10 AM. Some radiopharmaceuticals have such short stability following preparation that they should be used within five to seven hours. The compounding and dose preparation take about 45 minutes.

After I have finished with compounding, I have to perform quality control testing. I must make sure that the radiopharmaceuticals meet certain USP compendial standards, such as radiochemical purity, particle size (when appropriate), and pH. This is a process that most pharmacists rely on drug manufacturers to perform. For nuclear pharmacists, it's a daily responsibility that, like most things, must be documented.

Upon completion of dose preparation, I put the lab to rest. It's time for a cup of coffee, time to start assembling schedules for the next day and to review tests that have been ordered. If something seems inappropriate, I bring it to the attention of the ordering physician. At Bay Pines, record keeping is done a little differently than in most hospitals. For example, each patient has two charts – one containing a medication profile and the other the medical records. I go through both looking for clinical problems that might have an effect on the administration of nuclear pharmaceutical agents, such as other scheduled diagnostic testing procedures, drug-radio-pharmaceutical interactions, and certain medical conditions. Generally, I don't contact patients personally, but I do talk to VA pharmacists about their medications and to the nuclear medicine physicians about potential problems.

One of the exciting things about my job is the impact it enables me to have on patient care. For example, if a patient who comes in to be tested for cirrhosis of the liver also has an upset stomach and has been given an antacid that contains aluminum, we might produce a great lung scan but a very poor liver scan. My job is to catch such problems because if a $300 test doesn't turn out, it probably will not be repeated – reimbursement won't cover the additional cost. Instead, it's likely that the hospital will send the patient for ultrasound or other radiologic examinations. In such cases, the patient has to go through additional tests that wouldn't have been necessary if someone had been paying closer attention. It is important to get it right the first time, without having to order a battery of other tests to confirm or deny less-than-optimal diagnostic tests.

Not infrequently, patients come down to the nuclear pharmacy and express concern about the tests they are expected to undergo. Many are afraid that they are going to be injected with dyes, to which they may be allergic. I reassure them with the information that radiopharmaceuticals so rarely induce allergic reactions that perhaps one in 300,000 patients will experience a problem. That's a very small number – far lower than would be seen with traditional medications.

This specialty is so new that the long-term (50+ years) effects of working in nuclear pharmacy are not known. Consequently, there is some hesitation, especially among females of child-bearing age, to enter the field. It's true that the materials are radioactive, but if pharmacists take proper precautions, including wearing protective clothing, there is no evidence of hazardous effects. Here, drugs are appropriately shielded, and I draw the doses from behind leaded-glass protective barriers. Many of the materials I handle, especially vials and syringes, are kept in special shield containers at all times.

The badges I wear to detect radioactivity show that I am exposed to even lower levels than our nuclear medicine technicians, and that isn't much. The technicians must stay near patients during tests while they administer the drugs intravenously. In effect, patients become sources of low-level radiation, but I've never known anyone who has had a problem. On the other hand, if you were to break the rules and fail to take protective measures, you probably would suffer some consequences. For that reason, good lab and pharmacy techniques are important.

When I am not involved in clinical matters, I spend a great deal of time preparing lectures and journal articles. In addition, I am active in several local and national professional associations. I also have developed continuing education courses for nuclear pharmacists through the Florida Pharmacy Association, the American Pharmaceutical Association, and the American Society of Hospital Pharmacists. I'm not alone in my multifaceted professional participation because nuclear pharmacists are among the most active and vocal specialists in pharmacy. I believe this activism will ensure that we gain a greater role in patient care than we now enjoy.

In general, there is a critical shortage of manpower in nuclear pharmacy. Naturally, this creates many opportunities for students who choose to work in this rapidly growing practice setting. Currently, only a few schools of pharmacy (eg, New Mexico, Purdue, Mercer, Massachusetts) are producing 25 to 30 nuclear pharmacists annually. That's a terribly small number in view of the fact that a single commercial company has 80 openings each year. Even in hospital-based practice settings, there is finally a trend to have more pharmacy involvement both with radiopharmaceuticals and radiopaque contrast agents. Thus, in the years to come, the concept and scope of nuclear pharmacy practice may become known as radiologic pharmacy, reflecting pharmacy's involvement with the radiopharmaceuticals used in nuclear medicine, as well as agents used in radiology, including ultrasound, magnetic resonance imaging (MRI), and computed tomography.

Even with the high demand for nuclear pharmacists, salaries are lower than can be found in retail chain pharmacy, but are rising rapidly. In terms of health care dollars, this is a highly competitive industry. Test costs range from $400 to $1,000, but the physician's reading fee and hospital charges claim most of the money. Relatively speaking, the cost of the drugs we employ is small – between $10 and $200. This means that to be successful, pharmacies must sell many doses. It's a volume business.

The work day can be long and difficult for nuclear pharmacists. Diagnostic testing may require someone to be available around the clock. Because most hospitals start their day at 7 AM, commercial nuclear pharmacists might be hard at work by two, three, or four o'clock in the morning. During normal working hours, someone also must be available to prepare stat doses. This means that a typical two-person operation might be open from two in the morning until four in the afternoon. In such pharmacies, the pharmacists will rotate from the early to late shifts and wear pagers during the night and on weekends and holidays. Nuclear pharmacists working in hospital settings often have a regular work schedule, but after-hours emergency calls can always occur.

For students who seek clinical opportunities on the cutting edge of technology, nuclear pharmacy has much to offer. Patient contact may be minimal, but there are plenty of chances to serve in a clinical capacity. Moreover, few specialties give pharmacists more contact with other health care professionals, primarily physicians, and nuclear medicine technologists. We have a tremendous impact on diagnostic accuracy. And because effective therapy depends on that, our role in patient care is unquestioned.

Critical Care Pharmacy

Beth VanderHayden, PharmD, BCPS,
is an assistant clinical professor at the
University of Maryland, and a
clinical specialist in critical care at the
Shock Trauma Center at University
Hospital Systems in Baltimore.

A critical care practice offers a unique blend of clinical opportunities. For example, it gives the pharmacist an opportunity to work with some of the most advanced products available. In addition, the work calls on such independent cognitive abilities as therapy analysis, patient monitoring, and problem solving. Most important, the pharmacist is part of a team that cares for patients who are very ill.

My interest in critical care pharmacy grew out of a hemodynamics course I had during my PharmD studies. A major component of that course dealt with the pathophysiology of the critically ill. All the courses I had taken up to that point discussed conditions or disease states and their various treatments in very straightforward and linear terms. Critical care pharmacy was different. Manipulations of therapy were still outcome-based, but there were always other mitigating factors, such as multiple organ failure or infections that develop during treatment. As a result, I found the pharmacokinetics much more challenging.

Before committing to a career working with critically ill patients, I decided to get some hands-on clinical experience. After earning my PharmD at Purdue University, I enrolled in a two-year residency at the Medical College of Virginia Hospitals (MCVH). The residency split my time evenly between the hospital's emergency room and intensive care unit. In two years I saw a full spectrum of conditions, including presentations of severe asthma, liver malfunctions, head injuries, cardiac arrest, multiple stab wounds, gunshot trauma, kidney failure, and virtually everything in between.

While I wasn't drawn to work with ER patients, the experience I gained in that unit was very valuable. More than anything else, it taught me to be resourceful and to think on my feet. Also, after a year in the ER, nothing shocked me. We dealt with patients who were experiencing extreme conditions, and our primary objective was resuscitation and stabilization. A significant part of my job came down to reacting to whatever type of case was in front of me and anticipating what drugs and IVs the physicians and nurses might need next. Pharmacokinetically speaking, this was particularly challenging, because we never knew what type of case would come through the door next. And when the whole team was scrambling to resuscitate a patient, that's when I realized the depth of my knowledge.

Conditions in the ICU were as serious or even more so than those in the ER, but the atmosphere was less hectic. In general, I knew what kinds of cases I would be dealing with each day, and I had more time to analyze the patients' conditions. However, the treatments employed in that setting were extremely complex. In part, this was because most of our patients had just had liver or kidney transplants. Others presented with gastric bleeds, esophageal varices, or renal ailments. In addition to their primary conditions, many patients also suffered from multiple organ problems, infections, or, perhaps, pneumonia. Any one of these factors could affect the effectiveness of drug therapy. As a result, managing care depended heavily on monitoring outcomes, adapting treatments, and learning to anticipate what might happen next. Many of our patients were susceptible to infections and sepsis, and while these complications were not certain to occur, I had to be ready to alter care accordingly.

After completing my residency, I accepted a position as a clinical specialist in critical care at the Shock Trauma Center of the University of Maryland Medical Systems, in Baltimore. This job presented me with a new challenge: The hospital had never had a critical care pharmacist before. The pharmacy department gave me a general outline of what was expected, but I was given considerable liberty to shape this position as I saw fit. In essence, as a member of the critical care team, I was there to support the physicians and nurses. I could do this by sitting in an office, or I could participate directly. It was up to me to set the boundaries, build up the practice, and establish a practice relationship. It was a challenging opportunity, and in many ways it was quite intimidating.

The Shock Trauma Center is a Level-I critical care facility, offering the most intensive and highest level of care available. Naturally, this often includes complicated pharmacy with cutting-edge treatments. I was confident in my skills and knowledge, and I knew that my clinical abilities would enable me to make positive contributions to patient care. In addition, the prospect of getting to work was exciting.

However, on my first day I received a large dose of reality. One of the physicians greeted me and invited me to accompany the critical care team on rounds. I gladly accepted. Then he told me I would be there solely as an observer, not as a participant. I was welcome to look and listen, but I had to keep my mouth shut.

I was shocked. Throughout pharmacy school I was taught that pharmacists were valued members of multidisciplinary teams, embraced by physicians and nurses, and encouraged to contribute as colleagues in patient care. MCVH had a tradition of hands-on clinical pharmacists, so my residency there had done little to change my perception of pharmacists as vital contributors. But here, the physicians and nurses had no such traditions or philosophies. I was not considered a colleague or even a contributor – just a pharmacist the physicians had never met who was inserted into their team by the hospital administrators. That first day, I felt as though I was being tolerated more than anything else. It was a very sobering experience.

I don't blame the physicians or nurses. After all, they were used to clinical pharmacists who served as consultants, who stood back and prepared medications or made recommendations when asked. The concept of a pharmacist working as a hands-on clinician was foreign to them. I don't think they were resistant to the idea as much as they were skeptical. They found it much easier to deal with me in the same way they had dealt with pharmacists in the past. However, I had a different idea of how this practice should go.

I knew I had to prove myself. I also knew that if I started offering unsolicited opinions about treatments, dosages, and therapy selections, I would create more problems for myself than I would solve. The answer lay in working within their concept of what a pharmacist should be, while enhancing their recognition of what I as an individual could provide. I decided the best way to accomplish this was through pharmacokinetics.

During my first year I developed a pharmacokinetics service specifically for my unit. I monitored lab outcomes and various serum levels that were indicative of the effectiveness of drug therapies. In charts, I wrote detailed notes on the kinetics of therapies and anticipated dosage changes. After a few weeks, I was able to make comments in rounds about the kinetics in specific patients. I did everything I could to make this service helpful and necessary without posing a threat to anyone else on my team.

I also made a significant contribution in the dosing of infusions. Before I came to the unit, IV infusions were prepared as patient-specific concentrations and dosed according to the patient's weight. This was effective, but it wasted money because partially used (or even unused) drips had to be discarded. I went about standardizing all infusion drips at a certain concentration. This did not decrease the effectiveness of care. Nor did it significantly increase demands on the nurses. However, it dramatically decreased waste and saved my department about $80,000 per year. As a result, I gained recognition not only among the nurses, but among my colleagues in the pharmacy department.

Within a few months, my work began to be more appreciated, especially by the infectious disease physicians on my team. These physicians realized that I could make contributions, especially in the area of kinetics. They began to seek me out, especially to help them with the treatment of renal failures. I was becoming skilled at understanding what factors would affect treatment and adjusting dosage changes accordingly. As a result, the unit's rate of subtherapeutic dosing decreased significantly.

As my relationship with the infectious disease physicians strengthened, the surgeons and internalists took note and also began to seek me out. This is what I had worked so hard to achieve – an opportunity to practice more critical care pharmacology. But it was also intimidating. I knew that when a physician who had never asked me for an opinion before came to me for a consult, it would probably be my only chance. I would have to demonstrate that my knowledge could be helpful and that it could even add to his understanding. At the same time, I had to be diplomatic and remember that my recommendations could be overruled.

It took about a year and a half to establish among the physicians and nurses a trust and appreciation of my value as a member of our team. Then my duties expanded to include monitoring care, identifying proper treatments and doses, making adjustments in therapies in certain cases, and providing therapy recommendations to physicians and nurses.

In the five years since I've been at the Shock Trauma Center my duties have continued to expand, and I've been promoted. Today, I supervise 15 people, including technicians, pharmacists, residents, PharmD candidates, and a clinical specialist who filled the position I originated. My days start at about 8 AM and last until 6 PM. When I arrive, I usually do a chart review and go around and see new patients who came in during the night. Then I go on rounds with the physicians, nurses, and other members of the team. We discuss patients' progress over the last 24 hours and then create care plans for the next 24 hours. My students and residents round with me and see patients whom they have been assigned to follow. After rounds, I meet with the students and we discuss the rounds. Later that day, they will present their own patients to me and provide evaluations. We talk about treatment strategies and follow ongoing care plans.

I am on our ICU, therapeutics, and research committees. I also work with a group that creates pharmacy protocols. I am expected to keep up with new therapies that may have applications in our unit and to provide information about those products to physicians and nurses. I must attend to a number of administrative duties, especially in staffing, personnel, and staff development. I believe strongly in the development of clinical skills, and I am currently redefining performance standards so they incorporate more clinical objectives.

Away from the center, I teach bachelor's- and PharmD-level classes in critical care pharmacotherapeutics at the University of Maryland School of Pharmacy.

A PharmD is not necessarily required for this type of practice, but someone with a BS degree and no residency training would have to acquire a considerable amount of hands-on experience before working in critical care. This type of practice requires strong pharmacokinetics knowledge, good communication skills, proven problem-solving abilities, and the ability to work independently. The critical care pharmacist also should be somewhat thick-skinned. Teamwork can be tough, especially when pharmacists work hard to solve a therapy problem and then receive little or no credit for their efforts. It's always difficult to be overruled on therapy or dosage suggestions, but that's just part of the job.

For me, the positive aspects of my work far outweigh the negatives. I make more money than a staff hospital pharmacist or a chain pharmacist. Moreover, my job contains endless challenge and gives me tremendous personal satisfaction. But best of all, I know that my work contributes to saving lives. There's no better feeling than that.

Jay Mirtallo, MS,
is a nutritional support pharmacist
at the Ohio State University Hospital,
Columbus, Ohio.

The Nutritional Consultant

My job lives with me day in and day out. No matter where I go, I'm first a nutrition support pharmacist, and second Jay Mirtallo. I've learned to discipline myself so that I'm not always thinking about my job, but I never forget that the better I do and the more people I teach, the better patients who depend on my knowledge will fare. That thought both overwhelms me and keeps me going.

I didn't always know that I wanted to be a pharmacist. To be honest, I was more interested in medicine. I chose pharmacy because I believe it makes sense to establish a solid income. Then, if I still wanted to go into medicine, I'd have a good jumping-off spot. But after I graduated from the University of Toledo in 1976, I knew I wanted to stay with pharmacy. I entered the master's degree program at Ohio State University Hospital, and when I got my MS in 1978, a position was just opening up in nutrition support pharmacy at the hospital.

At the time, nutrition support was a brand-new field. It had not been absorbed by another specialty, and the job description had not been carved in stone. I considered those ground-floor circumstances to be a green light that freed me to create the position as I saw fit. I did, and today I can say that this is my job – in every sense of the word.

The fact that I was able to take all the knowledge I'd acquired in school and focus it on a single practice was very important to me. Because nutrition support is still an evolving discipline, the chance is small that my responsibilities will overlap with those of a physician. This means that instead of engaging in opinion duels, the nutrition support pharmacist usually has a clear field as the in-house expert. In short, I found a field in which I could make significant contributions while creating my own job. It's perfect for me.

My duties occupy four categories: clinical pharmacy, education, research, and management. Of these, the clinical category is the most demanding. It involves making rounds and monitoring patients' therapy, and it casts me in the role of consultant to other professionals who deliver patient care.

Pharmacy students complain about their biochemistry courses, because they ordinarily use very little of that training when they enter the real world. That is not true in this field, where the challenge is to develop ways of nourishing patients whose disease or treatment interferes with their ability to be nourished by ordinary means. Meeting that challenge depends entirely on applied biochemistry, which I've come to appreciate much better now that I understand its value and use it every day.

Because I work in an academic teaching hospital, education is an ever-present part of my job, whether I am making informal recommendations to physicians or meeting formally with students. In nutrition support, we collect a great deal of data from charts and lab reports and from nurses and physicians. Some students respond to this by complaining, "Hey, I didn't go through pharmacy school to become a clinical secretary." I love it when they say that, because it gives me an opportunity to emphasize the usefulness of all that information. On the other hand, some students are pleased to have found an activity that requires them to use all the information they can get their hands on. This is not spectator pharmacy, and by the fourth week of residents' four-week rotation, we expect them to take part in making real decisions about patient care.

Research is not every pharmacist's favorite activity. Many think it means no more than working with rats in a laboratory. That is not the case and I try to counter that image by having students redefine research as a process of finding scientific methods for solving problems in patient care. In nutrition support, we don't do abstract experiments. Instead everything is applied – done solely for the purpose of improving patient care.

Finally, I wear my management hat in dealing with strong personalities and in making certain that the treatments we employ are evaluated from an administrative as well as clinical point of view.

Of course, all these responsibilities have a way of overlapping, and management duties sometimes spill over into the science of the job. For instance, in reviewing a costly TPN solution and evaluating its risk-to-benefit ratio, I may find that patients can be treated just as well with a less costly alternative. In one case, we found that albumin was being overused as a means of increasing blood volume but was having no impact on the patient's recovery. As a result, we established protocols that restricted its use to selected situations, and we saved the hospital more than $100,000 a year, with no reduction at all in the quality of care.

They say even brain surgery gets boring. That's why I try to compartmentalize my duties. This gives me room to move around within the job, and I'm sure that's one of the reasons I'm still here after 14 years. It's widely believed that in order to succeed in a profession, it is necessary to change jobs periodically. I've been able to do this simply by shifting emphasis, putting in more or less time on different duties. Naturally, the ability to do this may vary according to the practice setting.

In my career, for the most part, I've chosen to take a consulting role, bringing a pharmacist's perspective to a multidisciplinary team that also includes doctors, nurses, and dietitians. In this way, I avoid practicing pharmacy in a vacuum. Each team member offers an opinion and we decide as a group how best to treat a patient. Of course, on any team, there is a potential for conflict, so it's important to have a good concept of team dynamics. In an environment that encourages strong personalities and opinions, I must have a clear sense about my own job. I have to know exactly what is expected of me – where my job ends and another person's begins – and I have to recognize where they overlap.

Sometimes tempers run high in this environment. I have been insulted more than once, and I've learned how important it is to keep my personal feelings separate from my work. Tomorrow I may have to deal productively with the person I wanted to punch yesterday. Shy, soft-spoken people can get gobbled up in an environment that is capable of producing such conflict.

There is no denying that my job can be stressful, but it's worth the struggle when I can see that my knowledge makes a difference. Not only does it benefit patient care to have a pharmacist's opinion on nutritional support considered, it also does much for pharmacy in general. If I contribute confident and useful opinions, then other health care providers will begin turning to other pharmacists for advice.

It's hard to describe a typical day. Usually, patient rounds take up the morning. Around noon, the team meets to consult on therapy, discussing whether and how it should be modified. Late in the afternoon, we see new patients. This schedule is constantly subject to change. What actually happens is that we simply sit down as a team and say, "Here's a day, let's fit everything we have to into it." We usually have about 20 to 25 patients, and sometimes that number goes as high as 40. I didn't bargain for a nine-to-five job, and most of the time I start collecting data at 7:30 AM. I go home when I'm finished.

Practicing nutrition support takes the pharmacist beyond the classic realm of hospital pharmacy. Although it is necessary for me to understand and be able to predict drug-nutrient interactions, I may not use my basic pharmacy knowledge for long periods of time. It is probably true that I focus so much on nutrition that I fall behind on other developments. Sometimes I have to remind residents that I can't keep up with every new drug that comes to market.

As I struggle to keep up with new products and technologies, I am frustrated to be asked the same questions over and over again. I often am amazed that the same issues still keep cropping up. I solve and re-solve the albumin problem year after year. Sometimes I am surprised that things I learned – and taught – a decade ago are still largely unknown and unpracticed. But I remind myself that I'm making progress. Now, at least, the students have someone to ask. When I started, there was no place to get formal training in nutrition support. I bounced around until I found a place where I could fit in, and then I taught myself what I needed to know by choosing discussion topics for weekly peer review meetings. I still don't have an advanced degree.

For today's graduate, I recommend a PharmD degree, followed by a residency in nutrition support. The additional training is likely to be a major asset in the early stages of a career.

Nutrition support is now one of only three certified specialties in pharmacy, and the health care industry actively seeks nutrition support specialists for consultation. Nevertheless, the number of practitioners is relatively small, and this makes it possible for pharmacists in the field to earn additional income through private practice or consulting. For a time I had a private practice that allowed me to still be involved with hospital patients who then continued their treatment once they went home.

However, freelancing requires a lot of extra work, and for pharmacists who must have more money, I'd recommend pursuing another aspect of pharmacy. Compensation for hospital pharmacy – even in this specialized field – probably represents the lower range of what pharmacists earn. I know I could earn more elsewhere, but I stay in the job because it is clear that I am able to help patients. The autonomy and associated perks are important bonuses. I do a fair amount of lecturing, even in Australia, Malaysia, and Peru. These benefits are available to younger people entering the field because there are so few of us. In fact, I think the opportunities I have to get involved beyond the job I was hired to do are more significant than in any other area of pharmacy. The lifestyle can be hectic, but well worth it.

Marvin A. Chamberlain, MS,
is director of pharmacy and materials
management on the Central Campus
of the Group Health Cooperative of
Puget Sound, Seattle.

The HMO Pharmacist

It is a big event for me when six months or a year after starting a project that at first seemed impossible, it actually comes together. Of course, it's rare that I can point to that day on a calendar. More often, I end up looking back and saying, "You know, we turned a corner last month, didn't we?"

On the other hand, I remember perfectly the specific day we started and the day we completed the multiyear process of decentralizing our pharmacy program. When I became director of pharmacy in 1982, people told me that I could never get funding for a decentralized program in a managed care setting like this. They said, "Hey, you won't find money for clinical pharmacy activities. That's not something the organization values."

Well, it turns out that the organization did value clinical practice. It took nearly six years, but we completely changed the entire clinical and delivery system that was in place when I came here. Now, the majority of the pharmacy staff practices on patient care units, and our pharmacists have their own specific clinical focus.

To accomplish this, I had to find a way to achieve my goals while working within the system. Finally, I succeeded in having all beds in the hospital covered by a decentralized pharmacy system. When that happened, my wife and I went out and celebrated.

I am responsible for all pharmacy and materials management functions on what Group Health calls Central Campus, which includes the referral hospital and a 70-physician specialty center. I direct 85 people, including seven managers, in the materials management, inpatient pharmacy, and ambulatory pharmacy departments.

Group Health Cooperative (GHC) of Puget Sound is a managed care, health maintenance organization that provides a prepaid health plan to people who voluntarily enroll, either as private individuals or as part of an employer's group plan. Group Health primarily operates a staff model delivery system, in which health care services are provided in facilities owned by GHC and staffed by our own physicians and other health care professionals.

Managed health care has grown significantly throughout the country in the last decade. In 1980, only nine percent of the population was served by managed care systems. Now, more than 30 percent of the population is enrolled in managed care health plans. Of these, about 15 percent receive care through HMOs, and the other 15 percent are covered by preferred provider plans.

In a managed care setting, practitioners are not reimbursed on the basis of what they do for people. Instead, compensation is based on the number of people who belong to the plan. Obviously, if everyone enrolled in a managed care plan is sick all of the time, what we would call a high patient acuity level, the company will do very poorly. Conversely, if most people are relatively healthy, the company will do very well. Managed health care plans have an incentive to keep their enrollees healthy through preventive care.

The most important thing to understand about working in a managed care setting is that the incentives are different than they are in a fee-for-service environment. The goal of managed care is to care for people and to hold costs down within a fixed revenue cap. Nothing is accomplished by putting everyone on pumps, by operating on everyone, or by ordering every lab test in the book. Our physicians are salaried, and they are compensated based on the care they provide to their "panel" of patients, not on how many services they provide. The incentive is to do exactly what is needed to get patients well and keep them well.

From the point of view of a health care consumer, one trades unlimited access to services and an unlimited choice of providers for the cost advantages of managed care. In a fee-for-service plan, the patient can look in the yellow pages for a family doctor and elect to call any physician listed therein. In a managed care plan, enrollees generally have a choice of physician or other health care provider, but they must choose from practitioners on our staff.

There are other limitations that enrollees must accept when they join a managed care plan. For example, we do not cover every medicine that's available. We make choices about what we feel will be most effective in certain situations. No managed care plan arbitrarily says, "Oh, this drug is too expensive, so we won't use it." We make our decisions based on what we know is safe and effective as well as cost competitive.

My job here at GHC is to see that my staff have what they need to get their work done productively and in concert with the departmental plan. To do that, I have to maintain a climate of teamwork and support. That means I attend a lot of meetings – meetings with my managerial team, residents that I am precepting during a given month, and other hospital and campus committees.

The biggest challenge of my job is to keep the level of enthusiasm high among members of the administrative team, especially during periods of adversity or organizational conflict. If I failed to do that, I couldn't accomplish anything in my position. Consequently, it is critical that I find time to support my people. When personnel and hospital issues come up that my managers have never dealt with before, they need constructive counseling and suggestions. I have to be an important source of that encouragement. This is no job for someone who doesn't enjoy interacting with people during periods of conflict as well as during periods of opportunity and success.

I was attracted to hospital pharmacy when I was a student. This was back in 1975, when there was so much to do and it seemed that so little was being done in that area of clinical pharmacy. There was such excitement about what pharmacy could and should be doing. It was clear to me that pharmacists could make a significant contribution to the hospital health care team.

I was the first resident in a hospital pharmacy program at the University of Washington. For me, that was a very exciting time. And an active one too: I remember staying up 15 or 20 hours at a stretch, preparing nursing units to convert from floorstock to a unit-dose system. I would go home and sleep for a few hours, then come back and do it all over again to make sure everything was done properly.

These days, the hospital environment is a little calmer for most pharmacists, but there is still plenty of excitement. Another difference is that the patient and the overall health care delivery system are more central to pharmacy issues today. Increasingly, we are concerned directly with identifying and resolving patients' drug-related problems.

After graduation, I worked as a staff pharmacist for a few years. Then I became a supervisor and an assistant director. I came to Group Health 10 years ago as director of pharmacy, and since then my job has evolved into what it is today. I have always enjoyed the challenge of being in management.

Pharmacy students who think they might like to go into pharmacy administration one day should consider a master's program or equivalent postgraduate training program in management. Not many schools offer such programs, so finding one may require a bit of research. This is not the only route to success because there are a good many who, over time, have acquired the skills needed to manage departments.

Whatever a candidate's educational background may be, in order to make a successful move into pharmacy management, it is vitally important to understand human resource management at a very, very basic level. It is essential to understand what motivates people and how that can change over time. The effective manager should be able to detect changes in individual staff members and be able to respond to their different needs. This can only be done by someone who truly enjoys working with people, sometimes in difficult circumstances.

The pharmacist-manager must be able to assess the capabilities of every employee and diagnose their needs for additional training and development. Moreover, the manager must be able to assign the right person to the right issue. A keen understanding of the planning process – and the ability to apply it – is essential for those who would be effective managers.

Whether you are interested in management or not, if you want to work in hospital pharmacy you had better think seriously about advanced training. There are still a few BS graduates in this setting, but the percentage is getting smaller every year. Now, pharmacists with advanced degrees and residency experience generally have a decided advantage over those who graduated even five years ago.

Tomorrow's pharmacists should work hard to differentiate themselves from everyone else. One way to do that is to choose a few professional areas in which you can gain a great depth of knowledge. This doesn't mean that I think everyone should become a specialist. However, there is tremendous value in getting extra experience and knowledge in specific therapeutic areas. Identify an area that interests you in particular, then learn more than you're expected to about it: computer systems, robotics, biotechnology, drug information retrieval, or home care. The pharmacist who hones his or her expertise in any of these disciplines is getting a head start on the future.

To succeed in a hospital setting, it is necessary to be skilled at relating to people on a number of different levels. In the past, pharmacists could get away with being introverted individuals who were comfortable working behind the counter, dealing with a product, and speaking with patients or physicians over the telephone.

Most hospital pharmacists don't work that way today. They're up on the floors working with nurses, physicians, respiratory therapists, and anesthesiologists. They often take their expertise to patients in their rooms. They are expected to know the therapeutic needs of each patient. They must have intimate knowledge of the issues in drug therapy in order to anticipate drug-related problems. And when problems develop, pharmacists are expected to know how to resolve them.

Hospital pharmacists must be able to assess the literature, identify trends in therapy, and say: "You know, that could have some application in this case. Let me tell you why." Staff-level pharmacists who can do that are extremely valuable.

I keep up with issues in health care by listening to my staff and management team. In addition, I have learned to skim the countless articles, papers, and journals that come flying through my office. I can't read everything, but I read enough to develop a viewpoint and opinion about a lot of issues, including the direction in which our profession is headed.

In the future, I believe technicians will have expanded responsibility, allowing pharmacists to become even more active than they are now in patient care. Even now, pharmacists are moving away from product manipulation and systems support into the more demanding world of therapeutics and patient assessment. In hospitals of the future, I believe pharmacists will be more closely aligned with nursing units than pharmacy departments.

In fact, the current model of so many different hospital departments is already starting to erode. Now, we're looking into integrated staffing models in which pharmacists get more involved with the therapeutics of specialized services such as oncology and internal medicine.

Over the next several years, robotics will change the basic operation of just about every large institutional pharmacy. The future activities of hospital pharmacists will not include manipulating, delivering, and transporting products. Those are tasks that will be performed by robots.

These changes will free hospital pharmacists to become even more involved with therapeutics. We've already made the separation from a product manipulation focus at my institution – most of our pharmacists work outside of the pharmacy in specialty areas.

There are still some locations in the country where hospital and retail pharmacists earn significantly different salaries, but I think the two income ranges are coming closer together. To make an accurate comparison, talk to pharmacists in both settings who have been practicing for five to 10 years. I think you'll find that hospital pharmacists have a greater sense of challenge and enjoy more job growth and enrichment.

If you are a graduating pharmacy student interested in working in a hospital setting, you will soon find that you have made a great career decision. If you look at the professional duties that are performed in a hospital, you will find that pharmacists engage in an unusually broad range of activities. From systems and logic to science and patient care, this can be an exciting career for you.

It certainly has for me.

Amy L. Shafer, PharmD,
is an operating room pharmacist at the
New England Medical Center in Boston.

The Operating Room Pharmacist

There are some people who can't stand to walk into the operating room but, for me, it is an exciting environment. I am amazed every time I watch a liver transplant or open-heart surgery when the patient's chest has been cracked open. I am enthralled by the almost miraculous feats surgeons perform in repairing the human body.

The OR team is like a little club. Everyone wears scrubs, and we work closely together. It's nice to be among those people, in a place where, traditionally, few pharmacists are seen.

Many hospitals have satellite pharmacies on patient floors, but few have yet carried this concept into the operating room. For students interested in an area of practice that is new and different, OR pharmacy is a choice to consider.

But be forewarned: If you adopt this as your specialty, your skills in long-term care may be dulled. You will care for patients in the OR and recovery room, and that may be the last you'll see of them. Pharmacy students who hope for extended relationships with patients will not find happiness in the surgical suite.

OR pharmacy is moment-to-moment, hands-on work. It's also quite routine, otherwise it would be too stressful. In this environment, drugs are needed immediately, and rapid responses are expected. The pharmacy is connected by intercom to each operating room, and the intercom can be used by the OR team to request drug information. Usually, responding is not a problem, but sometimes it's necessary to scramble for the right answer, because the drug in question needs to be administered in short order. Reference materials have to be instantly available, and the OR pharmacist must be able to handle the pressure of responding quickly.

I grew up in Ann Arbor, Mich. In high school, I enjoyed the sciences and wanted to work in a profession that would make it possible for me to help people. Pharmacy seemed to address those dual interests. I spent six years earning my PharmD at the University of Michigan. Following that, I spent one year in a hospital pharmacy residency at New England Medical Center. I've been here ever since.

During residency training, my major project was to justify for the hospital administration the value of establishing an operating room pharmacy. Midway through the project, my employer made an offer I couldn't refuse. "If the project is approved," he said, "you've got yourself a job." That was a great incentive for me.

About a month after my residency was over, my proposal was accepted, and several new pharmacy positions were approved. I spent the next six months setting up the pharmacy: ordering all the supplies, working with architects to design the little room it was to occupy, and working with the departments of anesthesia and nursing and the recovery room to set up a feasible system of drug distribution and controlled-substance accounting.

It was like having a baby; about nine months later, the pharmacy finally opened! We were then faced with proving the financial success of this new service.

Together with the anesthesia department, we worked to reduce the drug cost per case by a certain amount. During that year, we were able to save the equivalent of four pharmacy department salaries, and we proved that we were at least a break-even operation.

New England Medical Center is a 490-bed teaching hospital associated with Tufts Medical School. The pharmacy department is relatively large, with approximately 15 pharmacists on duty during weekdays.

On a normal day, I come to work around 5:30 AM. My first duty is to assure that appropriate medications are ready to be dispensed for the day's first surgical cases. One of the pharmacy's responsibilities is to make certain that controlled substances are correctly accounted for in the operating room. Consequently, we have a system for minimizing the possibility that these drugs can be diverted. Our anesthesiologists must sign out controlled substances on a triplicate request form.

By about 7:30, surgery is underway. At that point, I go over the schedule with my technician to determine what intravenous admixtures we will need to prepare. I will probably spend some time doing this and will run a computer printout describing medication being administered to patients on the acute pain service. I take the printout with me on my rounds. I may even pitch in to help label admixed drugs.

From 9 to 10:30, I round with the acute pain service. While I'm gone, my technicians run the satellite. At this point, the early surgical cases are starting to be completed and the next ones are about to begin. Anesthesia and nursing staff stop by the pharmacy to pick up new drugs and return those that were not used for the first cases. We dispense drugs separately for every case.

At 11:30, the other operating room pharmacist arrives. On alternating days, one of us will stay in the pharmacy during our overlap time, and the other can leave to take care of projects or attend meetings.

When patients hit the recovery room, it is our job to provide all the medications they need. We admix antibiotics, and a pharmacist checks all written orders before any medications are dispensed.

My shift is over at 2:30 PM. Even so, I rarely leave before 4:30. I spend that extra time taking care of projects that I haven't been able to complete earlier. Lately, I've used some of that time to help set up pharmacy services for our new labor and delivery suites.

An OR pharmacy offers three important advantages. One is an increased level of quality assurance. We now prepare many of the drugs that previously were prepared under nonsterile conditions by the anesthesia staff. We are able to do a much better job of storing drugs and checking for expired medications.

The second advantage we offer is tightly controlled substance accounting. This is an important function because controlled substances often are easily obtained but not so easily tracked in the OR setting.

The third benefit we provide is that a pharmacist is now available to provide drug information to the OR staff. There are so many areas, such as postoperative pain management, where our expertise can make a difference in patient care. The OR pharmacist knows exactly how drugs are being used intraoperatively and can provide useful data to hospital administrators.

Students who are looking for a field in which new ground remains to be broken should consider a career in OR pharmacy. This is a professional specialty that is still evolving, especially in the area of clinical services. No one has all the answers, and we currently function without rigid, preset standards. Pharmacists who serve the OR are in a position to move this specialty forward.

Beverly J. Holcombe, PharmD,
practices in the pharmacy department at
the University of North Carolina Hospitals
in Chapel Hill.

The Nutrition Support Pharmacist

"You can have it all – a home, a family, and a part-time job." That's how pharmacy was first described to me: a challenging career option for working mothers. I was attracted to it because of my interest in science and math, but I was not looking for a part-time career. It's fortunate that I wasn't, because my work in nutrition support is a demanding, full-time responsibility.

Although I was first interested in pediatric pharmacy, I had done well in the academic requirements for nutrition support, which in the early 1980s was an emerging field. I liked the fact that a new professional area was opening. But its strongest appeal lay in the fact that it would give me a chance to apply much of what I'd learned in school.

In short, nutrition support was new and it offered variety. Moreover, it promised the excitement of being in the vanguard of a pharmacy specialty. Because this field is still being formed, it seemed like a good place to make my mark.

And I have definitely been in the vanguard. During the last four years, I have been intimately involved with developing specialty certification for nutrition support pharmacists. Much of the field may be considered an art, because aspects of it are not yet backed up by hard science. For instance, when my hospital began doing lung transplants, we had almost no idea about how to administer optimal nutrition support. We called other institutions and got some ideas, but nobody had established a definitive course of action. Subsequently, we developed our own plan. Now, people call us for advice. There is considerable satisfaction in having come full circle from seeking advice, to formulating a plan, to having people come to us. Today, we're considered the experts.

I did my undergraduate work at the University of North Carolina, and then I earned my PharmD at the University of Tennessee at Memphis. While I was there, I applied for a nutrition support fellowship under the auspices of the American Society of Hospital Pharmacists Research and Education Foundation. Although students who enter the field are not required to do specialty residencies (training can still come from on-the-job experience), I strongly recommend them – or fellowships – because they help participants hone their skills in a specific area.

I returned to the University of North Carolina's teaching hospital in 1984. Here I work on a multidisciplinary consulting team that includes a physician, a nurse, a dietitian, and a pharmacist. In some circumstances, the team might be expanded to include physical and respiratory therapists and a social worker. For the most part, team members see new patients individually, divvying up the responsibility according to which of us has the most expertise in the patient's problem. We meet collectively every day to report on our patients and receive information from other team members. We combine that information with data from charts and records as well as from direct examination and interviews with the patient. Based on this, we decide on a course of therapy. Filtering all these data and trying to assign each element its proper importance is the unique responsibility of a nutrition support pharmacist.

I emphasize that this is very much a team activity, which is one of the reasons I like my job. Although physicians are usually deferred to as the "experts," in this specialty we are treated equally, and all of our opinions are considered valid. The daily meetings give team members a chance to ask questions about the other members' specialty areas. For instance, if I see that a patient is having trouble with an IV, I'll mention it to the nurse. By the same token, if someone has a pharmacy-related question, I'm the one they ask. Each member of the team serves as a liaison to his or her department or discipline.

After we develop a plan, we present it to the patient's primary physician. Although the physician has the authority to reject our recommendations, that doesn't happen often. Instead, we usually work together to fine tune a few points. Still, one of the most frustrating aspects of this job is recommending a treatment – sometimes over and over again – and not seeing it implemented. But because we work on a consulting basis, that frustration goes with the territory.

When our suggestions are accepted, we often help the physician implement the plan by completing order forms, setting lab parameters, and monitoring the patient. Length of treatment can extend from several days to a few months. In some cases, therapy continues into the home care environment, and this offers another career option for nutrition support pharmacists.

Because I work in a teaching hospital, I have an obligation to work with students, and I expect them to become involved in actual cases. I may be lurking in the background, but it's their responsibility to report information and assess the patient's condition. This involvement is high on the list of what they like about nutrition support. Also on that list is the variety of cases they see, the chance they have to apply what they learn, and the satisfaction they gain from practicing in a specialty.

Many nutrition support pharmacists spend only half their time performing nutrition-related activities, because their hospitals simply don't need a full-time person. Community hospitals also might have too few patients to warrant a full-time nutrition support specialist. If you choose such an institution, be prepared to perform other pharmacy duties. Depending on where you practice, your job description can vary widely. For example, I have heavy patient care responsibilities at this institution, but in a different setting I might also be given responsibility for an IV admixture service as well as for budgeting and managing personnel.

In many institutions, pharmacists are expected to be the team leaders and to coordinate the nutrition support service. A nutrition support practitioner who has moved into home care would surely have management responsibilities, including fiscal issues, quality assurance, and administrative tasks.

My job requires me to participate in several different areas, and because I like to have my fingers in a lot of different pies, I divide my time between patient care, teaching (I give lectures to undergraduates on nutrition support and am currently teaching a course in metabolic management), clinical research, and participating in professional organizations.

There is a variety of employment opportunities in nutrition support. Many of my colleagues work in home care or research, and consultation is another promising option. In fact, I have two friends who are forging exciting careers as consultants for pharmaceutical companies.

In describing qualifications necessary for success in this specialty, I would say the pharmacist must have a good understanding of metabolism, biochemistry, and fluids and electrolytes. An interest in and knowledge of a variety of disease states are requisite. Beyond that, the ideal practitioner in our evolving field should have a real commitment to bedside patient care and clinical research.

On the clinical side, the nutrition support pharmacist must be expert in both parenteral and enteral feeding formulations and in coadministration of medications. This person has to be thoroughly knowledgeable about the composition and compatibility of nutrients and the interaction between nutrients and drugs.

An exciting new aspect in this specialty is the use of drugs to alter a patient's response to stress, thereby altering metabolism and nutrition therapy. Because the patient's nutritional status can alter the pharmacodynamics and pharmacokinetics of a drug, this is an area in which nutrition support pharmacists can make important contributions.

Pharmacists in our specialty are responsible for reviewing and evaluating new products and for educating the patient and his family. Because nutrition support specialists are usually members of health care teams, they must be able to recognize and appreciate the skills of other members, and to mesh their own skills within that network. In order to work through the tough times that are sure to occur, people who practice in nutrition support must be flexible – there has to be a lot of give and take among team members.

Partly because of the importance of working with the other team members and the relationships that are built there, and partly because our work is specialized, nutrition support can be tremendously demanding. Sometimes I work long hours, because I know there will not be someone else to replace me after I go home. But I like that sense of individual responsibility. I think it increases my credibility as a pharmacist if I demonstrate my dedication in this way.

One situation I recall shows the impact we can have on patient care. We were treating an outpatient with throat cancer. The man had a feeding tube, but he could still talk and swallow a little. From outward appearances, the seriousness of his condition was not apparent. He was taking medication for another condition, and his wife administered it via the tube, as she had been taught to do. This drug was in microencapsulated-granule form, and it clogged the tube when she tried to pour it through. She brought the patient to the hospital, and we cleared the blockage. While they were there, I discovered that another medicine – a sustained-release agent – had been prescribed for the man. The woman intended to crush it in preparation for administration, but she hadn't yet given it to her husband. That was lucky for him, because crushing it would certainly cut down on the medication's benefit and may have resulted in toxicity. By anticipating this chain of events, I was able to warn her and arrange for a liquid substitute for the medication.

There are advantages and disadvantages to practicing in a relatively new and small specialty. One advantage is that the demand for practitioners is growing steadily – and, as of now, there are only 150 board-certified nutrition support pharmacists. Moreover, jobs are available in a number of practice settings, including hospitals, home care, and industry. Finally, nutrition support specialists can enjoy the challenges of applying new knowledge and technology in a dynamic field.

On the negative side, the demand for nutrition support pharmacists is still spotty, and practitioners often are expected to perform unrelated pharmacy duties. In addition, some health care providers still do not recognize the importance of nutrition therapy.

Because the specialty is so small, my network of colleagues is still manageable, and I can readily call professional friends around the country when I need information or advice. In fact, I actually know most of the other pharmacists in the field; they are not just a sea of names on an association's roster. Even more important than that, I enjoy my work and the people I'm associated with. I have no need to look elsewhere for job satisfaction, and I think that says a great deal about the rewards of nutrition support pharmacy.

William N. Tindall, PhD, RPh, CAE,
is executive director of the
Academy of Managed Care Pharmacy.

New Career Opportunities in Managed Care Pharmacy

Since the term *health maintenance organizations* (HMOs) was coined about 1972, there has been phenomenal acceptance of managed care, especially as Americans have become sensitive to the growing financial burden of health benefits. Although prescriptions represent only about seven percent of total health care benefits, managed care pharmacy is providing attractive, satisfying careers for thousands of pharmacists. More and more pharmacists are seeking careers in this setting because they find they are accepted as major contributors to the overall quality, efficiency, and efficacy of the American health care system. Their contributions are the result of the exciting and professionally rewarding opportunities that exist in managed care administration, education, research, and quality assurance, as well as in the application of traditional dispensing and clinical skills. These opportunities emerged when managed care pharmacists were given access to a deeper and broader base of information about individual patients or the population of patients enrolled in managed care programs.

To better understand managed care pharmacy as a career opportunity, one should first understand how health maintenance organizations, preferred provider organizations (PPOs), and the indemnity insurance industry have reconfigured health care delivery. The Health Insurance Association of America (HIAA) defines managed care as a system that integrates the financing and delivery of health care by adhering to four criteria. Such a system:

- makes arrangements with selected providers to furnish a set of comprehensive health care services to members
- follows explicit criteria in selecting health care providers
- establishes formal programs for ongoing quality assurance and utilization review
- offers significant financial incentives for members to use providers and procedures associated with the plan

Others see managed care as the application of contemporary business practices to health care delivery, while some, including Pete Penna, PharmD, of Group Health Cooperative of Washington, see it as a system that encourages giving value for the dollar on behalf of its members.

An objective of managed care is to balance quality of health care against the marketplace reality of managing cost. Thus, managed care plans compete in an open market. This gives rise to the many options and configurations that managed care plans take relative to their ability to offer health and prescription benefits, and this is what builds opportunities for pharmacists. Generally, it is accepted that managed care consists of HMOs, PPOs, and managed indemnity plans (eg, health coverage offered by traditional insurance companies). Within HMOs, there are four recognized models: staff, group, network, and independent practice associations (IPAs). Basically, all HMOs link enrollees, or members, to providers and then assume responsibility for the delivery and financing of health care benefits, including prescriptions. HMOs use incentives to encourage a team approach to the delivery of cost-effective health benefits and, simply put, they differ only in how they link their enrollees with providers. Staff-model HMOs employ physicians and pharmacists in their in-house facilities; group-model HMOs contract with multispecialty physicians in group practice and networks of community pharmacies; network-model HMOs are similar to group models, but network or contract with groups of physicians and pharmacies; and IPA-model HMOs contract with individual providers.

Preferred provider organizations generate contractual arrangements between providers and purchasers of health care. The PPO, like a broker or middleman, acts on behalf of an insurance company, a self-insured employer, or other firm to arrange a discounted price, based on volume, from providers of specific medical, hospital, pharmaceutical, and related care. Each provider bills the PPO for services, and because of the way a plan is marketed, it is the PPO that faces a business risk if overutilization of contracted services should occur.

All in all, managed care in the early 1990s is providing health care to nearly half of all Americans via one of four HMO models, PPO networks, or as a benefit of indemnity insurance plans. It is expected that this percentage will increase to 75 percent by 1995, and with that growth will come new, almost unlimited opportunities for pharmacists. For example, Kaiser Permanente, a large group-model HMO already employs more than 2,500 pharmacists throughout the United States and is constantly looking for more.

In carrying out their professional responsibilities, managed care pharmacists have a distinct advantage over traditional pharmacists – information. They have information about individual patients and information derived from large populations of patients. It is this extensive information that creates much of the specialization in managed care pharmacy and, ultimately, that supports pharmacists' influence on the quality and cost effectiveness of pharmaceutical care.

- For pharmacists interested in clinical and dispensing roles, managed care pharmacy becomes especially rewarding when they are given access to a patient's diagnosis, lab tests, and history, as well as the patient's compliance with prescribed therapy. Thus, managed care practice becomes a challenge to a pharmacist's clinical skills.

Careers in managed care pharmacy also can revolve around the data generated by large groups of defined patients, especially because of the emphasis on monitoring the economics of therapeutic decisions. Pharmacists are finding it professionally rewarding to:

- review an HMO's or PPO's Medicare and Medicaid contracts
- design and implement studies that validate the cost effectiveness of drugs, drug protocols, and compliance interventions
- participate in the sophisticated team process of formulary development. Today, nearly 80 percent of all formulary teams rely on the pharmacist to supply proof of a drug's effectiveness, advantages over alternatives, cost, and benefits to risks.
- provide specialized education for patients, prescribers, or colleagues. As a pharmacist-educator, one may provide groups of patients affected with such diseases as diabetes, hypertension, depression, cancer, or anemia with programs that help people understand why they must take their medication as prescribed and why lifestyle changes may be needed. Also producing in-service programs for nurses, physicians, and others has become a rewarding career opportunity for pharmacists.
- develop reimbursement methods used by HMOs, PPOs, and insurance companies to compensate contractual or in-house pharmacy
- provide concurrent, prospective, and retrospective drug utilization reviews of prescribing patterns and prescribed medication. Many pharmacists find professional growth in generating and supplying reports that support formulary review processes, the development of treatment protocols, and the selection of products.
- serve as an educational liaison to colleges of pharmacy. Colleges of pharmacy already are adjusting their curriculums to include experimental education in managed care settings. Some are inviting managed care pharmacists to lecture, and some use managed care pharmacists to coordinate consulting and research activities with pharmacy college faculty.
- serve as a vendor of pharmaceutical expertise to managed care plans. Great numbers of pharmacists have found immense professional satisfaction and rewards in companies that provide managed prescription benefit packages on behalf of a PPO or an employer. These third-party administrators (TPAs) offer a growing number of paths to satisfying professional careers based on the cost-effective nature of a pharmacist's education and expertise.
- for those with good negotiation, team building, marketing, financial, time management, and organizational skills there are exciting opportunities as administrators of managed care pharmacy plans among the 650 HMOs, 550 PPOs, and several hundred indemnity insurance plans.

That managed care pharmacy is rapidly changing is a reality that represents many opportunities. The new roles listed above when applied to the various configurations of HMOs, PPOs, TPAs, and indemnity insurance organizations extend expanding opportunities for pharmacists.

Today, managed care and managed care pharmacy are being woven into the fabric of health care. For the rest of the 1990s, they will surely be included in government and private sector health care reform. Managed care pharmacy's attractiveness as part of that reform is that it is a professional prescription for success. All pharmacists have to do is to accept, expect, initiate, lead, and manage change for the betterment of Americans who desperately need their pharmacists' help in getting the best use of their medicines.

Pharmacy in a Staff-model HMO

Michael Dillon, MS, RPh,
is director of planned pharmacy operations
for Community Health Plan,
a staff model HMO in Latham, New York.

Managed care organizations are proliferating so rapidly that they are creating an entirely new practice specialty in pharmacy. And because managed care can be provided in a variety of configurations, it affords practitioners a broad range of career options. One is the staff-model health maintenance organization (HMO).

Staff-model HMOs are distinguished by two main characteristics. First, the HMO maintains its own staff of physicians, pharmacists, nurses, allied health professionals, and other personnel. Second, these professionals work together in a centralized health care center to deliver a variety of ambulatory, primary care services. Such centers have imaging and lab facilities as well as a range of ancillary services. For example, in addition to primary care, the Community Health Plan (CHP) center where my office is located also provides dental, dermatologic, and mental health services. We have an ambulatory surgery center and a rather extensive oncology practice. Depending on size, the staff-model HMO may provide its care at a single site or in a number of locations. CHP has 43 staff pharmacists at 12 different sites.

Over 100,000 members use our staff-model facilities, and we provide other types of managed care for 100,000 more members. This makes us a mid-sized HMO. Most of our members have enrolled through their employers.

The staff-model approach to managed care is very much a multidisciplinary concept, with pharmacists constituting a vital component of our teams. The result is that pharmacists are not limited to a routine of dispensing, but participate in a variety of roles. Their duties include clinical activities, dispensing, education, and counseling. They consult daily with primary care practitioners and specialists to assist in drug selection and patient monitoring. There are opportunities for specialization, as with our pharmacists who work exclusively with the oncology service. They focus on chemotherapy, pain relief, and side-effect management, and they deal closely with patients and families. One of our pharmacists works in the OR with anesthesiologists and surgeons. She scrubs with the surgical team and is actively involved by controlling the substance inventory and preparing intraoperative medications.

Our pharmacists develop new skills by rotating through all of our specialty and general pharmacy functions. Rotations accomplish two things. They make staff members better and more valuable, and they help dispel the boredom that can develop in more routine types of practice. Together with compounding and dispensing, all of our pharmacists spend part of their time performing clinical activities, counseling, education, and drug utilization review (DUR). The result is a tremendous sense of professional fulfillment. The rotations are not restrictive. For example, pharmacists can choose an area of special interest such as diabetes education and then work with our health education department to develop patient programs for better diabetes management. Rotations are particularly valuable for specialists who experience burnout and want to take a break and explore other permanent options.

Historically, patient counseling has been emphasized strongly in HMOs, and it is no different at CHP. In fact, we have required counseling for many years, long before state and federal regulations mandating counseling were enacted. Counseling is important in increasing patient compliance and controlling costs. No matter what condition or illness patients are being treated for, they are more comfortable when they understand what drugs they are receiving, what these agents are supposed to do, and what side effects may occur. Also, patients who are more knowledgeable about their medications are more compliant. Ultimately, optimum compliance produces greater therapeutic efficacy and, potentially, reduces use of health care services.

Research and education are also essential components of our pharmacists' job descriptions. Most of our research is conducted in conjunction with physicians and is related to formulary issues. Pharmacists are members of the P&T committee that selects drugs and establishes usage protocols.

Educational services provided by pharmacists generally serve two distinct audiences: staff and patients. Most of our staff education is directed at physicians and is accomplished through a bimonthly newsletter called *Pharmacy Profiles.* This publication is managed by our clinical coordinator and written by our staff pharmacists. It evaluates new products and addresses physicians' questions about specific therapies. New product releases might generate articles profiling related drugs in that class and associated therapies. In-house seminars and one-on-one consultations provide opportunities for more extensive staff education.

Our staff pharmacists often write for *Subscriber News* and *Health Bulletin,* a newsletter that is sent to CHP members. Because of the audience, these articles require a certain amount of communication ability on the pharmacist's part. The challenge is to present information clearly and factually, but in a way that is not too technical or too simplistic.

CHP employs a number of pharmacy students as interns who work during the course of their school year. We also have externships for students from the Albany College of Pharmacy. Externs come for five-week rotations in our various services. And sometimes we even act as facilitators for student research projects. In fact, we are currently working with a PharmD candidate to develop a patient education program for pediatric asthma patients and their families. This young woman's research idea required a managed care environment, and she contacted us. We felt her project would have significant value for our patients, so we identified 100 patients in our pediatrics program who will participate in an educational session for patients and parents. The presentation will include a discussion of the patients' disease and various treatment options. Results will be determined through pretesting and posttesting of participants' understanding of asthma.

Our involvement with pharmacy students is good for them, and we benefit as well. The students gain valuable experience, credit towards their degree, and, in the case of interns, income. CHP gains quality assistance and, sometimes, the relationship leads to new employees. Several of our students have joined us permanently after graduation.

Requirements for entry-level pharmacists differ slightly among staff-model HMOs. At CHP, we look for a few specific skills in our candidates. A PharmD degree is unnecessary, but dispensing ability is critically important because we fill between 800 and 1,000 prescriptions per day. Such a heavy volume means that working in the dispensing area requires good drug information knowledge and the ability to evaluate a variety of therapies rapidly. In addition, we look for pharmacists who are capable of counseling patients of all ages and with all conditions.

We want people with good oral and written communication skills. Not only do our pharmacists have to be able to convey prescription instructions to the patient, they must also be able to explain details of drug therapy. This is so important because of the effect counseling has on compliance. Communication skills are also essential as staff pharmacists interact on a team with physicians and nurses. Written communication skills come into play when formulary research must be documented and when physicians must be alerted in writing to treatment information.

Beyond these qualifications we look for motivation in prospective employees. In other words, we want pharmacists who intend to grow within their profession instead of settling into the same job day after day, year after year. Because of the way our pharmacy rotations work, it's nearly impossible for a pharmacist to be doing the exact same thing month after month. In fact, with the wide range of patients we treat it would be unusual for anyone, except one of our specialists, to see the same type of patients repeatedly.

As for the benefits of working for us or any staff-model HMO, they are extensive. Our pharmacists are able to make a tremendous impact on care. By having access to patient records, pharmacists can be more effective in evaluating a patient's condition and in helping select and monitor therapy. At CHP, our multidisciplinary approaches confer authority on our pharmacists so they can have a direct effect on the quality of care while helping reduce costs for patients as well as for the HMO.

Salaries in staff-model HMOs tend to be competitive with those in hospital practices.

At CHP we offer some additional benefits. For instance, we have an education package that provides time and money for our pharmacists to pursue continuing education. In general, our work schedule is nine to five, Monday through Friday. Even though we do work weekends, our staff size makes it necessary for our pharmacists to work only one weekend in every 13. We believe in promoting from within and have thus far been able to offer continual opportunities for advancement because we open one or two new pharmacies each year. A number of CHP pharmacists have advanced into other professional areas. For example, a pharmacist is the administrator of one of our health centers, another is the head of marketing for one of our regions, and still another works on utilization management for all our clinical services. Not surprisingly, we have a low rate of attrition among pharmacists – this is a great place to work.

In the face of national health care reform, managed care is poised to assume an unprecedented role in tomorrow's pharmacy practice. No matter what type of career entry-level pharmacists are looking for, chances are they will be able to find it in a managed care setting.

Managing the Pharmacy Benefits of a PPO

James W. Stephenson, RPh,
is CEO of Stephenson and Associates,
which provides pharmaceutical benefits,
consulting, and management.

The proliferation of managed care systems and the escalation of costs associated with virtually every insurance plan's pharmacy benefit have combined to produce a growing phenomenon among health insurers: a greater appreciation for pharmacists' cognitive skills. Our drug information knowledge has become a powerful tool, allowing us to create new practice opportunities. One of the newest, most challenging, and potentially rewarding opportunities lies in providing consulting services to preferred provider organizations.

Preferred provider organizations (PPOs) contract with selected hospitals and physicians to provide services at discounted rates to subscribing members. Systems may include deductibles, copayment plans, and other features. Some PPOs also have a pharmacy benefit that may offer a variety of reimbursement features, such as flat prescription costs, maximum annual caps on reimbursements, fixed-percentage copayments or deductibles, or sliding-scale percentage arrangements.

In the past, most PPOs paid little or no attention to the pharmacy benefit, allowing members to have their prescriptions filled at any pharmacy. As costs began to escalate, some PPOs entered relationships with selected chain retailers, and some turned to such basic economy measures as formulary management. More recently, PPOs have been searching for other methods of cost containment. However, the experience of HMOs during the early 1970s showed that blindly pursuing cost containment of pharmaceutical products was not a totally effective strategy. Short-term savings might be realized, but evidence quickly mounted that these savings came at the expense of quality of care and in many cases eventually caused escalations in long-term costs. Moreover, these long-term cost increases carried beyond the pharmacy benefit, surfacing also in lab tests, hospital stays, surgical procedures, and other areas. As a result, in the 1970s and 1980s, HMOs turned to a new philosophy that placed appropriate use of pharmaceutical products at the forefront of their pharmacy benefit coverage philosophies. This eventually demonstrated that a comprehensive approach to managing the pharmacy benefit could produce positive effects in what had been considered unrelated components of the entire care package.

My own involvement in managed care began nearly 20 years ago. I had been active in retail pharmacy since the late 1950s and had a small chain of pharmacies in southern California. Part of my business was in providing consulting services for a small number of nursing home facilities. This experience helped lay the foundation for my decision to join with business associates in order to start an HMO in the early 1970s. The organization, a federally qualified HMO, was called Family Health Services (FHS), and I was a partner and pharmacy director. After several years our HMO was acquired by Maxicare. I left at the time of the acquisition and developed a pharmacy program for Equicor (a joint venture between Hospital Corporation of America and Equitable Life Society). Then in 1990, Equicor was bought by CIGNA and I decided to take a retirement package. However, I had acquired substantial knowledge in retail, consulting, and HMOs, and I was not yet ready to stop practicing pharmacy. I wanted to stay in touch with the profession and perhaps do something entrepreneurial. I could see that PPOs were beginning to experience the same changes HMOs had endured in the 1970s and 1980s, and I knew I could make contributions in this area. So, in late 1990 I began offering consulting services to PPOs and other employer groups.

My practice essentially involves going into a PPO, examining its existing pharmacy benefit structure, and creating a strategy for improvement. While each provider has a different objective and philosophy of care, there are six basic areas that can provide the keys to determining the effectiveness of the company's benefit.

I generally start by evaluating the existing pharmacy involvement. Does the PPO even have a pharmacy benefit? If so, what type of patient management exists? How much information do patients receive about their prescriptions? Do they have a general idea of how the medication is supposed to work and what its ultimate outcome should be? Do they receive active counseling? I also want to know whether a pharmacy network has been established, what type of compensation plan is in place, and what system is used for managing drug use.

My second concern involves formulary incorporation. Is there an internal formulary system, or will I have to develop one? If there is an existing system, how broad is its purview and how well does it work? Is it a closed system or open to modifications and substitutes? Are there incentives to use products approved for the formulary?

Formulary incorporation is an important element in physician involvement, which is the third area of analysis. What type of communication exists between the PPO and member physicians? Does the PPO maintain a prescribing profile of member physicians? Do physicians have active input in formulary creation and modification? Do member physicians accept the established formulary, or do they go outside of its recommendations and protocols? Are there incentives for compliance and penalties for noncompliance?

Next, I examine the PPO's benefit design. Does it include deductibles or patient copayments? Are certain classes or types of drugs excluded from reimbursement? If so, what is the reasoning behind each exclusion? And what impact would modification of this design have on members?

Claims processing is the fifth area to be evaluated. Does the PPO process claims internally, or does it use an outside contractor? Are the data on each form carefully analyzed, or is this information used more as an accounting tool? Are transaction costs tracked and quantified?

Finally, I look at the PPO's drug utilization management system. How are challenges to the formulary handled? Are pharmacy interventions permitted for such occurrences as inappropriate usage or modification of dosage? If so, how are these facilitated? Are there systems for identifying and charting medication overuse or misuse, doctor hopping, and hospitalizations that result from misuse of drugs? Can patients be identified who are candidates for wellness programs and other preventive measures?

Of all these components, two are most commonly misinterpreted by PPOs. The first is the perception that eliminating a pharmacy benefit will save money. The reasoning behind this usually is a simplistic understanding of escalating costs; the organization believes that halting reimbursement for drugs will cut the overall cost of care. Initially, this may prove true, but studies have shown it to be an ineffective long-term strategy. Apart from the experience of HMOs, there is strong evidence that patients who are not reimbursed for their prescription medications are less likely to use them. This lack of compliance may lead to more serious problems that require additional doctor visits and more lab tests, and is likely to result in a higher hospitalization rate. PPOs that eliminate the pharmacy benefit eventually discover the hard way that it is more efficacious and cost effective to have a properly managed pharmacy benefit.

Claims processing is a subject that is prone to a different type of neglect. Many organizations see this function as little more than bill collecting and payment disbursement. However, claims can provide invaluable data on the products that are most commonly prescribed and for what conditions. Claims also can help organizations create patient profiles that can be used to identify candidates for preventive measures, behavior modification programs, or specialized counseling. This can reduce the development of expensive risks. The prescribing habits of physicians also can be monitored through claims, and this can help dramatically improve formulary compliance. In addition, special studies can be initiated based on the data generated by claims.

After analyzing key components, I prepare a proposal with a careful presentation of disciplined steps that can achieve the clients' goals, improve quality of care, and reduce costs. My proposal may include components that are not delineated above, such as employing an outside formulary management service. Part of the proposal process is selling the idea of the improvements to the prospective client.

My work is not over when the proposal is accepted, because managing the new system may be a component of my consult. This can call for regular monitoring, improvements, and modifications based on the client's own assessments of its needs and desires. The responsibilities for ensuring results can be just as challenging as the development of a working system.

The consultant must stay current with new developments that can help his clients. For example, I am helping develop a system that will make the information exchange in PPOs similar to that in staff-model HMOs. Briefly, this will be accomplished through a modem-based computer system that gives participating physicians and pharmacists access to all patient records and then displays formulary choices. It can reduce the time physicians and hospitals spend gathering patient information at each visit. Moreover, the dispensing pharmacist will be privy to patients' histories, conditions, and all current medications, and thus be able to screen for interactions, alternative dosages, and specialized counseling needs. A current system costs less than 26 cents per patient inquiry.

As much as I enjoy my work, there are aggravations in this type of practice. One is that it's frustrating to do an analysis of a client's system, come up with a new system that can produce a dramatic improvement, and then have the client do nothing. It also is upsetting when clients fail to understand what proper management of the pharmacy benefit can accomplish. The components of many benefit systems enable pharmacists all the way down the line to contribute more cognitive services in improving patient care and cost effectiveness. Unfortunately, many clients still believe that the role of most pharmacists is to count, measure, pour, and, perhaps, provide some counseling. Using pharmacists as information resources to analyze claims information; as patient managers for diabetics, hypertensives, and asthmatics; and as patient educators in general is not in most clients' frame of reference. Even more frustrating is the lack of quantitative studies showing that cognitive services performed by pharmacists reduce costs and improve the quality of care in a way that merits reimbursement.

Nevertheless, the satisfactions prevail over the frustration, and the challenges to a pharmacist's cognitive abilities are outstanding in a practice like mine. No two clients present the same mix of problems, and yet each depends on the consultant to come up with a solution that meets its needs. And because the results of the consultant's effort have such an impact, there is a potential for exceptional financial rewards. For me, this is a retirement activity, and I am generous with my time. However, we bill our pharmacy associates out at about $1,000 per day plus expenses. One warning: overhead costs can be high, especially in the start-up phase. The managed care consultant will have to keep up with huge amounts of information about databases, products, and innovative systems that can affect a client's pharmacy benefit. Accessing all this information can be quite expensive.

Students interested in managed care consulting should first spend a few years practicing in a busy hospital or a managed care setting that lets them participate actively in cognitive analytical services. Organizational skills are essential. Often, I find myself confronting massive amounts of data that I must organize to create order out of chaos. Of course, working for a consultant who does exactly this type of work would be ideal, but landing such a job also would require a few years of practice.

In addition to analytical and problem-solving skills, a pharmacist in this field must be able to communicate effectively. Making proposals to clients involves oral presentations to people who may have knowledge of the systems and concepts discussed. Proposals also entail written documents that must provide quantifiable – and understandable – evidence in support of the oral presentation. There is also a strong sales component.

Few people provide this type of consulting right now, and yet there is a tremendous need for it. This need is likely to increase rapidly within the next few years as the country's health care system moves toward managed care. Consequently, it's a great field that offers pharmacists a great chance to have an impact on the quality of U.S. health care.

*Norrie Thomas, PhD,
is president and COO of
Clinical Pharmacy Advantage in Minneapolis.
She also is adjunct professor of social and
administrative pharmacy at the
University of Minnesota.*

The Pharmacist in a Specialty Managed Care Company

In virtually every health care plan that covers the cost of prescriptions, the pharmacy benefit is the most complex component. As a result, health maintenance organizations (HMOs) and similar types of providers have begun looking for ways to manage pharmacy costs without compromising the quality of care. This search has created new opportunities for pharmacists in the broad spectrum of managed care activities. Companies that provide specialty managed care offer pharmacists a chance to separate themselves from dispensing chores and to concentrate on using their analytical skills.

Like Clinical Pharmacy Advantage (CPA), these new companies are independent entities that manage some or all of another organization's pharmacy benefit. At Clinical Pharmacy Advantage, we function essentially as an HMO, focusing entirely on managing the pharmacy benefit. Our clients include self-insured employers, preferred provider organizations (PPOs), HMOs, and insurance companies. Companies such as ours are so new in pharmacy that less than a dozen exist today. However, many experts predict that they will proliferate rapidly.

At Clinical Pharmacy Advantage, our pharmacists work to manage costs, improve the efficacy of the prescribing process, and increase the quality of pharmaceutical care for all our clients. To do so, our system is based on the drug utilization review (DUR) work that was pioneered in the 1960s and 1970s, and was enhanced by the expansion of personal computers during the 1980s. In the 1990s, an integral feature of our business is the ability to maintain computer access to our clients' patient files. We strive to make sure providers get the right drug to the right patient at the right time, and in a cost-efficient manner.

My own involvement in managed care began in the late 1970s. I had been working in hospital pharmacy for a few years and decided it was time to go for a graduate degree in pharmacy administration. My studies included an exploration of how to design pharmacy information systems that would support drug use review. This led me into research with one of the HMOs here in the Twin Cities and set me on a 13-year career in managed care.

In 1990, the company I worked for was bought by Aetna. Soon after, I became Aetna's vice president for pharmacy programs and began designing managed care products. But I wanted a different kind of career challenge. I really wanted to design a managed care system where pharmacy is the driving force, not a system in which pharmacy is just one of many segments. Ultimately, in August of 1991, these ambitions led to my decision to start Clinical Pharmacy Advantage.

Who uses our services? Primarily PPOs, HMOS, and insurance companies. We also serve large and medium-size self-insured employers, one of our fastest growing client groups. Although self-insurance used to be a cost-effective alternative for many American companies, most of these businesses are now facing medical crises of their own. Their health spending is escalating dramatically for both current employees and retirees. And at many companies, retirees alone are using the majority of the pharmacy benefit. This problem is compounded by new tax laws that increase the financial liabilities attached to providing health care to retirees. Even though many employers want to provide health care coverage, including pharmacy benefits, they finally must ask whether they can afford the cost.

We help employers understand why they are spending so much money and how they can begin spending more effectively. This can be a challenging undertaking. For example, some of our clients have said, "We are not going to cover birth control pills anymore; it's too expensive," or even, "We don't want to cover pharmacy benefits at all." Our challenge is to show how these costs can be brought under control. Not only is it possible for a well-managed pharmacy benefit to have a positive impact on the medical premium, but it's also possible that eliminating the pharmacy component may cause other health care costs to rise.

The keystone of our service – and of virtually every other managed care pharmacy company – is an examination of the products used by a client. We look at how a drug is prescribed to determine whether other, more beneficial therapies are being overlooked. A drug formulary is essential, and continued scrutiny is needed to eliminate drug duplication. Another obvious feature of this process is that it enables us to determine the cost effectiveness of therapeutic options. We assess patient compliance as well as the quality of prescription monitoring by dispensing pharmacists or prescribing physicians. Finally, we are an important source of clinical information on appropriate drug use and efficacy and safety.

We continually analyze our clients' claims, looking for ways to develop and implement solutions that are carefully tailored to clients' needs. We might discover that the formulary needs to be reconfigured, or that physicians need to be shown the benefits of a new prescribing regimen. We may even write to patients with suggestions for enhancing compliance. As consultants, we also visit with physicians to review relevant data on commonly prescribed medications.

We conduct ongoing programs to analyze specific problems for several of our clients. For example, we developed a system that can track patients who use their asthma medications incorrectly. The program evaluates both underutilization and overutilization in order to identify patients who may get into trouble. In this case, we targeted heavy users of beta-antagonist inhalers and monitored their compliance with steroid therapy. Studies have shown that patients use inhalers because of the immediate benefit, but don't adhere to a steroid regimen because the relief is not immediate. This behavior leads patients to overuse inhalers, and can aggravate the disease. By analyzing the use of both therapies, we can identify misuse or underuse of the inhalers, the steroid therapy, or both.

Our large pharmacy information database allows us to track patients in this manner. In the study of asthma therapy, we reviewed each day the claims for prescriptions dispensed to asthma patients. We were able to follow several parameters, including all conditions being treated and the length of time each patient had been using the same prescription. Careful analysis of the results allowed us to design interventions that improved pharmaceutical care before problems led to emergency room visits or other complications. This was not prospective DUR because we didn't intervene before the patient received the drug. But we did intervene within 48 hours after targeted patients received their medications. This permitted us to take relatively quick action to alter therapy.

Even with our reliance on computer databases, our pharmacists stay in regular contact with physicians. They also have extensive interaction with patients, although not at the bedside. We work with unions, for example, educating members in the specifics of their pharmacy coverage. When it's called for, we provide on-site patient education seminars. For example, one of our union customers had a number of enrollees who were diabetic, so one of our clinical pharmacists conducted a seminar on the specific needs of these patients and how their benefit plan covered them.

A number of our clients cover retirees. For these companies, we conduct brown-bag seminars on particular conditions, or on the employees' benefit packages in general. Patients who attend are urged to bring all of their medications. After the seminar, each patient is invited to sit down with a pharmacist who reviews the medications and provides appropriate drug information. If we find a medication conflict or a compliance problem, we work with the patient and his or her physician to find a solution.

These examples illustrate the biggest advantage of practicing in managed care: Pharmacists can use their analytical skills to improve the quality of patient care. Our work is to solve problems by designing interventions that make a big difference, often very quickly, in the health care of a large number of patients. Some pharmacists on our staff have completed residencies in cardiovascular care, psychiatry, and other specialties. They have extensive clinical experience and highly developed skills. They are attracted to this environment because it allows them to use their abilities in a professionally satisfying way, and with great impact.

Specialty managed care also appeals to pharmacists with an interest in business. Being able to present clients with care-versus-cost evaluations or to defend the value of specific drug therapies takes a certain amount of marketing savvy. So does selling providers on the benefits of managed care. For pharmacists who have earned double degrees – perhaps a BA or MBA in business in addition to a pharmacy degree, specialty managed care companies offer tremendous career opportunities.

When we hire pharmacists, we look for people with analytical abilities. Do they have strong pharmacokinetic and clinical knowledge? Are they experienced at communicating with patients and physicians? Have they served on a P&T committee or performed a DUR? Do they have strong verbal and written communication skills? Do they have experience in a specialty? These are our concerns.

Students who want to work in managed care should explore opportunities for relevant externships. Clinical Pharmacy Advantage is affiliated with many universities, including Minnesota and North Dakota, and we have 14 or 15 students in externships and routine rotations. If this option doesn't exist for you, try working through your academic advisor or call a managed care organization – you may be able to create your own for-credit experience, even during the summer.

Beginning in July 1993, CPA's vice president of clinical operations, Dr. Donna Schmidt, will be conducting one of the first residencies in pharmacoeconomics for managed care. Dr. Schmidt worked with our resident to design a program that met the student's needs, would be eligible for accreditation, and would be valuable to CPA's members.

Performing analytical pharmacy services is work that pharmacists are well trained to handle, and it is very rewarding. However, once students get out of school, there are few opportunities to use these skills outside of a large hospital or clinical setting. A practice in specialty managed care is an alternative to these settings and as it continues to proliferate, it will present pharmacists with exciting options and possibilities.

Allan Zimmerman, RPh, MBA,
is national director of pharmacy operations
in the health care operations and
research division of the Prudential Life
Insurance Company of America
in Roseland, New Jersey.

Managed Care Pharmacy in an Insurance Company

More and more insurance companies are embracing managed care and, increasingly, they are providing new practice opportunities for pharmacists. One of these is active management of the pharmacy benefit within their health care delivery systems. This work enables pharmacists to use their cognitive skills; to analyze and evaluate large amounts of information; and to collaborate with other health care professionals and administrators in an effort to enhance the quality and decrease the cost of the prescription drug benefit. Pharmacy in managed care is challenging and very rewarding.

At the Prudential Life Insurance Company of America, pharmacists work on teams that manage the pharmacy benefit for an array of managed care plans and individual client employer groups. Because these plans are tailored to the needs of local market environments and individual client groups, they often include different benefit designs. Despite these benefit design variations, however, managing each package involves common managed care strategies aimed at enhancing quality and reducing costs.

First among these strategies are those aimed almost exclusively at decreasing the ingredient cost of drug therapy. This can be accomplished by implementing programs that maximize discounts available from vendors. For example, an insurance company might develop a discounted network of pharmacies to service plan members. The company may simultaneously negotiate discount drug purchasing contracts with the pharmaceutical industry, develop and manage maximum allowable costs (MAC) programs, and arrange for discounts with drug wholesalers.

The second strategy is to develop and manage programs directed at physician prescribing. These may include development and management of drug formularies and drug utilization evaluation (DUE) programs. Our manager of clinical pharmacy operations spends significant time on these issues as well as in discussions with physicians about appropriate drug therapy and related clinical information.

Many Prudential pharmacists serve on the company's pharmacy and therapeutics (P&T) committees, which develop working formularies, develop protocols and usage guidelines for drugs, and determine which drugs and drug classes to target for DUE. When making P&T decisions, the issues most often considered are efficacy, safety, improvement of quality of care, and cost. This requires a thorough review of literature that describes currently available treatments, working with our manager of pharmaceutical contracting to compare costs of similar products, evaluate efficacy, and, perhaps, perform a database analysis of current utilization and trends of certain products. Once a product has been chosen for the formulary, the selection rationale is documented by the P&T committee, and decisions are communicated to all participating physicians.

Merely disseminating this information to physicians without monitoring adherence can cause such efforts to fall short of the expected benefit. A large part of the job of managing clinical pharmacy operations is to analyze prescribing practices in order to determine whether physicians are following recommended standards and protocols. These efforts are globally defined as drug utilization evaluation programs.

If, for example, the manager wanted to see what is being prescribed for patients with certain conditions in a specific age group, he could review relevant histories to see if prescribed therapies follow the indicated protocol. If these activities reveal prescribing deviations, the pharmacy manager may initiate a review or communicate directly with the physician. Some insurance companies make compliance a mandatory quality-assurance issue, subject to enforcement by their quality-assurance committees. For instance, proper compliance with protocols may bear directly on whether the plan will continue to use the physician as a provider.

In addition to ingredient-cost and physician-targeted strategies, benefit design is also necessary. Benefit design will establish which drugs or classes of drugs are covered; what deductibles, copayments, and generic incentives are to be administered; and whether certain delivery systems, such as mail order, are to be included.

Marketing is a new part of the job description for many pharmacists in this setting. Undoubtedly, this trend will continue as pharmacists take part in converting conventional indemnity health insurance to managed care plans, and as they compete in a marketplace with increasing numbers of pharmacy benefit management companies.

Although enrollments have been steadily dropping in the past few years, indemnity health coverage is still a very active product for many insurance companies. Management of the prescription benefit in the indemnity environment has typically been predicated on the efficient payment of claims submitted to the insurance company. The typical indemnity plan that includes a drug benefit in the certificate of coverage usually allows enrollees to fill prescriptions at the pharmacy of their choice and to submit the claim for reimbursement. This claim is paid at a predetermined rate, typically 80 percent. Other than making rudimentary checks on whether certain drugs are covered, or whether the dispensing pharmacy's charge was reasonable, little is done to manage pharmacy claims.

While there are still those in the insurance industry who think that indemnity insurance coverage is the most appropriate means of providing health care coverage, the managed-competition approach is now clearly the favorite among the majority. Though many clients want a more managed environment with better controls and lower administrative costs, some have been slow to embrace many of the strategies necessary to enhance quality and cut the cost of drug benefits, such as establishing formularies or limiting coverage to defined networks of pharmacies.

At many insurance companies today, pharmacy benefit managers are being chosen to promote managed care to large indemnity clients or to those internal customers responsible for selling to indemnity clients. Based on their own experience, those professionals are able to explain the positive aspects of managed care, demonstrating that it is a valuable tool for improving the quality of care and lowering costs.

Although marketing is a new duty for most pharmacists, their comprehensive knowledge has made them highly respected spokesmen. I believe that this new responsibility will come to represent very important new career options. Yet, many pharmacists shortchange themselves by failing to realize the value of their knowledge and the strengths they can bring to a variety of settings.

Here at Prudential, a small group of four pharmacy managers oversee a range of pharmacy activities. Our clinical pharmacy operations manager deals primarily with formulary issues, DUE programs, and outcomes and quality-of-life research. A manager of pharmacy operations deals with other components of pharmacy, including network design, systems and claims adjudication, and data management. In addition we have a manager of drug information and a manager of national pharmacy contracting. In a company like ours, a new pharmacist might start as a support staff member or an assistant to a manager. We believe that the skills and attributes needed for those jobs include not only a strong orientation to details and a comprehensive knowledge of drugs, but also strong strategic planning and organizational behavior skills. We also look for people who have good analytical skills and the ability to communicate well.

From all indications, managed competition may well be the future of our nation's health care delivery system. Even now, managed care is presenting pharmacy graduates with tremendous opportunities, many of which can be realized upon graduation from pharmacy school. This is the one environment that makes it possible for pharmacists to maximize their potential in virtually every practice arena. Unfortunately, I believe the importance of managed care is misunderstood in many schools of pharmacy and by curriculum committees and those who teach courses on the subject. Consequently, I urge students who feel they are not receiving enough information on managed care to seek their own experiences through internships or professional associations. It will be worth the effort because pharmacy practitioners in this setting use their skills to the fullest while quickly building management abilities. Here, pharmacists can exert a tremendous impact on health care.

Opportunities in Consultant Pharmacy

R. Timothy Webster
is executive director of the
American Society of Consultant Pharmacists.

Since its inception only 25 years ago, consultant pharmacy has evolved into an exciting practice option for more than 10,000 pharmacists. In the broadest sense, a consultant pharmacist is one who provides services to a health care facility on a contractual basis, rather than as an employee of the facility. For several reasons, many people equate consultant pharmacy practice with nursing home practice. The evolution of consultant pharmacy practice was influenced strongly by federal regulation of the nursing home industry. Also, because nursing homes typically do not employ pharmacists or have on-site pharmacy facilities, they must contract with a pharmacist to provide needed services.

Consultant pharmacy practice encompasses two distinct functions: the information-based role of consulting, or consultant services; and the distribution of drugs, or provider services. Consultant services to nursing homes are mandated by federal law. To qualify for Medicaid reimbursement, a nursing home must have the drug regimens of all residents reviewed by a pharmacist each month (this is known as drug regimen review, or DRR). This was the first clinical pharmacy service recognized in federal statutes.

Some pharmacists in this practice area offer consultant services or provider services only, while many offer both. In addition to practicing in nursing facilities, today's consultant pharmacists practice in a wide range of environments that provide long-term patient care. These include residential care facilities, hospices, prisons and jails, acute care hospitals, substance abuse rehabilitation centers, psychiatric institutions, homes for the mentally retarded, health maintenance organizations, and even patients' own homes.

Most consultant pharmacists are based in independent community pharmacies, or independent pharmacies that serve nursing homes only. However, many consultant pharmacists are employed by hospital pharmacies, chain pharmacies, pharmacies located in long-term care facilities, government health facilities, and home health care agencies. Some work as independent contractors from their homes or offices.

Because the emphasis in consultant pharmacy is on information services, pharmacists who choose this practice setting must have strong clinical ability and good communication skills. To be successful, consultant pharmacists must be able to collect and evaluate information that relates to a resident's drug therapy, identify and resolve drug-related problems, and then communicate recommendations to physicians, nurses, and other health professionals involved in the care of the resident. Providing pharmaceutical care is not a new concept to most consultant pharmacists. Their practices center on the patient, and they know that their services have a profound impact on each resident's quality of life.

In promoting quality care for all residents, consultant pharmacists do not limit their activities to monthly drug regimen reviews. Instead, they take an active interest in all facets of medication use in their client facilities. Consultant pharmacists help facilities learn how to order, store, and administer medications in the most effective and efficient ways possible. They may be called on to counsel patients and patients' families about prescribed therapies and the need for compliance. Consultant pharmacists routinely present educational programs to nurses in order to bring them up to date on the latest drug therapy information. They also participate on interdisciplinary committees in their client facilities, dealing with such issues as quality assurance and infection control.

When consultant pharmacy was a relatively new practice area, most patients who needed long-term care were elderly, and they resided in nursing facilities. Today, the phrase *long-term care* encompasses many levels of care and many different types of patients. For example, elderly patients in assisted-living settings may be quite healthy, but need a pharmacist to help them sort out their complicated medication regimens. Thanks to the advent of "patient friendly" infusion-therapy systems, many patients with serious conditions are able to receive care in their own homes and avoid lengthy hospital stays. Special-care facilities focus on the medical problems that are unique to certain disease states (such as AIDS and Alzheimer's disease) or to certain types of patients (such as those with head injuries). Hospices offer care, including pharmaceutical care, to patients with terminal illnesses. Other facilities are devoted to helping patients overcome substance abuse problems. Consultant pharmacists apply their expertise to ensure optimal patient care in all of these settings.

Consultant pharmacists have something that no other health care professional has in long-term care settings: specialized information about drug therapy, administration, and monitoring. Phenomena such as the graying of America and the trend toward shorter hospital stays ensure that the markets for consultant pharmacists' knowledge will continue to grow. Innovative, entrepreneurial pharmacists seeking to escape the limits of traditional practice settings will not be disappointed by the many opportunities available in consulting. In fact, most consultant pharmacists find their opportunities to be limited only by the time they have available to take on new business. If you are looking for a practice setting that lets you combine clinical, management, and communication skills, the challenges and rewards of an exciting career await you in consultant pharmacy.

William J. Okoniewski, BS, RPh, FASCP,
is president of Okie's Pharmacy
in Wilson and Newfane, New York.
He also is a long-term care consultant.

The Consultant in Retail Pharmacy

Any technician can count pills and pour liquids. But it takes a professional to make sure the right drug is being used for the right patient and to make sure the patient knows the proper way to take it.

Because of that, insurance companies and third-party payers are becoming increasingly aware of how important pharmacy consultants can be. For example, it has been estimated that up to 20 percent of hospital admissions are the consequence of drug problems caused by people who overdose, underdose, forget to take medications, or don't take them properly. If this demand on the health care system can be reduced, money can be saved.

As the demand for consultant pharmacists grows, more and more retail pharmacists are discovering that consulting is a way to get out from behind the counter – to apply more of their education. In fact, the membership of the American Society of Consultant Pharmacists has more than doubled over the past three or four years. And about 90 percent of those new consultants are part-timers.

I own two pharmacies in small towns in western New York. I also consult to two local long-term care nursing homes. One of our pharmacies services five long-term care facilities. A separate vendor pharmacy contract is made with each facility. In addition I consult to two of these facilities. That's the way the American Society of Consultant Pharmacists encourages it, and that's the way I believe it should be. My pharmacies provide the pharmaceuticals for the facilities I consult for, but we keep the services separate. I don't give away my consulting services in order to keep the vendor business.

I started consulting in 1973 when I was asked to conduct an audit for a local nursing home. The administrators were happy with my work, and they asked me to serve as their pharmacy consultant. Once I became involved, I learned that consulting is the greatest opportunity in the world for retail pharmacists. It is really exciting to use my knowledge and to work on a team with other health professionals.

One of the best things about consulting is that I can arrange my schedule any way I like, mainly because federal and state regulations require that certain things be done only once a month. So, except for meetings or special situations, if it's sunny and I want to play golf on Tuesday, I play golf on Tuesday.

I work as a consultant because I like the work, not because it is essential to my economic survival. That's not to say that I don't make good money consulting. The hourly compensation for a pharmacist consultant in this area is between $20 and $30 per hour.

One nursing home I work for has 175 beds; I visit it at least twice a week. I usually spend one day a week at a second home with 82 beds. Although I check in with my drugstore managers daily, I spend only a half day at each store every other week.

I can afford to take time away from my pharmacies because I hire excellent people I can trust. I employ 25 people, five of whom are pharmacists. Except for a fellow consultant pharmacist who fills in for me when I go on vacation, I am the only one who consults.

The pharmacists who work for me enjoy the freedom to run the stores pretty much the way they like. It's almost as though they own their own stores. Sometimes I may seem to be too much of a hands-off owner, but as long as we're showing a profit, that's the way it's going to be.

In addition to a good salary, pharmacists who work for me enjoy many benefits. For example, they can take time off whenever they need it, and they can take advantage of generous in-store buying policies. I think it also helps that the pharmacists and I are approximately the same age. The result is a very low turnover rate: One pharmacist has been with me since 1968, another since 1973, and two others since 1980 and 1985. There isn't much turnover around here.

I love small towns. I was raised in big-city Buffalo, and during my last three years as a pharmacy student, I worked for city pharmacies and a hospital. After that, I went to work in my uncle's small-town pharmacy. I decided that I was never again going to work in the city or suburbs.

To practice pharmacy the way I thought it should be practiced, I knew I would have to go to work in a small town. I wanted to get to know my customers, to know more about them than their names and how much money they spend. I wanted to talk to them about their families and how they were feeling – counseling them at a time when pharmacy clients seldom received this kind of support. In addition, I prefer the friendly competition among small-town pharmacies to the fierce competition among city pharmacies who depend on high volume.

In 1968, I bought my own drugstore in Wilson, NY. Five years later, I opened a brand-new pharmacy in Newfane – only eight miles away. The long-term care facilities that I consult for are in those same small towns. For that reason, I already know about 10 of their patients at any one time. Many have been my store customers. Those patients appreciate the fact that I stop by and talk to them when I come to the nursing homes. They know that I truly care about them.

I spend 75 percent of my time as a consultant conducting monthly drug regimen reviews, looking for drug interactions, missed doses, and inappropriate prescriptions. I consult with the nursing staff to learn how the therapies are working: Are the patients getting better? Are the drugs doing their job?

I am responsible for all of my clients' pharmacy policies and procedures.

I conduct quality-control audits to make sure the medications are being administered properly and that policies and procedures are being observed. I also provide in-service training to ensure that staff members are performing their medication-related duties as they should. I supervise storage of medicines as well.

Even though the nursing homes I work for don't have formularies per se, we do work with a modified version. For example, we try to limit the products each home has in inventory, and I ensure that the drugs on hand are the best products available.

Consulting is extremely competitive. And because of the strict federal and state regulations that govern long-term care facilities, pharmacist consultants now have tremendous responsibility for the quality of drug therapy. This has prompted pharmacists to consider consulting as an alternate type of practice. Today, there are many, many consultants doing small amounts of consulting – and the numbers are growing.

My reputation gives me a competitive edge. If I'm doing a good job and the nursing home administrator knows that I am, it isn't likely that I will lose my contract to hungry newcomers. However, one of the administrators I work for had been approached by other pharmacist consultants who offered to do my job for less. Each time, the administrator decided to stick with me.

The biggest challenge I have had is in winning the confidence of physicians, and this was especially true when I first began. When I started, physicians were very skeptical of consultant pharmacists. At that time, many pharmacists in this field were paper consultants who would stop by a nursing home, sign the paperwork, and then leave. Besides, the older physicians had little confidence in the skills of a pharmacist.

In the beginning, one particular physician ignored every suggestion I left for him. Yet within 30 days he implemented those same suggestions without acknowledging my input. I'm happy to say that over the years he has learned to trust me. Now he doesn't wait a month to talk to me about my recommendations, and he does so willingly.

Younger physicians are more open to the concept of working as part of a health care team. Of course, they are the most important part of the team, but in this setting, they probably see the patients less often than anyone else – once a month or two for three to five minutes. They now realize they have to rely on input from other professionals when making critical decisions about patient care.

With our increasing acceptance and credibility comes challenge, too. When I give advice to a physician, I had better be right. If I'm not, and my recommendation is unsound, the physician will say, "Boy, this guy is dumb. He doesn't know what he's talking about. I'm never going to listen to him again." That's why I always explain my reasoning for each recommendation. Now the physicians with whom I work have enough faith in me that they seek my opinions.

In the future, I would like to be able to consult for other types of clients – hospices, prisons, mental institutions – where I believe the need for more drug therapy monitoring and drug information services is great. In fact, I sometimes think I may sell the pharmacies and do consulting full time.

Pharmacy students who are interested in the retail setting should consider consulting on the side. This provides an opportunity for direct patient care that simply is not available in other areas of community pharmacy.

Over the last 20 years, I have seen the number of independent pharmacists in western New York diminish greatly. New pharmacists believe they should start making money right away, so they go to work for chains at an excellent starting salary. Many don't want to do what I did, working eight to 12 hours a day, seven days a week to develop a business. Unfortunately, new pharmacists can't just go out and buy a business, hire employees, and make money – not unless there is a rich uncle to bankroll the enterprise.

In addition, the cost of starting a pharmacy today is very, very high. The smallest of my two pharmacies has only 1,500 square feet, but almost $130,000 in inventory. It probably would cost a quarter of a million dollars to start a new pharmacy today. Where does a new graduate get that kind of money? The answer is that it's hard, especially in the major cities and suburbs. However, for students who are sure that independent pharmacy is for them, there is still plenty of opportunity in retail and consulting in small towns. There, it's still possible to make a profit and practice pharmacy the old-fashioned way.

Lorrie Packer Lattari, BS,
works as a consultant pharmacist with
Insta-Care Pharmacy Services
in Woburn, Massachusetts.

The Long-term Care Specialist

The chief responsibility of consultant pharmacists in nursing homes used to be making sure that the drug a physician ordered was the drug the patient received. Today, we play an even more essential part in patient care, ensuring that patients receive the right medication at the right time, and in the right form.

Any nursing home that receives money from either Medicaid or Medicare, and more than 90 percent do, must have a pharmacist review medication charts and write a progress note on every single patient every single month. It's mandated by law. Also, any nursing home that receives government funding has to comply with annual state inspection surveys. These surveys are mandated by the federal Health Care Financing Administration (HCFA), the government agency that determines how Medicare and Medicaid monies are allocated. An important part of the consultant pharmacist's job is to critique procedures and advise nurses as they prepare for the surveys.

I work for Insta-Care Pharmacy Services, which was founded in 1960 by Richard Berman. He is known in the industry as the father of consultant pharmacy. As a young man, Berman helped bring new business to his father's corner pharmacy by soliciting business from nursing homes. Over time, his father's pharmacy began to package drugs for nursing homes. The Bermans employed the "bingo card" drug distribution system that we still use today. Another result of this early experience was the development of quality-assurance programs to ensure that drugs were distributed properly. Before this, nursing home patients were largely unsupervised when it came to administration of their medications.

Insta-Care has contracts with nursing homes, pediatric facilities, home health care agencies, group homes, some prisons, rehabilitation facilities, and head trauma facilities. The company has more than doubled in size since I started working here in 1986. We operate in Massachusetts, Florida, Alabama, Georgia, Louisiana, Texas and, most recently, Connecticut. In Massachusetts alone, we have 25 full-time consultant pharmacists, and we employ close to 50 pharmacists in total. In Massachusetts, we service about 5,000 patients through four pharmacy sites. Our Florida operation is nearly as large.

After graduation from the Albany College of Pharmacy, I did a postgraduate residency in hospital pharmacy and began my career at Rhode Island Hospital. I enjoyed most of my duties, but I sometimes felt I was spending all my time in the basement counting pills. After three years, I decided it was time to look for something different so I answered an advertisement for Insta-Care.

The advertised position involved little more than dispensing and answering the phone, and neither I nor the woman who interviewed me felt I'd be a good match for it. Then the woman asked if I had ever thought about going into consultant pharmacy. I said, "What is that? I've never heard of it before."

When she described it to me, my ears perked up. Then I spent a day with a consultant, learning more about the job and the company, and I knew I had fallen right into a new career.

I now have dual responsibilities as a senior consultant pharmacist (75 percent of my job) and regional education coordinator. As education coordinator, I am responsible for Insta-Care's marketing and education programs throughout New England.

As a consultant, I work mainly with skilled nursing facilities, which provide the highest level of long-term care. They serve patients who are least able to care for themselves. My responsibilities extend to 12 homes with nearly 1,000 beds.

I usually work from 8 AM to 5:30 PM, and most of my time is spent visiting nursing homes where I review patients' charts. Every month, I review each chart and make progress notes for each patient. I go over medications to make sure there are no problems with dosages or interactions. I also read doctors' and nurses' chart notes and lab results, and I watch for side effects.

Sometimes, progress notes are quite simple – a patient may be taking a multivitamin and nothing more. At other times, the notes can be quite involved. If I find any irregularities, I am required by law to bring them to the attention of the director of nursing and the attending physician. Because physicians make their visits once every 60 days, the nurses are most likely to hear from me about harmful side effects.

Among my other duties, I'm charged with making sure the nursing homes I work with comply with federal regulations. For instance, for every medication that's prescribed, there must be a corresponding diagnosis. If a patient's chart does not show a diagnosis for a particular medication, it's up to me to request one from the doctor. On rare occasions, I've had rude responses to my requests, but these usually come from physicians who do not know me or do not understand the consultant pharmacist's role. In most cases, I have good rapport with physicians, and there have been instances when a doctor has discontinued a drug because of a question I raised. At Insta-Care we work hard to see that patients are taking only medications that are essential for their well-being. Nationwide, nursing home patients take an average of 6.1 drugs. The average in facilities served by Insta-Care is only 4.5.

Medicating the elderly can be tricky because new drugs are often tested on younger volunteers. However, the elderly metabolize drugs more slowly than young people, primarily because of impaired liver and kidney function.

There is a second problem in predicting a new drug's effect on the elderly: In the aging process, muscle mass decreases, while fat mass increases, thereby altering the distribution of a drug throughout the body.

Every three months, I meet with the quality-assurance committee of the nursing homes I serve. If there has been a theft of a narcotic, I help trace records to determine how the theft occurred, and I provide advice and consultation in complicated cases where patients may be taking several different medications. When my company contracts with a nursing home, we sponsor educational programs for the nurses – at least one every quarter. These programs usually last an hour and feature a lecture on a drug category or disease state. In Massachusetts, we provide the continuing education nurses must have when they renew their licenses. My own continuing education includes a great deal of reading so that I am informed about the most recent developments in pharmaceuticals.

The future will bring additional challenges to the consultant pharmacist. For one thing, as our population ages, more people will be in nursing homes. For another, patients in these facilities will be sicker than ever because those who are able to care for themselves will be sent home. Naturally, these challenges will translate into opportunities for students who elect to practice in this expanding field.

Kathleen M. D'Achille, PharmD, MEd,
is a consultant pharmacist for
Health/Med Information Services
in Easley, South Carolina.

The Freelance Consultant

There were no clinical pharmacy jobs to be found.

That's what I discovered in 1980, when my husband and I moved from economically depressed Toledo, where I worked as a clinical pharmacist and a professor, to Winston-Salem, NC. If I wanted to work, I was going to have to create my own job. That's how I began my career as a freelance consultant.

The term *consultant pharmacy* usually suggests nursing home care and, indeed, much of our work is in long-term care facilities. However, that connotation is restrictive because consultant pharmacists also may work on educational programs, with corporate health care coverage, and in hospitals, hospices, and even patients' homes.

I've always been interested in health care, but it took me a little while to settle on pharmacy. I knew nursing wasn't for me after I did volunteer work as a candy-striper, and I rejected medical technology after a year's study in college – I knew I wanted more contact with people. My first exposure to pharmacy came courtesy of a neighborhood drugstore, where I worked as a clerk. The pharmacist there described the profession as one that offered a respectable income and a schedule flexible enough to leave time for a family.

In 1973, I earned a BS degree in pharmacy from Wayne State University, but when I graduated the job market was grim. Not many community pharmacies were in a financial position to hire full-time pharmacists, and my classmates were going to work for chains. That didn't appeal to me because I didn't think a chain could give me the freedom I wanted.

As a result, I decided to get a PharmD degree and to complete a hospital pharmacy residency, which I financed by working as a hospital staff pharmacist. I've never regretted my decision to get advanced training. After I finished, I went to work as an assistant professor of pharmacy at the University of Toledo. My responsibilities included teaching in a family practice center.

Five years later, I moved to Winston-Salem and became a pharmacy consultant. In the early phase of my new career, I held several jobs. For instance, I worked with a health insurer to develop a cost-effective and accessible prescription plan. I consulted with a group practice to analyze the costs of an in-house pharmacy. In one job, I helped establish pharmacy educational services at a hospital clinic, as part of a multidisciplinary, comprehensive health care team. Eventually, these experiences led me to full-time work at the University of North Carolina in 1984. Continuing education had become mandatory, and I was given responsibility for surveying the state's pharmacists to find out what they needed. I also served as an ad hoc public relations person for the program, easing the fears of alarmed pharmacists who hadn't participated in organized education for years.

In the late 1980s, I earned a master of education degree in community health education at the University of North Carolina. Until then, my background was mainly in clinical pharmacy. The master's degree gave me a broader understanding of teaching, training, and human behavior. It helped me develop a better grasp of the health care system in general and of the value of prevention in particular.

Interestingly enough, although I had previously avoided working for a chain, I was recruited into long-term care by a large pharmacy chain that serviced nursing homes. While I had to do some on-the-job learning, I had amassed a good deal of experience by then. My education and work in clinical pharmacy had prepared me to review drug therapy, communicate with other medical staff, and develop alternative plans of care. In fact, I think clinically experienced pharmacists from any setting are well equipped to work as consultants in long-term care.

Any long-term care facility that receives Medicare or Medicaid funding is required to use the services of a consultant pharmacist, who is responsible for making certain that pharmaceutical therapy meets government standards. Indeed, the field of consultant pharmacy owes its growth, in part, to federal regulation. Although the government's intervention sometimes creates problems, by and large it has produced important benefits in the quality of patient care.

Consultant pharmacists develop a system for monitoring every aspect of drug use in client facilities. We visit our clients approximately once each month to review drug therapy and to alert the medical director or nursing staff of any problems or recommended changes.

Sometimes the problems we find are easily fixed. Perhaps, for example, the staff simply needs to be shown that a patient's regimen can be simplified. During each visit we check on the use of a targeted drug or class of drugs, such as sedatives or antipsychotics. Government regulations stipulate that patients receive no unnecessary medications. Every drug a patient receives must be scrutinized according to the stringent criteria included under these regulations.

Sometimes, the consultant encounters resentment. Physicians who are not accustomed to a team approach to health care may be unresponsive to recommended changes. They don't like having someone looking over their shoulders, and their reaction may be to complain. The nursing staff also may be wary of the consultant, at least initially. To overcome this, I try to enlist the nurses' assistance in communicating with the appropriate people about problems I find. If they are included in the information loop, they usually learn to anticipate my requests.

When physicians learn that I am analyzing drug therapy rationally, rather than simply spouting regulations at them, they tend to become more cooperative.

Everything the consultant pharmacist does should contribute to better patient care. We're there to identify problems, and it's preferable for us to catch them before the government surveyors do. Obviously, diplomacy is a commending feature of our work. I once mentioned a nursing problem to a facility's director of nursing and found out that she had used the information to upbraid a particular nurse in front of her coworkers. Naturally, that put me in a difficult position, because I work very hard to maintain credibility and convince the staff that I'm there to help, not get them in trouble. If I learn that I *have* gotten someone in trouble, I go directly to the person and straighten things out. As far as I know, I haven't alienated anyone. But I do have to remind administrators that they should concentrate on education – it doesn't work to anyone's advantage to use my findings to punish the staff.

In 1991, I began work with a company that provides pharmacy services to nursing homes in South Carolina. Several consultant pharmacists are employed by the vendor pharmacy I contract with, and we meet once a month to compare notes, review common problems, and discuss strategies. We provide a sounding board for each other.

Another resource I use frequently is the American Society of Consultant Pharmacists (ASCP) electronic bulletin board, Consult Net®. If I encounter a problem I haven't seen before, I can put out a call for help and get responses from across the country. Because I work out of my home and can't consort with my colleagues around the water cooler, this is an ideal way to stay in touch with other professionals.

I find consultant pharmacy rewarding because it blends the stimulation of using clinical knowledge with the satisfaction of helping people. Not only am I using my knowledge in a challenging practice, I am also able to see the results of my work in terms of improved patient care. An example of this occurred with a female patient I saw recently. She was extremely confused and withdrawn. And because she had no supporting diagnosis, I requested that her psychoactive drugs (an antipsychotic and a sleep medication) be reduced and then discontinued. Since then, she has exhibited no aggressive behavior and still sleeps well at night. And she's become progressively more physically active, spending much of her time visiting with the staff and responding well to hugs. One nurse said to me, "We've discovered that she really does have a personality, and we like her!" Statistics validate this empirical evidence that long-term patient care is improving with closer scrutiny of drug use.

Scheduling flexibility is another advantage in this field. I tailor my days to revolve around my children's car pool schedule. Right now, I work only 20 to 30 hours a week, but even when I was working full time, it was possible to have free days during the week if I worked evenings and on weekends. And because I'm essentially a freelancer, I can pick and choose my assignments. Most of my work is in long-term care, but I sometimes consult with drug distributors. I also write and, under the auspices of ASCP, I authored a model policy and procedures manual for use by long-term care facilities. I am using my health education degree by consulting on an employee health-promotion program with a small company. Seldom am I involved in a job I don't like.

When I work as a consultant in long-term care, I am paid a monthly fee as a subcontractor. When I work with an employer or consult with a drug distributor on the regulations that govern the way products are handled, I charge by the hour. As a contributor to journals, my writing fees are negotiable. In general, consultant pharmacists' income probably is comparable to or more than that of pharmacists in retail practice.

A big plus in consultant pharmacy is its growth potential, which is almost guaranteed with the aging of our population, increasing government regulation, and new niches for consultant work in AIDS care and hospices. As of October 1991, federal regulations require prescription drug wholesalers to establish standardized policies and procedures for handling medications. In South Carolina, this is overseen by the Board of Pharmacy, thereby opening another door for consultant pharmacists.

I think all this is indicative that consultant pharmacy is breaking away from the narrow image of nursing home care and is beginning to establish itself as a complete field. More and more, the terms *pharmacy consultant* and *consultant pharmacist* are becoming synonymous. I look forward to the day when consultant pharmacist describes all of my diverse activities.

William J. Taylor, PharmD,
is vice president of
clinical services at the
Family Biomedical Health Services Division
of Biomedical Home Care in
Burlington, North Carolina.

The Home Infusion Consultant

I have been very fortunate in pharmacy because I have worked in several settings and could have had a satisfying career in any of them. For me, home infusion therapy has been the most rewarding of them all. As a matter of fact, my job as vice president of clinical services for Biomedical Home Care gives me what I have wanted for all the years I've been in pharmacy – opportunity to work as a clinician within a pharmaceutical environment. As far as I'm concerned, it's the epitome of pharmacy.

When I was growing up, one of the people I admired most was the local pharmacist, who was one of the few professional people in our rural North Carolina community. He encouraged my interest in pharmacy and science, and when I attended the University of North Carolina, I studied for a BS in pharmacy.

My desire to practice pharmacy was cemented when, through the U.S. Public Health Service, I participated in the Commissioned Officer Student Training Externship Program (COSTEP). The summer before my senior year, I was placed in the Food and Drug Administration's generic drug division, just when generic drugs were beginning to make news. At the FDA I became acquainted with two pharmacists who held top-level positions, and I credit them with inspiring me to set my sights high.

The following summer I had an experience that sparked my interest in clinical pharmacy. There was a nursing shortage at the time, and pharmacy students were trained to become medication nurses. I participated in the university's medication assistant program, working on hospital wards, following rounds, and giving medications. Unfortunately, that program is now defunct.

For two years I was chief pharmacist at Fort Yuma Indian Health Hospital in Yuma, Ariz. I was the first full-time pharmacist the clinic and hospital had ever had, and I did whatever was needed. In fact, during my first three days there, I delivered two babies – something I never expected to be part of a pharmacist's job.

The Indian Health Service (IHS) is an excellent organization, probably one of the most progressive in the profession. The service is a clinical organization, but we performed traditional pharmacy duties as well. We ran a 25-bed hospital and saw close to 100 patients a day with a team of two physicians, a pharmacist, two nurses, and a lab technician. We all were on call every night, so it was essential that whoever picked up a patient's chart be able to see what the previous caregiver had done for the patient. In those days, I learned how effective a physician and a pharmacist can be when working together as a team.

At Yuma, I was more than a pharmacist: I was a public health servant and an integral part of the community. We taught patients how to use their medications, and we convinced the federal government to give the reservation money to build streets and houses and install an air conditioning system on the reservation.

After leaving the IHS I enrolled at the University of Tennessee to work toward my PharmD degree. Subsequently, I was named chief resident in pharmacy at Buffalo General Hospital in Buffalo, NY. I then held several academic positions – assistant professor at Duke University, associate professor at the Medical College of Georgia, and clinical associate professor of neurology at the University of South Alabama Medical School.

When I began to teach, medicine had just begun to embrace clinical pharmacy. In teaching residents the subtleties of pharmacotherapeutics, I spent more time at patients' bedsides than I did in the classroom. It was generally agreed that a pharmacist was well qualified to teach therapeutic drug monitoring (TDM) as well as clinical pharmacology and adverse drug reactions.

During this period, I worked as a consultant pharmacist for long-term care facilities that were associated with the medical school. I discovered that the reach of a consultant pharmacist is a long one: I saw nursing home patients only once a month, but I still participated in their care long after my visits to individual facilities.

After I left academia, I became director of pharmacokinetics and education at Roche Biomedical Laboratories in Burlington, NC. I remained involved in patient care, but for a larger population and at a greater distance. My expertise was in therapeutic drug monitoring. This experience was followed by a three-year stint as managing director of a small manufacturing concern in the Netherlands. Many European companies strive to meet FDA standards so they can sell their products in the United States. While in the Netherlands, I was able to draw on my internship experience at the FDA and facilitate an understanding of the regulatory aspects of the pharmaceutical industry in this country.

In the late 1980s, I became interested in how home care companies operate, and I was attracted to Biomedical Home Care because of its dual focus on patients and clinical pharmacy.

Biomedical Home Care is a pharmacy-driven company in a pharmacy-driven industry. We have more than 100 employees, and we have an interdisciplinary team of pharmacists, nurses, metabolic nutritionists, and respiratory therapists. Our pharmacists are on clinical call 24 hours a day, seven days a week, to provide clinical consultation, drug information, and pharmacotherapeutic education.

My main responsibility as a clinical consultant pharmacist is to help develop systems and direction for a range of activities that go beyond clinical pharmacy services. The truth is that I work with more nurses than pharmacists. I formulate management and policy approaches on such issues as whether a medication can be given safely in the home. I also am instrumental in making certain that drug information is available to those who need it. For example, when a new AIDS drug came on the market, I informed physicians about proper dosages and delivery methods. I talked with third-party payers about reimbursement for that medication, and I taught nurses and patients how to administer it safely.

A clinical orientation is an absolute requirement for home infusion therapy, and that's what makes it such an exciting and demanding area of pharmacy. In home infusion therapy, outcomes are critical: If a patient's infection doesn't clear up, the blame for the failure may be shared by the pharmacist and other members of the health care team.

The Joint Commission on the Accreditation of Healthcare Organizations (JCAHO) offers voluntary accreditation to companies that provide home care infusion services. In most specialties, pharmacists are not required to document or notify physicians if adverse reactions occur. However, in the home infusion environment, daily monitoring of patients' reactions is essential in coordinating and communicating the events of patient care. In a real sense, the pharmacist in this specialty is the liaison between the patient and other health care providers, and a primary duty is to participate in designing drug regimens. In fact, because home infusion pharmacists interact with patients more frequently than physicians do, the clinical pharmacist leads the home health care team.

When home infusion therapy was introduced in the early 1980s it was meant primarily for stabilized patients. At that time, home IV care was a $50 million-per-year business and was considered appropriate for approximately 20 diagnoses. Since then, acceptance of this treatment has made it a $4 billion-per-year industry, and there are now more than 900 diagnoses (including AIDS) for which home infusion therapy is used.

I believe pharmacists in this field should have advanced degrees and clinical training. We hire those with extensive training and experience in IV therapy and clinical pharmacy. Beyond that, we look for candidates with expertise in IV pharmaceuticals, infectious diseases, metabolic nutrition, and chemotherapy.

Not all pharmacists want the decision-making responsibility and accountability that go with home infusion therapy. Some prefer to leave the job's problems behind at the end of their shift. Unfortunately, that simply isn't possible for most consultant pharmacists because we have to answer to the physician, the public, and the regulatory agencies.

For those who do choose to work in home infusion therapy, the compensation is competitive with that found in hospitals and ambulatory facilities. However, opportunities are greater in home infusion care than in hospitals, where most pharmacists can expect to reach a certain level and go no further. Home infusion therapy is oriented toward the marketplace, and skilled pharmacists who have accumulated experience in this field are likely to find that their services are in great demand.

Armon B. Neel, Jr., BS,
is president of Institutional Pharmacy
Consultants in Griffin, Georgia.

The Innovative Consultant

My partner and I stopped dispensing drugs in the late 1970s because we decided that our goal was to focus on patients, not products. We wanted to spend time working with new ideas, methodologies, and technologies that could improve the quality of life for geriatric patients. We intended to take a holistic approach to consulting that would include all of the professional disciplines involved in long-term care, not just pharmacy. Today, we have 39 employees, 22 of whom are specialists – nutritionists, registered dietitians, registered nurses, occupational therapists, activities and social directors, and, of course, pharmacists.

We had been working as consultant pharmacists for long-term care facilities since 1965, when Congress passed Title 18 and Title 19. Experience had shown us how the quality of long-term care depends on the successful melding of all these disciplines. Today, we serve 60 facilities throughout Georgia – nearly 10,000 patients.

In addition to our work in long-term care facilities, we serve a broad and unusual set of clients. We design forms, drug delivery systems, and nutritional systems for acute care facilities. We evaluate cases for attorneys, in order to determine whether they have potential for malpractice litigation. We also provide expert witnesses in cases that have to do with drug therapy.

We also work for insurance companies, evaluating the validity of claims and charges. For state agencies, we develop programs to help them inform the long-term care industry about new laws and regulations. We also provide such agencies with temporary managers for nursing homes that have regulatory problems.

The funny thing is, I never set out to be a consultant. I am the fifth-generation pharmacist in a family that recently celebrated its hundredth year in retail pharmacy. But even with such a long family tradition, I just couldn't get interested in the nonpharmacy side of the business. Besides, I wanted to be more directly involved with patient care.

I quit working in my father's store soon after graduation, and I opened an apothecary shop behind the hospital in Griffin, Ga. When patients brought in their prescriptions, I prepared them and then we would adjourn to a counseling booth. I counseled patients about their therapies, measured blood pressure, and talked with mothers-to-be about prenatal care and other matters. Patient counseling is pretty routine today, but it wasn't back then.

Joe Pittman became my business partner 23 years ago because we shared the same philosophy about pharmacy, and he, too, was patient oriented.

Later on, we got into the consulting business when a local nursing home administrator asked us to provide pharmacy consultation.

When we started consulting, it quickly became obvious that there was a tremendous need for the expertise of pharmacists as long-term care developed. Administrators and regulators had taken existing acute care policies, procedures, protocols, and customs and tried to apply them in long-term settings. It just didn't work – primarily because hospital stays for acute patients lasted only a few days, but long-term patients were likely to be institutionalized for years.

Because there was no precedent for operating in the long-term care setting, we developed many of our own pharmacokinetic programs – very good ones – and conducted our own research into drug therapies. We shared our research with the physicians and nurses we do business with.

All long-term care facilities are required by law to employ the consultant services of a pharmacist and a dietitian. But they don't have to hire consultants who offer the sophisticated services we have developed. So, clearly, the administrators who hire us are committed to providing excellent patient care.

Our consultants rotate constantly among client facilities, and this is an important way to assure quality. If the same people always work in the same place, productivity would soon begin to fall. It's human nature: Our consultants would settle in and make friends. A certain degree of complacency would be inevitable.

By having so many different sets of eyes on our client locations, at least two positive things happen. First, the consultants perform quality-assurance checks on each other. This makes it difficult for problems to remain hidden for long. Second, because each of our people has a particular area of expertise, we are able to render a very broad spectrum of services.

One of the reasons our drug therapy evaluations are so well done is that we look at our patients – we see them in person. Our consultants don't just sit in the nurses station and read charts. If we spot any potential for trouble we visit the patient and personally check his or her physical condition.

Whenever I go to meet with an administrator, conduct an in-service program, or just stop by to say hello, I never fail to go out on the floor and visit with patients. I do this because I enjoy interaction with patients, and frankly, I just like old people. I especially enjoy their insight and philosophy of life.

The consultant pharmacists we hire are expected to feel the same way. When we bring pharmacists into our group they go through a year-long residency and participate in a program that highlights positive patient outcomes. If they come to us with any orientation toward products, we soon convert them to patient-oriented professionals.

Whenever I visit an institution, I conduct a procedure we call "body scanning." In fact, our consultants train every worker in every facility to do this. We all have been trained to be on the alert whenever we walk through a facility. We look carefully at every patient we pass, alert for signs that something is out of order. Is this man slumped in his chair because he is too weak to pull himself up straight? Why isn't that patient's hair combed? If patients are wearing shoes that don't match, we consider that an insult to their dignity. Any such problem is reported immediately to the nurses and is resolved.

Our commitment to quality care is responsible for the positive reputation we enjoy within the industry. We rely on that reputation to get new clients, and it works. We never make cold calls. In fact, we don't make any sales presentations at all unless we're asked to do so by a facility administrator.

Consulting in the long-term care market is a rewarding experience for pharmacists – both professionally and financially. Last year, our business grew by 16 percent, the smallest growth we have experienced for a number of years. The year before, we grew by 28 percent.

We owe our success to the fact that we offer a top-quality product that clients need to buy. If the facilities we serve are willing to adopt our guidelines and accept our recommendations, there is no question that the quality of their patients' lives will improve substantially. For example, during the last review, 50 percent of our clients were declared deficiency free. Such a high level of quality is unusual in the long-term care industry, but it is not at all unusual among our clients.

Consultant pharmacy will continue to grow. The number of people in the United States who are age 65 and over is growing by 6,000 or 7,000 people a day. There are 1.6 million people in long-term care homes right now. In 25 years, the number will rise to nearly seven million. Obviously, there's no end in sight to opportunities for the consultant pharmacist.

Each day, the territory of pharmacy consultants is expanding further into the private sector. We already consult for many clients who are not involved in long-term care. And, someday, I am sure that we will begin offering our services to individual patients, much as I did in my old apothecary shop.

The need for this service is clear. In this era of specialization it is not uncommon for patients to have prescriptions from three or four doctors. When that happens, someone has to be coordinating drug therapy. That's the service we plan to provide.

The biggest challenge I have is to anticipate tomorrow's health care needs and prepare my company to meet them. One way I prepare is by hiring the best people I can find. We pick the brightest stars. We hire experienced pharmacists who have practiced in different disciplines, and we hire those who have never filled a prescription. We look for pharmacists who genuinely like people and who have high levels of intelligence, creativity, and reliability. We might interview 60 people before we select one new consultant.

Partly because we are so careful about hiring, we don't lose many pharmacists to attrition. Some of our employees have been with us for 22 years; about half of our staff has been here more than 12 years.

Every person who works here is made to feel like a part of our family. Each consultant enjoys a competitive salary, profit-sharing, excellent benefits, and a company car. Mostly though, I think our employees stay because they are proud of the work they do here.

Students interested in consulting should definitely get a PharmD degree. Right now, we hire people without doctorates, but that is going to change. Soon, the PharmD degree will be necessary for a pharmacist just to get a foot in the door of any consulting firm. In the near future, graduates will need the level of knowledge and prestige of a PharmD to function in consultant pharmacy.

There is no way to diminish the importance of education and solid skills in consultant pharmacy. We take it for granted that people we hire come equipped with those features. We don't take it for granted that they genuinely like and are concerned about people, and that is the ultimate determinant of success in this business. Without it, how could we help our clients provide the kind of care their patients deserve? But most of all, successful consultants – particularly in the long-term setting – genuinely like people. A consultant's first concern should be to help clients provide the best patient care possible.

Carl E. Trinca, PhD,
is executive director of the
American Association of Colleges
of Pharmacy.

Planning for Careers in Pharmaceutical Education

By the time you read this guide to careers in pharmacy, the chances are good that you already will have embarked upon your professional education. Eventually, your commitment will culminate in nearly two decades of learning, during which you will have experienced a wide variety of teachers and teaching styles. By now, you can spot the difference between teachers who are exemplary and those who are not quite as effective. You know that the best educators not only help you learn, but they also guide, motivate, and evaluate. We hope that some professor along the way has urged you to consider a career in pharmaceutical education. Regardless of how seriously you might have taken this suggestion, and no matter what practice area you finally choose, your responsibility will extend to teaching our future generations of pharmacy students.

This can be accomplished in two ways. If you elect to practice pharmacy in one of the many forms described in this guide, you must set aside time to serve as a practitioner-educator: a pharmacist who assists a school or college of pharmacy as an adjunct faculty member. This duty can be discharged by delivering guest lectures in a classroom setting, by working as a discussion leader during case-study recitations, and by accepting a student to work side by side with you in a pharmacy practice experience.

The second way in which you might help prepare future pharmacists is by becoming a full-time faculty member in a pharmacy school. Today, there are approximately 3,000 full-time faculty members who teach, conduct research, and render patient care in the nation's 75 colleges and schools of pharmacy. Of this number, approximately 25 percent are women. Many faculty, including deans and department chairs, consult with local, state, national, and international agencies and organizations. A significant number are leaders in their communities as well as in our profession.

Almost without exception, a faculty position at a college of pharmacy requires an advanced, graduate level, doctoral, or professional degree. Additional education and training, such as fellowships and residencies, also may be desirable. Depending on your chosen field, your choice of a BS or PharmD as your first professional degree, the requirements of the graduate program you select, and the nature of your research, preparing for an academic career normally takes between three and six additional years of study.

Graduate study is rewarding in its own right. Those who complete doctoral programs have grown accustomed to stiff competition and have

257

learned the value of teamwork. They have developed keen multidisciplinary skills and understand the complexities of the scientific method and research. Their oral and written communication skills have been sharply honed. So have their powers of observation and analysis. They know how to manage their time and resources. Pharmaceutical educators and scientists are idea people who can articulate and defend their positions.

Even though most pharmacists who complete graduate study exercise the option to join the faculty of a school of pharmacy, there are substantial shortages in all disciplines: medicinal and pharmaceutical chemistry, pharmaceutical analysis, pharmacognosy, pharmacology, toxicology, pharmaceutics, pharmacokinetics, pharmacy administration, and clinical pharmacy science.

Does the idea of working with students, scientists in the pharmaceutical industry, educators in other disciplines, and leaders in all fields of endeavor appeal to you? If so, you should consider planning for a career as a pharmaceutical educator. Here are some suggestions.

Graduate programs in the pharmaceutical sciences need to be investigated rigorously because no two are alike. Although choosing among the 205 graduate programs offered by schools and colleges of pharmacy may be confusing at times, this diversity almost guarantees that students will find a program to satisfy their individual interests. But before making any final decisions, carefully weigh academic, outcome, cost, and personal factors. And never base a choice of this importance on written material alone. Visit the program. Interview current students and faculty members. Learn the best time to take the Graduate Record Examination (GRE) as well as any other required or optional tests. Examine policies governing credit transfers, off-campus learning opportunities, typical modes of instruction, availability of laboratory space, faculty commitments, and financial aid.

Make certain the program you choose will help you achieve your career goals. Be sure the required course work falls squarely within your area of interest. And, consider how your advisor will be chosen. If you haven't yet selected a discipline or specialty, will the program enable you to sample various research experiences? Are there any health risks associated with your area of study?

You must evaluate the reputation of any prospective program. Look closely at the background and number of faculty. Examine the credentials and reputation of each member. Ask how the program is funded and consider its attrition rate. How many students have successfully completed the program in the last five years? What are recent graduates doing now? What are they earning?

Examine the costs of any program that interests you. Will it waive your tuition costs? Are teaching or research assistantships available? Will it be necessary to moonlight in order to make ends meet? More important, is moonlighting allowed? Can you afford application fees and loan obligations?

If you will be away from family and friends during graduate school, how much personal and academic support will you need? Remember, getting used to the cultural and social environment in which you will be spending the next several years may be one of the biggest adjustments you will ever have to make.

Rely most on those who know the ropes – the current graduate students. Take advantage of the strong support systems in and among graduate programs. Remember, these students were in your shoes a few years ago. By asking questions they forgot to ask you can learn much from their experiences – and from their mistakes.

The American Association of Colleges of Pharmacy (AACP) is another resource to which you can turn for help. Our association can provide information and discussion as you begin to consider graduate study. We can suggest programs to pursue and questions to ask. And we can offer a network of support during your graduate studies. When you become a faculty member, we can help with faculty development and leadership opportunities. Simply write or call our Office of Graduate Education, Research and Scholarship; we will be pleased to help you.

Without a doubt, the most important resource available to you are the faculty members at your current school. These men and women know you, and they know your potential. Moreover, because they are active in their disciplines, they are ideally positioned to help you find information through their network of colleagues.

Graduate programs are demanding and require years of hard work through intense study and research. Often participants must make significant temporary sacrifices of time, earning potential, and energy. Consider, though, that you will be practicing your career for 30 to 40 years or more. In the long run, such an investment in academia will pay off.

Still, graduate school isn't for everyone. The men and women who flourish there enjoy teaching and the sciences. They seek professional advancement, intellectual challenge, and expanded earning potential. They have considered the negatives but have not lost sight of the positives. To them, a graduate degree provides a sense of accomplishment and a sense of personal and professional growth. If this is for you, pursue a graduate degree in the pharmaceutical sciences. Join with the dedicated professionals who are making a difference in pharmaceutical education and science.

Larry E. Boh, MS,
is an associate professor of
clinical health sciences
in the School of Pharmacy at the
University of Wisconsin, Madison.

The Pharmacist as Educator

Without question, educator-practitioners like me enjoy more autonomy than other pharmacists. In fact, the major reason I'm a faculty member instead of a full-time practitioner is that I like to establish my own hours and set my own goals. If I want to work on Saturday and Sunday, I can do that. If I want to work until one o'clock in the morning, I can do that. Obviously I have commitments to be available for patient care at certain times and to be with students at particular times, but the rest is up to me.

As a result, there is no typical day in my life. Nor is there a typical week for that matter. For example, even though I have to discharge my responsibilities to patients and students on certain days of the week or during certain hours of the day, the balance of my week may be taken up with work on committees, administrative tasks, professional organization duties, or research. What I do varies from day to day, and it's accurate to say that variety is the spice of life for me.

Clinical faculty members at my school wear four hats: They must have the combined skills of educator, practitioner, researcher, and service provider. As clinical educators, we do not center our work around traditional stand-up lectures, although we do deliver some of those. We have a much broader mandate: We are charged with teaching students how to apply their professional knowledge in actual patient care settings. We teach them to be patient advocates for medication therapy as we seek to optimize the therapy and minimize the adverse effects.

As practitioners, we are involved actively in patient care. We're not ivory-tower people who sit in an academic environment, writing about how patients respond to drug therapy, or about toxicities that are evident. Instead we work directly with patients: we actually *use* the drugs. As a result, we know how they work – and how they don't work. We see first-hand the real concerns patients have.

As researchers, we confront issues in patient care settings, and we design and conduct studies to resolve them. Why does a patient fail to respond to a particular drug? Why are certain lab test values altered when a particular drug is given? In addressing these questions, we design the research, we get necessary funding, and then we carry out the study. I find great enjoyment in the researcher's role.

The service aspect of a clinical faculty member's life is broad. We provide service to our profession and our university or statewide community through leadership and insight into issues that will determine where pharmacy is going or where, ultimately, it needs to go.

I enjoy wearing the different hats in the clinical faculty wardrobe. Of course, I can have good and bad days with each of them. But the flexibility I have to switch from one to the other is rare in most fields. It's the challenge of balancing all those roles that makes my job exciting.

If I had to name one thing that is most important to me professionally, it is the opportunity I have to combine the teacher's role with patient care. It's exciting to take pharmacy students who have spent years sitting in a classroom – who have never seen drug therapy at work – and give them their first significant contact with patients. Once students are able to see the knowledge they gain in class applied in real situations, they do not quickly forget it.

Unfortunately, my administrative duties as a program coordinator prevent me from dealing as directly with students as I used to. Frustrating as that may be, I do enjoy being able to organize the whole system and make it work. Wearing my administrative hat, I am expected to provide direction for experiential education at our school, to determine where it should be going, and how to make certain we maintain a top-quality program. In addition to these responsibilities, I still maintain a practice in rheumatology, and I still conduct my own research.

With all the chores and obligations in academia, burnout is a common problem among educators, and certainly it can be a problem in clinical education. Fortunately, clinical pharmacy professors have so much variety in their jobs that I think they have a better chance of avoiding it. For a period of time, focus may be on patient care. Then it shifts to research. Soon it will shift again – say, to teaching or committee work. Not infrequently, the educator-practitioner finds himself juggling several projects all at once, but those variations make our work fun and rewarding. For most of us, there simply isn't time to get bored, let alone burn out.

One of the greatest rewards in academia has to be the recognition we get for our contributions, whether they be in scholarly matters, research, publishing, or just day-to-day successes in teaching. In my view, recognition by my students and my colleagues is the best of all rewards.

Because this is a relatively new field, and because it's possible that a more standardized PharmD degree will someday be required for all pharmacists, there is a tremendous amount of opportunity in academia. In many programs, the experiential component of the degree will be expanded from the current three-to-six-month period to full-year programs. And because this will double the requirement for one-to-one instruction, all of our existing manpower will be tapped. Clearly, this will require us to develop creative ways to provide instruction, and it will require additional clinical educator-practitioners.

The people who make the best educators in a clinical field are those who have good communication skills and who enjoy working with patients and with other health care professionals. These educators are never satisfied with their knowledge. Indeed, they become relentlessly inquisitive. They are forever analytical, always looking at therapy situations and data, asking "Does this make sense? How does it relate to the patient's response to drug therapy?" To me, this inquisitive impulse that inspires them to search for more information is more important than anything else.

These same qualities apply not only in teaching and patient care, but also in research. The person with what I call the mentality of a two-year-old – the person who is always exploring and searching – makes the best clinical practitioner and researcher. Like children, these practitioner-researchers look at the world with fresh eyes, as if they have never seen it before. The person who can communicate the importance of those traits, and wants to serve as a model for students, makes the best educator.

Self-discipline is an essential character trait of a clinical educator. Without it, things just don't get accomplished, because most of us have the freedom to set our own schedules for doing things. As a result, the clock can actually be our worst enemy since we do have project deadlines – deadlines that we have set for ourselves. Indeed, the biggest challenge for me is knowing where to be when and juggling my responsibilities to make sure they are performed effectively.

I suppose I chose a career in academia because I enjoy patient care, I like to learn, and I like to teach. I waited until my last year of pharmacy school before deciding which area of the profession was for me. By then, I had worked as a student pharmacy technician in a hospital. There I had a chance to work directly with patients and to associate with pharmacists who were doing what I considered exciting work. They were deeply involved in patient care.

However, it still is possible to teach at the preceptor level without a doctorate. Indeed, I don't think this will change, because there is going to be an increasing need for quality preceptors who maintain active practices, solving drug-related problems in patient care settings rather than in the classroom. Some preceptors hold only a BS degree, and some have a doctorate. Some may not have completed residencies or fellowships. For all, their practices are the focus of their professional lives. The teaching they do is mostly on a clerkship level and is supplemented by occasional lectures. These practitioner-educators are responsible for much of the one-to-one learning experiences that students receive in pharmacy schools.

In order to become a full-time faculty member at a school of pharmacy, a PharmD degree is essential. Moreover, it is becoming obvious that even after a student has earned a doctorate, more education will be required. For example, a residency is necessary for specialized training in a particular area. Beyond that, fellowship training is important for those who want to refine their research skills. Currently, not all programs require candidates to have residency and fellowship training. However, there is definitely a move afoot to make them mandatory. In my opinion, both are critical in giving students a foundation that will enable them to flourish in an academic setting.

263

I predict that in the future the faculties of pharmacy schools will have a growing need for what we call clinical scientists, people who have earned not only doctor of pharmacy degrees, but also PhD degrees in clinical sciences. Here at Wisconsin, we offer a combination PharmD/PhD degree that builds a strong theoretical framework that will allow recipients to analyze and conduct top-quality research.

If you choose to become an educator-practitioner, I offer my congratulations. Your clinical involvement will be dynamic and rewarding, and your opportunities will be nearly unlimited. You may experience frustrations as you seek to establish your academic and clinical niche, but these will certainly be balanced by the freedom and independence you'll find in this corner of the profession.

You will never be bored, I promise.

The Pharmacist in Education and Research

George R. Spratto, PhD,
is associate dean for professional programs
and professor of pharmacology,
and
Robert K. Chalmers, PhD,
is Bucke Professor of Pharmacy Practice in the
School of Pharmacy at Purdue University.

Perhaps no other job in pharmacy has as far reaching an effect as that of an educator. In academia, one can excite young people about pharmacy and lay the groundwork for continuing advances in the field. Although education's traditional tools (lectures, assignments, and exams) have not been abandoned, educators now realize that for many students competition for high grades sometimes supersedes the goal of mastering a subject and its applications. To shift the emphasis back to true learning, teachers now encourage more hands-on experience in the lab, in recitations, and in the field. Another stimulus to learning is feedback: By becoming more like coaches in their response to students, educators can encourage students to apply and interrelate their learning. In addition, peer evaluation is being recognized as a useful way of helping students assess their performance.

It is exciting to watch a student decide on a career path and mature professionally. As faculty members progress in their career, inevitably they are asked to take on more administrative duties for program leadership. Despite this additional involvement, we cannot imagine not having some teaching responsibilities.

For most educators, the link with students is their touchstone to reality. This interaction is both pleasant and challenging. In academia, educators cannot simply sit back and be satisfied with the status quo. They have to keep up with their subject. One thing is certain in teaching: Working with students keeps us feeling young.

Another source of satisfaction is research, which goes hand in hand with teaching duties at most universities. Pharmacy educators are expected to get involved in scholarly activities, such as research and publication of research findings. Much has been written about the pressure on educators to perform extensive research and, in many instances, the pressures are great. Still, students who are considering a career in education should realize that research has many facets and may encompass more than working in a laboratory with test tubes or animals. In fact, much important research is done by individuals who never enter a laboratory.

Many researchers strive to find better ways to teach and to evaluate the effectiveness of educational innovations. Others study such contemporary aspects of pharmacy administration as cost containment and the impact of managed care. Moreover, research into systems for monitoring therapy and drug integration will always be necessary.

Only rarely does research lead to award-winning discoveries. Nevertheless, there are great rewards in knowing that one's work may improve understanding of the action of drugs and chemicals and increase awareness of the general practice of pharmacy.

The availability of positions in academia is variable. Yet, as is true in every profession, if students have high standards and a good work ethic, they will find jobs. This isn't to say that opportunities are unlimited. Nevertheless, bright new doctoral-level faculty members will almost certainly find interesting areas in which to work.

It is difficult to predict what will happen to prospects in academia in the future. In the past, when forecasters saw few opportunities, there turned out to be an abundance. The converse has also happened. Even so, it is doubtful that the opportunities that presented themselves to pharmacy educators during the 1960s and 1970s will be seen again. Still, there will surely be a continuing need for teacher-researchers in both pharmacy and medical schools.

Why would a pharmacist choose to be a teacher instead of a practitioner? There is no simple answer to that question, and many young people forge careers that incorporate both options.

Pharmacists who succeed in academia and research are outgoing and well organized. They must be able to communicate well, both orally and in writing. Innovation marks their efforts as teachers and researchers, and they also will have learned to admit when they are wrong. In this field, the ability to think critically, make decisions, and work collaboratively are as important for professional success as knowledge of one's subject.

Though academia offers faculty members a great many advantages, including the freedom to work independently on research, instruct students, and become involved with professional organizations, it does have its shortcomings.

One is that salaries in academia probably will never equal those in industry. Consulting, as long as it doesn't interfere too much with academic duties, is one way to make up the difference. Moreover, many educators believe that the disparity in earnings is balanced by the cultural activities and other advantages of life in academia.

The university structure can be cumbersome and frustrating, especially when politics come into play. In this setting, we must deal with the upper administration and its impact on such crucial areas as project funding and faculty promotions. Also, the emphasis of a school of pharmacy – its objectives and where it fits into the university at large – may be subject to various influences.

The person who wants a nine-to-five job with a great deal of predictability should not expect to find happiness in the university setting. Indeed, the demands of academic activities eliminate any possibility of a 40-hour week. Most educators are at work from 8 AM to 5 PM, but they are likely to return in the evening or work at home.

Faculty burnout is a problem in any university. Although this has been addressed in other areas of academia, we are only now beginning to deal with it in pharmacy. All too often faculty members don't realize they're suffering from this syndrome until it is too late. Usually, the most pronounced symptom is declining productivity.

One way colleges try to alleviate the problem is by offering time away from work in the form of sabbaticals. These are usually six- to 12-month periods of study, training, and writing and are designed to encourage the development of new professional perspectives and skills. As costly as sabbaticals are, both in time and money, most universities are willing to underwrite the expense for valuable faculty members.

Goals should be set and evaluated regularly in academia. This will help faculty members see where they are going and identify the difficulties they are experiencing in meeting those goals.

Though not all teacher-researchers are drawn to administration, this area is full of opportunity. Administrative positions range from department head to dean to academic vice president. In the purely academic realm, one can advance through the ranks from assistant professor to associate professor to full professor.

To follow any of these paths, a PhD or PharmD degree is almost mandatory. In addition, because events change so rapidly these days, anyone contemplating an academic career should develop the practice of keeping up to date with the pharmaceutical literature and the latest developments in teaching methodology. For example, today's academic world is governed by two trends: an emphasis on student ability outcomes and on faculty effectiveness outcomes. Much effort is being applied to developing meaningful ways to document and evaluate these academic outcomes.

Most academic positions are advertised by word of mouth, by letters to the department or school where you are getting your graduate degree, and by ads in professional journals. Alternatively, it's possible to look for work through a placement service at a national meeting.

Students should maintain good relations with former professors and employers. You also should take care to develop as a good reputation as possible. Make sure people know that you can get a job done and that you are sensitive to the needs of others.

No matter how you look for a job or where, remember that teaching is a viable and exciting alternative to working in industry, a hospital, or community pharmacy.

The Pharmacist in Science and Research

Jack R. Cole, PhD,
is director of graduate education,
research, and scholarship for the
American Association of Colleges of Pharmacy
in Alexandria, Virginia.
At the time of the interview for this guide,
he was provost and senior vice president for
academic affairs at the University of Arizona.

When I was a pharmacy student at the University of Arizona, I was asked to work with a professor on his research projects and to help teach some lower-level courses I had already completed. I enjoyed both activities so much that as graduation approached, I knew I had found my niche in pharmacy. I also knew I needed to obtain a PhD, at that time the necessary qualification for a career in research or academia.

In 1957, I completed my doctoral work at the University of Minnesota. Almost every day since then I have looked forward to going to work because my duties as researcher, professor, and administrator have provided endless stimulation. It is hard for me to imagine a more rewarding environment than the university setting.

Pharmacists who are interested in research can find challenging opportunities in industry, government, and research institutes, and many of my students have done so. However, usually only in a university can research activities be combined with the opportunity to teach. The decision to seek that opportunity is mostly a matter of individual preference; but, in my case, fate played a part.

As I was finishing my last year of graduate study, the University of Arizona asked if I would return as a faculty member. The idea appealed to me, so I worked hard to finish ahead of schedule. I started my career as an assistant professor that January.

In time, I became an associate professor and then a full professor. My research projects began to build and, eventually, I developed a research group that was funded continuously by government and industry for 31 years. It could have gone on longer had I not become increasingly involved in higher administration.

On average, the research team included 15 people – six PhD candidates, three or four postdocs, a couple of technicians, and several undergraduates. In addition, we had a number of support staff because of the continual need to publish results and prepare grant proposals. Some of my colleagues had larger teams – 50 or 60 people or more – but I preferred a smaller number. With 12 to 15 people, I felt I was better able to maintain personal interaction. Also, that made it easier for me to teach my classes, attend meetings, and take part in extracurricular activities. In short, I believed that a small team made it easier for me to share my knowledge with the group and learn from them as well.

I was fortunate because my group was quite competitive, and we received a number of grants. Our major project was supported by the National Cancer Institute (NCI). We were looking for new cancer drugs from plant sources. Other researchers and I were the contractors, and the NCI would assign us plants to investigate. We would meet periodically to discuss details of each other's plants.

In the end, we found a number of chemical compounds that were potentially valuable. Some of the compounds were found to be useful against cancers in experimental animals. We believe we made a number of contributions to science, and that, to a great extent, drives us all.

Researchers have been saying for years that it is getting tougher and tougher to secure funding. This may be true, but if researchers have good ideas and present them intelligently, they can be successful. In fact, at the University of Arizona, research dollars increased about 15 percent every year until the time I left last year. Funds are available every year, but not always enough in every area of interest. I believe that pharmacy programs now have such high standards and produce such high-quality people that graduates who pursue careers in research ought to be able to compete effectively for funding. Most of them do.

Researchers who have the educational background, the facilities, and the ideas usually get funded the first time they apply. It is not terribly difficult because there are many new investigator programs, and review panels are always looking for promising new investigators.

Once funding has been granted, you must prove you are worth the investment. Nevertheless, if your ideas are sound and you can prove it with experimental data, you should be able to maintain funding. The fact that I received my first grant within two years after I earned my PhD and had continuous funding until I became provost in 1990 does not necessarily indicate brilliance on my part. Those facts just mean that I had some good ideas and was willing to work hard. As is true in most endeavors, when those attributes are coupled with the ability to work with people, success usually follows.

Somewhere along the line, I was asked whether I would be interested in administration. At first, I said no, because I was enjoying teaching and research. However, administrators have a way of appealing to one's sense of community, and they suggested that my efforts could improve the educational programs of students while helping faculty develop and enhance their research programs. In other words, I was co-opted into administration.

The goals in administration are the same as those in teaching and research. However, the mechanism by which they are achieved is different. A faculty member and research director will be deeply immersed in teaching undergraduates and, perhaps, graduate students. When these duties are added to those of supervising dissertations and research activities and directing a research staff, the result is a demanding full-time job. Of course, those who are successful at this also will be busy presenting their work, consulting to government and industry, and serving on study sections that review grant proposals. There won't be many free moments in their days.

But it's possible to get caught up in the challenges of administration and discover that one actually can make a difference. I also discovered that if you do a good job, someone at the next level will be watching, thinking, "Well, if he did a reasonably good job for the department, maybe he could do a good job for the college. If he did a reasonably good job for the college, maybe he could do a good job for the university." And so on.

As a result of that reasoning, by 1991 I had experienced almost every job at the University of Arizona (including a short stint as acting president when the president had surgery), so I decided it was time to move on. The American Association of Colleges of Pharmacy (AACP) offered me a position that provides new challenges and allows me to maintain my interest in research and higher education. As director of graduate education, research, and scholarship, I hope to be able to help other colleges enhance their graduate and research programs.

In Arizona, we were able to build programs with minimal resources. When I left as dean of the college of pharmacy, it could claim $6 million in grants, up from a few hundred thousand dollars little more than 10 years earlier. During the same period, the number of faculty members had increased from a dozen to 40. The PharmD degree had replaced the bachelor's degree, and we occupied a brand-new building of our own, complete with all the latest technology. Of course, the economics and the times were different then than now, but I believe there are still opportunities to do many of these things.

There is no doubt that opportunities in the pharmaceutical sciences are excellent. Our society is in dire need of additional medicines. Unfortunately, too few pharmacists are interested in education and research. Perhaps we have done too good a job leading students toward the practice of pharmacy, which offers excellent professional and economic rewards. Today, it is difficult for students to trade those immediate benefits for three to four years of additional study when the financial payoff is likely to be a lower starting salary.

The bad news is that unless more students enter this field, we will soon have a shortage of professionals who are capable of developing new drugs or, for that matter, of teaching pharmacy students.

There is a disparity between the short-term financial rewards available to academic researchers and the compensation of pharmacists who enter practice at graduation. But in time, the researcher-educator will catch up and even take the lead as success brings promotions and higher salaries.

Before making your final career decisions, I urge you to talk with faculty at your school who are interested in clinical science research as well as basic science. Ask about their work, and ask them to describe the financial and humanitarian rewards they experience. Observe their enthusiasm over the contributions they are making to the profession, coupled with the pleasures of their association with highly talented and motivated colleagues and students. This may persuade you that the university setting offers the best of all pharmacy worlds.

Careers in Clinical Pharmacy

William A. Miller, PharmD, FCCP,
is professor and chairman of the department of
hospital pharmacy practice and administration
at the Medical University of South Carolina
in Charleston,
and
Robert M. Elenbaas, PharmD, FCCP,
is executive director of the American College
of Clinical Pharmacy
in Kansas City, Missouri.

The future of pharmacy and pharmaceutical care lies in clinical pharmacy. This may seem like a bold statement, but it reflects changes that are taking place in pharmacy and throughout the nation's health care system. To understand the evolution of clinical pharmacy as the standard for pharmacy practice instead of a specialized exception, it is helpful to consider exactly what clinical practice entails.

In simple terms, clinical pharmacy practices have four basic elements. They are patient focused, the practitioners are drug therapy experts, practices take place in an interdisciplinary environment, and pharmacy clinicians have access to patients' charts and histories. This is far different from the common stereotype of the pharmacist as a dispenser. Clinical pharmacists still handle and prepare prescriptions or drug orders, but the vast majority of their time is spent performing such cognitive services as formal consults for medical staff, exploring therapy solutions, and monitoring treatments. Moreover, clinical pharmacists provide a wide range of drug information services and education for physicians, nurses, patients, and even patients' families.

Over the last few years, clinical pharmacy has emerged as a vital component in numerous care settings. The heightened awareness of services a highly trained pharmacist can provide in this field has produced distinct career tracks: general clinical practice, specialty clinical practice, academically based practice, and research-based practice.

Most practitioners who provide services in small and mid-sized hospitals, long-term care facilities, ambulatory care centers, home health care settings, and similar environments tend to have a broad-based practice and expertise. Theirs can be a very demanding career track because of the range of therapeutics, conditions, and patient populations they encounter. Like practitioners who have chosen a more narrow focus, they work as members of multidisciplinary teams and are responsible and accountable for the outcomes of drug therapy.

Some pharmacists have focused their professional practice on a single specialty, disease state, or patient population. Areas of professional concentration read like a medical index, including cardiology, critical care, infectious disease, oncology, pediatrics, psychiatry, organ transplantation, and dozens of other choices. Specialized practices usually are found in large medical centers or university hospitals, where clinical pharmacists work as members of multidisciplinary teams and, along with the cognitive services listed above, are responsible for therapeutic recommendations, dosing adjustments, monitoring, and outcomes.

Every pharmacy student is familiar with academically based practitioners, because these clinicians bring their practice experience directly to the classroom. Often, they bring their students to their practice experiences. Together with the classroom instruction they provide, most academic clinicians serve as instructors during clerkships and residencies. Most universities require these clinicians to remain active in practice and to participate in research projects. In fact, many clinicians have faculty appointments with academic responsibilities. For instance, a specialty practitioner also may be a university professor, with clerkship and residency teaching responsibilities. The same may be true of a researcher, who instructs students in their laboratory work or internships.

Research-based practices in hospitals and universities also tend to be extremely focused. In these practices, the patient's bedside is often an important part of the researcher's laboratory. These pharmacists strive to improve existing treatments, apply individualized treatments to rare or unique cases, and help pioneer new therapies. Generally, researchers choose their areas of specialty and paths of inquiry, but their work is not performed in a vacuum. In fact, physicians, nurses, pharmacists, other health care professionals – and patients themselves – play crucial roles in the research process. Outside the hospital environment, clinical researchers work for contract research firms or pharmaceutical manufacturers, where they frequently concentrate on development and testing of new products, postmarketing surveillance, and providing drug information. Their work is diverse and may focus less on specific patient populations or conditions and more on how therapies perform.

Clinical pharmacy career paths are by no means limited to these areas. Indeed, because these pharmacists are so highly skilled, they develop a high degree of creativity and adaptability. Consequently, they can be found working in ambulatory care, consulting, drug development, community settings, and sales.

Regardless of where they practice, the success of clinical practitioners depends on particular abilities and attributes. Certainly, skills in relating to people are important because, to be effective, clinical pharmacists must be able to influence patients' understanding of and compliance with drug therapy. Because clinicians almost always are members of a health care team, they also must be comfortable interacting with professionals from a variety of other health care disciplines. And apart from the day-to-day cognitive services they provide, the clinical pharmacists often must make educational presentations to their teams, other health professionals, and administrators.

Even practitioners who are comfortable with people may lack good communication skills. In fact, many people interact well with others and are experts in their field, but find it difficult to communicate what they know. Being articulate is essential, but to be truly effective a clinician must be able to explain processes and treatments to people who lack depth of knowledge. For instance, one would not explain the characteristics of an antihypertensive drug to a cardiology nurse in the same terms as to a recovering MI patient. Similarly, a clinician may know of a better therapy than has been recommended by the attending physician. Conveying this information without challenging the physician's abilities, or those of anyone else on the team, requires a certain sensitivity. Finally, one of the most important and overlooked elements of effective communication is the ability to listen. So much of what the clinical pharmacist learns about a patient's condition and treatment comes from verbal description, either by the patient or a caregiver. However, for one reason or another, such observations often don't find their way into patients' charts. Listening to what is said and understanding what is meant is as much a part of communication in a clinical setting as being able to articulate one's own thoughts.

Clinicians must have good problem-solving abilities. They face different scenarios each day. Even in the academic setting, students may ask questions or encounter situations that the professor has never considered before. In such circumstances, there is not always a clear path or protocol to follow. In each setting, the pharmacist must balance strong pharmacokinetic and drug information knowledge with reason, common sense, and what can be observed. Pharmacists must be able to think on their feet and apply their knowledge even in unfamiliar situations and under the pressure of time.

What kind of training and education prepares the clinical pharmacist for this demanding environment? Certainly, a PharmD degree is required by most employers. And because clinicians are accountable for their patients' drug therapy, residency training is also advisable as a means to further develop clinical practice, communication, problem-solving, and patient care skills in a "real world" environment. In addition, pharmacists who wish to concentrate their clinical practice in an area such as cardiology, infectious disease, or psychiatry will want to complete a specialty residency. Individuals interested in a career in clinical research can develop the requisite knowledge and skills in a research fellowship.

In the last few years, three areas of clinical pharmacy practice have been officially recognized by the Board of Pharmaceutical Specialties as pharmacy practice specialties: pharmacotherapy, nutrition support, and psychopharmacy. Other practice areas are certain to gain specialty recognition over the next several years. Pharmacists planning to pursue a career as clinical practitioners should seek certification in a specialty appropriate to their practice. All of this most certainly lengthens the pharmacist's formal education, but if it takes a dozen or more years to acquire the skills of a physician, it surely takes more than four or five years to become a true drug therapy expert.

The concept of pharmaceutical care describes a practice model in which the pharmacist is seen as a drug therapy expert who provides services that are essentially cognitive. In other words, it highlights the pharmacist's clinical responsibilities. This model moves pharmacists from a passive role to a more active one in which we have responsibility for ensuring the appropriateness of drug therapy. There are several reasons for this role change. One is that it produces quantifiable increases in the effectiveness and efficiency of care. Another is that it reduces the cost of drug therapy. Moreover, increasing pharmacists' responsibility cuts the incidence of drug morbidity or mortality.

This model has been evolving for decades in hospital pharmacy practices. Indeed, nearly every hospital in the nation has moved or is moving to reduce its pharmacists' dispensing duties while increasing the cognitive services they provide. Clinical practice is an increasing reality in the retail setting.

We see this as a very positive change, because many students want to practice in a community setting. And no matter what the setting, all students want to use their skills to help patients. Herein lies the basic appeal of clinical pharmacy: Its practitioners end each day knowing that their skills and knowledge have been actively used to improve patient care.

Darwin E. Zaske, PharmD, FCCP,
is director of pharmaceutical services
at St. Paul-Ramsey Medical Center, and a
professor at the University of Minnesota
College of Pharmacy.

A Career in Clinical Research

Questions are a part of every pharmacist's daily experience. On-the-spot problem solving produces answers to many, and the literature will answer others. But some remain unresolved, leaving the pharmacist no choice but to move on.

Clinical research pharmacists are challenged with finding answers to some of the more difficult questions that present themselves. And it goes without saying that their efforts can produce benefits on a variety of levels. Not only does research improve – sometimes dramatically – the quality of patient care, it also enables pharmacists to execute therapy decisions at a higher level. As a result, the pharmacist's value to the health care team increases.

A clinical research pharmacist must have a deep foundation of knowledge. The cornerstone of this foundation is usually a good PharmD program. Of course, "good" is relative to one's goals, but in this case it signifies a program that requires intensive study of pharmacokinetics, drug information, and pathophysiology, with emphasis on the relationships between pharmacokinetics and pathophysiology. Though clinical researchers must be familiar with the theories and projected outcomes of various treatments, we do not operate in a vacuum. Instead, we work with actual patients who have real symptoms and conditions, some of which don't appear in textbooks.

Consequently, it's important to choose a PharmD program that has an established clinical component. In addition, any patient care experience the student can get will be useful. Beyond that, the successful clinical researcher must be self-motivated, determined, and capable of pursuing a question doggedly. Yet despite these characteristics of independence, the researcher must appreciate the importance of teamwork.

Strong clinical skills permit the clinical research pharmacist to identify aspects of patient care problems that warrant further study. Our work demands a strong grasp of the ways in which pathophysiological and pharmacokinetic components interact, because this enables the pharmacist to assess a patient's degree of illness. Then it facilitates the process of determining appropriate therapy. Finally, clinical expertise allows us to monitor patients and interpret their response to drug treatments.

What other skills are needed?

The ability to communicate clearly is vital in this field because it's necessary to work closely with physicians and nurses. In this setting, effective pharmacists know how to present their abilities in a way that adds to the efficacy of therapy without compromising the concept of teamwork. Communication skills also come into play when we make presentations about new drugs or therapeutic approaches, and when we craft written descriptions of our research findings.

The research pharmacist also has to be able to communicate with patients and their families about treatments and procedures. While this must be done with honesty and clarity, it must reflect compassion for the patient's condition and frame of mind.

No physician is going to allow a pharmacist to participate in making decisions about patient care until that pharmacist first establishes credibility with drug information and therapies. This includes knowledge of dosing, therapeutic alternatives, and new drug developments. This reluctance can make the first year of practice a bit tense because the new pharmacist will probably feel he is being constantly tested. However, once others on the health care team learn they can trust their new colleague, acceptance and support – and full responsibility – soon follow.

Acquiring this experience takes time. If a pharmacist fresh out of a PharmD program intends to study a specialized patient population, it may take a year or more before research opportunities present themselves. Pharmacists who want work in a more generalized area may need two years of experience. There is no set formula for progress because it finally comes down to an individual's experience and willingness to put in the time, day after day.

For the most part, my own experience demonstrates these realities. After graduating from a PharmD program in 1973, I began a clinical practice in which I worked extensively with burn victims. As the physicians came to know me better and realized what I could provide as a pharmacist, and as I became more confident in my abilities, I was given a voice in patient care decisions. Almost from my first day on the job, I saw situations in which I thought investigation into regimens or drug applications could produce benefits for our patients. However, more than a year passed before I acquired enough experience to gain the confidence of my colleagues. Only then could I begin initiating research projects.

I was drawn to this work because I am inquisitive by nature and enjoy applying systematic methodology in finding reasonable, quantifiable solutions to problems in patient care. Unlike many other professional activities in pharmacy, clinical research offers an almost unlimited amount of subject material and ideas to pursue. One can study specific treatments, dosage questions, regimens, outcomes, drug delivery systems, dynamics of drug response, adverse reactions, or a variety of other topics. Best of all, it is difficult to sustain boredom in research. There are endless hypotheses to test, and once the researcher begins answering one question, almost instantly two or three new ones are generated.

In the beginning of my career, I was lucky to have had experience helping perform ongoing research projects as a PharmD candidate. Some programs still allow students to have such exposure, but this is less true than it used to be. I believe clinical research is a natural extension of clinical practice. As a result, I think it should be cultivated along with clinical skills in PharmD programs.

If you are interested in the field, then it will be to your advantage to seek ways to work on research projects. Try to find investigators who will allow you to work with them on a part-time or for-credit volunteer basis. This really is a different culture and interested students should be exposed to it as deeply as possible.

One of my first research projects began about a year after I started clinical practice. My focus was on burn victims, specifically on their response to treatment for ecthyma gangrenosum, an insidious, deadly infection that was not uncommon among these patients. The infection occurred for two reasons. First, the extreme damage to the skin created an environment in which it is relatively easy for infection to develop. Second, because of the way burns traumatize the body, the effectiveness of the immune system is dramatically reduced. This reduces the body's ability to fend off infections, especially such bacterial types as gangranosa. Unchecked, the infection can spread to organs throughout the body, killing the patient in just a few days.

There was an established treatment for this infection, but it had little or no effect in our burn patients. In fact, once the infection had taken hold, there was an almost 100-percent mortality rate. A study of the patients' serum concentrations revealed that the drug was exiting the body so rapidly that it was unable to produce a therapeutic impact. We initiated a study that sought to combat this by dramatically increasing dosages in order to achieve a target serum value. Careful serum analysis would tell us how much of the drug was being absorbed by the body.

We saw positive results almost immediately. Then, by fine tuning dosage levels (in some cases up to six times the recommended dosages) we were able to convert the near 100-percent mortality rate to an 80-percent survival rate. The study lasted nearly two years before it produced a publishable procedure that could be employed in other institutions.

A research pharmacist's work need not be confined to a specific area. Indeed, because of my success with the gangrenosum study, the head of our pediatric neurology department contacted me about a problem being seen in premature infants. These patients were highly susceptible to convulsions. There was an established therapy for convulsions, but here, too, the condition of these babies seemed to negate positive outcomes. Moreover, there had been almost no study of convulsion therapy for neonates. After examining case histories and holding detailed discussions with the physician, we hypothesized that the effectiveness of therapy might be increased through dosage changes.

It took nearly three years to generate significant evidence that, in neonates, the initial absorption rate of this drug was lower than in adults or even older infants. Consequently, by increasing the loading doses and then scaling back to maintenance doses we were able to manage the convulsions. Even though I wasn't especially expert in pediatric pharmacy, my clinical skills and background in research enabled me to complete the neonate study successfully.

In all of my clinical research the primary laboratory site is the patient's bedside because I believe that only direct observation of patients' responses can produce the quantitative data that constitute accurate findings. Certainly, the work of clinical researchers requires a great deal of work in actual laboratories, but in this field, everything must revolve around the patient.

The knowledge gained through research studies has practical applications that can be used in the classroom. That's why many clinical pharmacists have practices that are tied in some degree to academia. But for pharmacists who aren't drawn to university life, there are significant opportunities in manufacturing and with contract research firms.

As the researcher's career advances, opportunities for administrative work will present themselves. Perhaps that is true because clinical investigation sharpens one's ability to make decisions and to think quantitatively. Both of these skills are important in management.

If it sounds as though I am describing the perfect career, let me offer some caveats. Rarely do significant events happen on schedule; often, they don't even happen during normal practice hours. As a result, clinical research can place tremendous demands on the pharmacist's time, requiring frequent sacrifices of personal activities. Also, there are plenty of opportunities for anxiety over whether a hypothesis is correct and whether a chosen project is the best way to spend valuable time. Imagine the frustration of working for months, only to discover that a hypothesis was flawed.

The tension can be terrific at times, especially when working with infections that can kill patients quickly. Time is not the clinical researcher's ally, and problems are almost never resolved quickly.

For all those drawbacks, this is a wonderful field whose practitioners have great influence on patient care. In addition, the financial compensation is good, and there's plenty of opportunity for professional and personal growth. Above all else, we are able to make a real difference in the quality of therapy – and in people's lives. What could be more rewarding than that?

James Cloyd, PharmD, FCCP,
is associate professor and head of the
department of pharmacy practice at the
University of Minnesota College of Pharmacy.
He also is a clinical pharmacist in the
Minnesota Comprehensive Epilepsy Program.

Clinical Pharmacy in Academia

For me, practicing academically based clinical pharmacy is the best job in the world. In a single day, I can go from the clinic to the laboratory to the classroom. At each site, I practice a different aspect of pharmacy and have ample opportunities to influence drug therapy and improve patient care. In the clinic, I apply what I've learned through my studies, research, and other practice experiences. Through research and teaching I improve my therapeutic skills and, I hope, the skills of others. I am in a position to take questions and problems that come up in practice or the classroom and submit them to rigorous investigation. I stay busy and have what, for me, is a satisfying blend of responsibilities.

Teaching clinical pharmacy allows me to empower students in two important ways. First, in passing on information and guiding students, I am participating in the age-old tradition of helping instill a foundation of knowledge. There are few things more rewarding than the realization that my students will go on to become pharmacists and make meaningful contributions to society.

My work as a clinical pharmacist enables me to share experience with students. This may seem like a simplification, but not long ago few if any faculty in pharmacy schools practiced actively. That circumstance may have resulted in adequate education when pharmacists were restricted mainly to dispensing activities, but that era is ending. More and more, today's pharmacists are required to make important cognitive contributions, especially in providing safe, effective, and economical drug therapy. It is here that the clinical academic pharmacist shines, because we are experienced in the real world and deal regularly with patients, evaluating their treatments and solving problems as they occur.

What is taught in clinical pharmacy cannot be learned by rote. In fact, the beauty of this field is that it is evolving so rapidly. For example, if I taught today the lessons and examples I used 10 years ago, the material would be uselessly out of date. Clinical pharmacy preceptors don't carry around those yellowed lecture notes that often are associated with many faculty lecturers. This is because changes happen so fast that we have to rewrite our presentations every year and, sometimes, every semester. As fundamental developments take place, whether in molecular biology, genetics, physiology, or dozens of other areas, they must be incorporated into our coursework.

A continuing challenge for me is trying to enhance the learning process. In a broad sense, students come to pharmacy school to learn about drugs and drug therapy – why medications work and how they can be made to work safely and more effectively. However, within this general area, every student has individual expectations, learning styles, attitudes. It is my job to help each student get the most out of the learning experience. The rapport between faculty member and student has to be a positive one in which both individuals are moving toward a common goal. That's the ideal learning environment.

Sometimes, the circumstances under which students learn is less than ideal. For example, in many classes the professor gives a lecture and the student takes notes, hoping to recall the information more or less verbatim on an exam. Not every student is good at learning that way. Those who are not may find themselves in a lot of trouble, at least in the eyes of some instructors. One of the greatest challenges for any teacher is to tailor his efforts to the needs of each student.

The teacher must work rigorously with thought-provoking material. In clerkships and other out-of-the-classroom settings, the demands can be even greater, because learning takes place in the context of actual patient care. Here, circumstances are neither static nor easily controlled. The type of patients being treated, their history and current ailments, the environment, the capabilities of the student on hand – all these elements are subject to change. Working within these parameters requires flexibility and innovative skills. I submit that clinical instruction can be more demanding than classroom work.

Clinical instruction gives students an early view of what they can expect in their future practices. It allows them to gain experience in taking and analyzing medication histories, helping select appropriate drugs, individualizing dosages, evaluating and managing responses and adverse reactions, and helping develop education programs for patients and their families. In general, the patient populations with which they deal are determined by the preceptor's interest. For example, I've worked in neurology for most of my career. In fact, 16 years ago I established what I believe is the country's first clinical pharmacy practice that focuses on epilepsy.

Epilepsy is managed almost entirely through drug therapy. Most of my practice centers on an inpatient unit with refractory patients – those who have been treated with conventional therapy but continue to have seizures. They are admitted to one of our units for a three- to six-week stay during which they undergo a meticulous work-up in an effort to identify their problem. Then we assess their drug therapy in an effort to maximize response and minimize toxicity. The students who accompany me – undergraduate students doing clerkships, PharmD candidates, or post-PharmD fellows – work with this highly specialized population. Along the way, they learn to communicate effectively with patients and other health care professionals. They also learn to work on an interdisciplinary team, and they refine their drug information abilities. All of these are useful skills in clinical practice.

When I am on service, I usually arrive by 7 AM to check on my patients and review the records of new admits. At 8:30, I begin rounds with the physicians and nurses. During rounds or just after, I consult with physicians and make decisions on therapy management. After that, I spend time with my students, supervising them as they interview patients or prepare treatment plan reports. Later, I may do an in-service for physicians or nurses, or lead a medication class for patients.

As is true of most academic clinical pharmacists, my practice is interlocked with research. Over the last 16 years I've had an opportunity to examine a number of interesting questions on the pharmacotherapy of epilepsy and, in some cases, I have had a direct impact on its treatment. For example, 15 years ago valproic acid was introduced in the United States to treat epileptic seizures. The package insert and relevant literature indicated the drug should be given at no more than 30 mg per kilogram of body weight per day and no more often than three times per day. At the time, I worked primarily with children. Yet, when a colleague and I began to use this drug in children, we didn't achieve the results we expected. As a result, we initiated some studies to determine why not. In the process, we discovered important factors that cause children to absorb and eliminate valproic acid differently than adults.

The problem lay not with the drug itself but with the recommended frequency of administration and dosages. We found that children required far higher doses given much more often than had proven effective in adults. Subsequently, we were able to help a number of children with our modified regimen. We published half a dozen papers on our findings.

This example is indicative of how all the elements of a clinical academic pharmacist's practice can evolve. I encountered a problem in my practice that stimulated research. My research led to a positive solution for my patients. The results of my study were passed on to my students at the undergraduate, graduate, and postdoctoral levels. Sometimes the cycle differs. A student's question may initiate research that leads to enhancements in therapy. Or the results of research may inspire a new direction of inquiry that yields a positive outcome for patients. Whatever path these developments follow, none would be possible outside an academically based practice.

Because of the way my practice is set up, I am able to focus my research, patient care, and – to a large extent – my teaching on whatever area interests me. The academic clinical practice also gives me a great deal of flexibility in apportioning my time. For example, during several months of the year I may spend most of my time on patient care and teaching, devoting less time to research. At other times, I may be occupied more with research and patient care, and my teaching duties will diminish. Few jobs in pharmacy afford this much freedom of choice.

For all the positive features, there are negatives to be found in this type of practice. And even though I believe this is the world's best job, not everyone would agree, because the demands of being a good teacher, an effective researcher, and a skilled practitioner can seem overwhelming. However, in my view, one need not be the very best in every area as long as he or she has enough proficiency in each to move comfortably and effectively among all three. Acquiring this proficiency makes it necessary to structure one's career in a way that takes advantage of personal strengths and minimizes weaknesses.

For some people, another negative is that recognition and career advances are rooted in academia's publish-or-perish mandate. Much of one's ability to publish is tied directly to research projects and practice experiences, and obtaining research funding can be a frustrating ordeal. The researcher has to be a little lucky as well as good. And even when funding is found, it may cover such a brief period that it becomes difficult to build a program or hire research assistants or technicians. In this field, it is necessary to rely heavily on collaboration with physicians, nurses, and other pharmacists. If crucial contacts leave, a practitioner can find himself in a position of having to start all over again.

Students sometimes accuse clinical pharmacy faculty members of not being "real world" practitioners. To a certain extent, that is true. We do practice, and we are involved in patient care, but our practice usually is limited to a single disease state. Our patients are similar and certainly do not represent the range that would be seen in community practice or in a hospital.

Finally, there are the disparate demands of practicing in three different areas. Lesson plans and lectures must be prepared. Research activities cannot always be performed on schedules that comfortably accommodate the need to attend meetings, conferences, and classes. There is an endless need to study the literature. Administrative duties can be burdensome, too. For instance, as department head I must chair meetings, make faculty evaluations, and work as a liaison between the faculty and other administrators.

Despite these shortcomings – and every career has some – the positive aspects of my work far outweigh the negatives.

For interested students I recommend a PharmD degree, preferably from a program that offers plenty of clinical experience and a quality faculty for clerkships as well as classroom instruction. I also recommend postdoctoral work in a specialized clinical residency and probably a post-PharmD research fellowship as well. Basically, prerequisites for success include a great deal of self-confidence, an inquiring mind, and a talent for communicating effectively.

Students who meet those requirements can expect to enter a profession that is rapidly changing its orientation from products to patients. Academic clinical pharmacy practice will be in the vanguard of this change, and I can't think of a more exciting place to be.

*Thomas Sisca, PharmD, FCCP,
is a board-certified pharmacotherapy specialist
and director of clinical pharmacy services at
Memorial Hospital, Easton, Maryland.*

Clinical Pharmacy
in a Community Hospital

Many students believe that choosing a clinical hospital career limits the pharmacy professional to two practice options – academic teaching or research. However, there is a third choice, one I've enjoyed for the past 20 years: community hospital-based clinical practice.

A practice like mine offers the individual a chance to work on a critically important health care team. Unlike pharmacists who are based in large hospitals or university facilities where clinical pharmacy tends to be extremely specialized, clinical pharmacists in a community hospital work with a broad range of patients, situations, and health professionals. The result is a fast-paced, dynamic environment where the pharmacist can and often does make a real difference. This environment also can give innovative pharmacists numerous opportunities to grow and expand their practices in ways they probably could not in larger, more specialty-oriented facilities.

My current practice at Memorial Hospital in Easton, Md., is a good example of how a community hospital-based clinical practice can provide opportunities and growth.

I came to Memorial 20 years ago, after completing my BS and PharmD studies at the Philadelphia College of Pharmacy and Science. While I was in those programs, I did rotations and internships in several community hospitals in the Philadelphia area, and I gained experience that gave me great appreciation for community hospital-based practice. I enjoyed the intimacy of 150- to 300-bed facilities. I also liked the fact that the pharmacist was treated as an active participant in the clinical services and care procedures. When I earned my PharmD in 1972, I went to the ASHP placement service in search of a community hospital-based clinical practice. I specifically wanted a practice that concentrated on patient care. I also wanted that practice to be under a hospital's aegis. My reasoning was that if clinical pharmacy was funded by the hospital, there would be administrative and collegial support for what I did. I wanted to focus solely on interacting with my colleagues and patients and did not want to have my practice dependent on a university and teaching duties.

In 1972, clinical pharmacy was in its infancy, and only two or three community hospitals were advertising for clinical pharmacists. The closest was Memorial Hospital. I had never been to Maryland and didn't want to live away from the Philadelphia area. However, I wanted this type of position enough that I pursued an interview at Memorial. As a safety valve, I applied for a clinical residency elsewhere. If the Memorial opportunity wasn't what I wanted, I would still have access to a good career option.

The Memorial job combined the duties of a clinical pharmacist with those of a staff pharmacist on a 60/40 basis. During my interview, I discovered the director had not defined exactly what a clinical pharmacist would do. However, he had recently installed unit-dose and IV-additive systems and knew the next step was to hire a clinical pharmacist. He was also a strong proponent of advancing pharmacy. The interview went well and I received an offer. The director would allow me to define the clinical pharmacist position. In essence, he was going to allow me to spend 60 percent of my time doing whatever I thought the job required. It was a wide-open opportunity, and I couldn't pass it up. I canceled my other applications and moved to Easton.

I immediately began providing drug information services, looking for drug interactions, and monitoring drug therapy. I also reviewed the literature and took medication histories. I offered myself as a specialist who could be a valuable resource in how drugs were prescribed and dispensed to patients. I also offered to accompany the physicians on rounds. This was my vision of what my practice could be at Memorial. However, at the outset, I encountered a conflict in visions.

In the beginning, the physicians I worked with were very uneasy. Most had never worked with a PharmD, so I encountered some strong resistance. The physicians simply didn't understand why a 190-bed facility on the eastern shore of Maryland needed a PharmD when Johns Hopkins and the University of Maryland got along very well without such professionals. Basically, the perception was that the administration must have hired me to reduce the cost of drug therapy. Anything else I tried to do was seen initially as overstepping my bounds as a pharmacist.

For someone like me – fresh out of pharmacy school, working at my first real job – this posed a serious challenge. I decided the best way to handle it was to take a proactive stance and try and show everyone what I could do. This was tricky because if I became too assertive, I would be viewed as pushy or arrogant and I would get nowhere. On the other hand, if I were too passive, I would be shunted off to the side and this would validate the physicians' original perceptions of my position.

I decided my best course of action was to become as visible as possible and let my actions do most of the talking. This meant getting out of the pharmacy as much as possible and working with the physicians. I asked a group of four internists if they would let me make rounds with them every day. Three of the four were not very supportive. Fortunately, the fourth physician was interested and enthusiastic, so I was allowed to go along. Even with his help it wasn't easy.

On the first day, I approached one of the physicians, introduced myself, and held out my hand to shake his. He said, "I know who you are," and turned away. Two of the others were more polite but equally noncommittal. However, the fourth physician took me around with him as if we were established colleagues, and he let me talk with his patients.

Over the next few weeks I made rounds every day. I even came in for rounds on Saturdays and Sundays. The first weekend, one physician asked me why I was there. I said, "Well, you're here making rounds, why shouldn't I be?" After a few weeks my persistence started to pay off, and the other physicians began to accept me and my services.

A month or so later, the next barrier fell when a patient presented with hemolytic anemia. The physician asked me to do a drug history on the man. As it turned out, he was on a medication that is capable of causing hemolytic anemia, and the drug seemed to be the cause. I gave the physician several articles to document the etiology. He went to the chief of surgery and said he wanted to present the case at grand rounds, an all-physicians meeting held every Friday to discuss interesting cases. The internist went a step further and asked if I could present my information as well. I had previously tried to become included in grand rounds but was told that it was no place for a pharmacist. However, at the urging of the internist, an exception was made. I would be allowed to do my part of the presentation, but I would have to leave as soon as I was done.

I went to grand rounds that Friday, gave my presentation – complete with handouts – and then I answered some questions. All together, it took about 15 minutes. When I was done, I left. Later that day I was making my regular rounds with the internists, and they said they really liked my presentation. In fact, everyone was really pleased with the handouts because no one had ever done anything like that before. As we were talking, I looked down the hallway and saw the chief of surgery walking toward us, calling my name. I thought, "Oh boy, here it comes." But he told me he liked my presentation. "I didn't realize you had such a positive contribution to make," he said. "Please come every Friday." After that, I was readily accepted by all the physicians in the facility.

With my credibility established, my practice expanded in its scope. I went from the 60/40 designation to a full-time clinical pharmacist and, eventually, was promoted to director of clinical pharmacy and drug information services.

Today, clinical pharmacy services at Memorial include three distinct components. We still provide drug information, which I believe is completely necessary, but we also have a formal drug protocol service and a formal consult service.

Drug therapy protocols involve active monitoring and prescribing of pharmacotherapy for approximately 75 drugs. For example, if a patient with an acute myocardial infarction presented with ventricular tachycardia, the physician would assess the situation and, perhaps, order a pharmacy protocol for heparin infusion and lidocaine infusion. When the therapy was chosen, we would retain the responsibility for dosing, supervising the lab tests, and monitoring outcomes.

Our service allows us to be considered a formal consultant just like a gastroenterologist or neurologist or any other specialist. This service is utilized when a patient presents with a condition that involves or may involve a drug-related problem. The attending physician requests a consult with our staff to evaluate the patient. We evaluate the patient's history, review the chart, and assess the information. Then we review our drug information resources, examine the literature, do a *Medline* search, and go through our files. Finally, we dictate a formal note and within 24 hours our consult will become part of the patient's chart.

As an example, we recently did a consult for a patient who wasn't responding properly to anticoagulation therapy. The physician asked us to access the patient's therapy for potential drug interactions in order to find out why he wasn't responding. We went through the consult process and discovered that there was indeed an interaction. We recommended a change in therapy, the physician concurred, and the patient soon responded positively.

Consults usually require a 24-hour turnaround time, but sometimes they need to happen quicker. Consequently, we have a pharmacist available on call to perform this service 24 hours a day. Most of our consults are therapy related. They involve such areas as congestive heart failure, pharmacokinetics, adverse effects, infectious disease, and toxicology.

Last year we did 292 formal consults. Of these 175 were therapeutic, 40 were for adverse effects, and the rest were pharmacokinetic- or toxicology-related.

Our protocol service manages approximately 75 different drugs and follows an average of 50 to 55 patients per day. We are involved in the whole drug therapy process – P&T evaluation, prescribing and monitoring the patient's outcome, and monitoring for adverse effects.

Through our affiliation with the University of Maryland School of Pharmacy, the Medical College of Virginia, and the Philadelphia College of Pharmacy and Science, we get fifth-year students and PharmD candidates for rotations, and we sponsor an ASHP-accredited, post-PharmD one-year residency in pharmacy practice.

All of these services demonstrate a tremendous amount of trust and respect by our physicians, nurses, patients, and administrators. They also reflect a natural progression of the professional ties and specialized services which were established early on. Once we were accepted as drug information experts, the physicians saw no reason why we could not perform formal consults. Because some of the first consults involved drug-management issues, it became clear that the next step would be for us to participate in prescribing and monitoring therapy. Then, as therapy became more involved over the years with continuous infusion and more complex pharmacokinetics, it was logical for the pharmacists actually to dose the medications.

What does a student need to pursue a community hospital-based clinical practice? For starters, I recommend a PharmD. A post-PharmD residency in pharmacy practice would also be advantageous. Good problem-solving skills are essential. The practice can be very dynamic and interactive, so practitioners need to be able to solve problems quickly. Communication skills are important, too, because being a poor communicator or saying the wrong thing can really put a damper on essential relationships with physicians, nurses, and patients.

Though starting salaries may be lower in community hospital-based practices than in academic-based practices, the career potential is excellent. There are many small community hospitals in the country, and they provide a fast-paced, interactive environment that encourages practitioners to be creative and innovative. And as my experience proves, they offer no end of challenges and daily opportunities to have a direct impact on patient care and outcomes.

Dorothy A. Wade, RPh,
is vice president for professional relations
at the National Pharmaceutical Council.

Opportunities in the Pharmaceutical Industry

As pharmacy students examine career options in the pharmaceutical industry, most are impressed by the tremendous number of opportunities for professional growth and the variety of positions that are available.

In this chapter I will provide a brief overview of the industry, a breakdown of areas that hold the most interest for pharmacists, and some tips for seeking employment in the industry. I'll also share a bit with you about the path my own career has taken. I hope this chapter contains the information you need to make an initial assessment of your interest in a career within the pharmaceutical industry.

The backbone of innovation in the development of new medicines in our country and throughout the world rests primarily in the research-intensive pharmaceutical companies conducting business in the United States. In addition to this backbone of our industry, there are many other fine manufacturers conducting limited research or simply manufacturing and distributing medicines. This core industry offers ample employment opportunities for the motivated pharmacist who has a particular interest in business, manufacturing, research, or in trade, professional, government, or public relations.

According to the Pharmaceutical Manufacturers Association, our industry spent an estimated $11 billion on research and development of new medicines in 1993. This compares favorably with the whole of the National Institutes of Health's budget for 1993, which was an estimated $9.5 billion. In 1990, the United States pharmaceutical industry employed 320,000 people around the world. Approximately 170,000 of those worked in the United States. It is not certain how many pharmacists are employed in the U.S. pharmaceutical industry, but experts estimate the number is over 6,500 and growing.

Each pharmaceutical company has its own personality and attributes. And because the industry is so diverse, there is no shortage of opportunity for today's pharmacists. If you are interested in forging a career in the industry, your first step should be to conduct some research in order to discover which companies could offer you the most opportunity. There are many avenues to be followed as you look for information about various corporations. You may wish to begin by speaking with pharmaceutical sales representatives (sales representatives often visit schools during recruitment drives), or by discussing company profiles with professors, deans, community pharmacists and physicians, or other health care professionals. You also may want to talk with company employees who can be found working the exhibit areas at national pharmacy meetings; these men and women will happily advise students interested in the industry. For further information, consider writing to a company's headquarters for a copy of its annual report. The National Pharmaceutical Council [1894 Preston White Drive, Reston, VA 22091, (703) 620-6390] will provide a list of addresses for its member companies.

Again, once you have researched the companies' backgrounds you will have a better understanding of those whose activities most closely parallel your own interests. If, for instance, you have a special interest in other cultures and world travel, you may wish to work in the international division of a company with a strong world presence. On the other hand, you may be interested in viral research or, specifically, in a company focusing on AIDS or cancer research. If cardiovascular or metabolic research holds a special appeal for you, learn which companies are strongest in those areas. If you hope to go into sales, you may find one or two companies that are involved in large-scale recruitment of new sales representatives. If your expertise is in pharmaceutics, you may able to gain insight from the American Foundation for Pharmaceutical Education [P.O. Box 7126, North Plainfield, NJ 07060, (908) 561-8077], which can provide information on companies with a current need in that area.

Although it is necessary to prioritize your choices, it is important to include on your list as many companies as possible. This will increase your chances of finding a new employer. Some new graduates would be pleased to work for any reputable manufacturer, and these people will, of course, have the greatest probability of being hired. If your primary goal is to move up the ladder within the pharmaceutical industry, you may consider focusing on getting your foot in a company's door – even if it is not your first choice – in order to begin building your experience base.

Keep in mind that making a satisfactory and challenging match begins with careful research into which companies provide the best opportunities for *you*. And as important as this step is, you must remain flexible and remember that, to a large degree, your success will depend on which companies are hiring at the time you are looking for a position.

More than 60 percent of the industry's pharmacists are involved in sales or marketing. Traditionally, the area of pharmaceutical sales has been a primary entrance point for pharmacists. Indeed, most companies are well disposed to hiring pharmacists as sales or detail representatives because of pharmacists' knowledge of pharmacology, the marketplace in general, and such health care issues as compliance and the cost effectiveness of medicines. From presidents and CEOs on down, most of the industry's leaders started in sales.

Excellent communication skills, interpersonal skills, and a knack for business are requisite qualities for a successful sales representative. Once hired, every sales representative goes through intensive training. A successful tenure in sales will open new opportunities to move up the ladder to the positions of district and regional sales manager.

Marketing is related to sales, but is more focused on the development of programs that promote and track product sales. A logical move from sales to marketing would be for a district sales manager to come into headquarters as a product manager and, later, to be promoted to director of marketing or sales.

Marketing activities include market research, product management, advertising, promotion, and pricing. In some companies, professional and trade-relations activities also fall within the marketing department's purview. Pharmacists who have served in sales for a number of years often move to marketing as their career goals broaden. As former sales representatives, these men and women bring with them an important understanding of the needs of customers, including those of community pharmacists, formulary committees, government purchasers, and managed care administrators.

Students interested in research are appropriate candidates to enter the industry. Although bench scientists with no more than BS degrees can find opportunity in the pharmaceutical industry, those with advanced degrees are almost certain to move upward more rapidly. The applied basic sciences – pharmaceutical chemistry, pharmacology, drug metabolism and toxicology – all can lead to entry-level jobs through which the pharmacist can begin an involvement in conducting basic research.

The areas of pharmaceutical formulation (tests on a medicine's chemistry, stability, and final dosage form) and clinical research are natural progressions for researchers who want to expand their horizons within a company. Clinical research in animals and, especially, in humans is a critical aspect of drug testing, and these areas offer interesting opportunities to pharmacists.

For exceptional students with a strong interest in research, the National Pharmaceutical Council (NPC) offers 10-week, research-intensive internships every summer with member companies. Applications must be received in NPC headquarters by November 30th of the preceding year. Normally, about 10 students are selected for these positions. Applications may be found in the dean's office, the office of the faculty advisor for the American Pharmaceutical Association (APhA) Academy of Pharmacy Students, or may be requested from NPC. NPC also offers a general internship program that gives a 10-week overview of the primary areas of the pharmaceutical industry, and has limited positions available for clinical internships in drug information.

Medicine development forms a bridge between research and production. Pharmacists working in development will be involved in testing new products, setting production standards, and performing preformulation experiments.

Actually transforming raw materials into finished products and ensuring that exacting manufacturing standards are maintained are both related to production and quality control.

Because research and development are linked so closely to production and quality control, many R&D pharmacists find themselves moving to manufacturing.

A major objective in drug manufacturing is the 100-percent adherence to the exacting FDA standards for production of a given product. Therefore, an ability to understand and implement FDA standards and to interact positively with FDA representatives is essential. Fortunately, the training you receive as a pharmacist will go a long way toward preparing you for this role.

Pharmacists in quality control oversee hundreds of tests and assays to assure consistently high quality in every product. Quality control is an excellent area for pharmacists with BS degrees, as well as for those who hold advanced degrees.

Outgoing, high-achieving pharmacists are especially qualified for performing the public relations-type activities directed toward health professionals, trade representatives (including wholesalers, chains, and managed care groups), and government and regulatory policy makers.

Pharmacists with a history of civic involvement, leadership positions within pharmacy and school groups, and with diplomatic and speaking skills may be qualified for these positions. Pharmacists who have worked for the government, the FDA, or other regulatory groups often have excellent backgrounds for this type of work.

You may be interested to know that my first job after receiving my pharmacy license was working for my Congressman in Washington, DC. I started in his office as an intern and was later offered a full-time staff position. I spent one year on his staff learning how government and policy makers work and becoming familiar with the legislative process and press activities related to health issues. From Capitol Hill, I moved to the National Association of Chain Drug Stores (NACDS), where I was director of pharmacy programs. For three years I oversaw professional issues for NACDS, oversaw the Pharmacy Affairs Committee for the chain industry, and gained exposure to the White House and the Department of Health and Human Services while working on joint projects. These activities led to my current position at NPC, through which my colleagues and I represent America's research-intensive pharmaceutical manufacturers. My current position as vice president for professional relations affords me satisfying opportunities to further the interests of manufacturers while working with the leadership of pharmacy and other professional groups.

The backbone of a good business is a sound management and administrative team. Many pharmacy professionals can be found managing departments and people throughout pharmaceutical companies. In fact, it is estimated that over 16 percent of the industry's pharmacists have risen to positions in middle and upper management. The most likely candidates for these positions hold advanced degrees or have had specialized business training.

In examining various opportunities within our industry, you will find that many unique and stimulating positions are available to the motivated and conscientious pharmacist. Depending upon your chosen field, you may find your opportunities are enhanced if you hold an additional degree in business, health policy, economics, or communications.

A major benefit of working in this industry is that some companies will consider underwriting some or all of the cost of additional education for qualified employees.

Newer areas of growth for pharmacists in pharmaceutical companies will proliferate as a result of the macroeconomic and policy changes facing health care in general and our industry specifically. Health care reform activities may herald major changes in the roles of all health care professionals, and almost certainly will for pharmacists in the pharmaceutical industry. These changes will present tomorrow's pharmacist with previously unrecognized opportunity.

In addition to traditional roles in research, marketing, sales, and quality control, opportunities for pharmacists are growing rapidly in health policy, government, and professional and trade relations.

In the end, a positive attitude and a record of persistent achievement will best position those who are dedicated to working within this industry. The reward – an essential position in one of the most respected industries in the world – is worth the effort. You will be an important member of the nation's health care team, and you'll be directly involved in improving the quality of life and cost effectiveness of health care in the United States and throughout the world.

The opportunities in the pharmaceutical industry are dynamic and diverse. The challenge of finding the right position in the right company should be met with a positive outlook, as well as determined and persistent commitment. Good luck!

Salvatore J. Giorgianni, PharmD, is senior associate director for the U.S. Pharmaceuticals Group of Pfizer Inc.

Opportunities in a Manufacturing Company

A pharmaceutical corporation is a highly complex organization, including not only the myriad of departments and operating sections found in most large firms, but also departments that conduct and manage basic, clinical, and pharmaceutical science as well as federal regulatory functions.

This blend of basic science, pharmaceuticals, and business provides tomorrow's pharmacist with many options for both entry-level positions and career development within the industry.

The pharmaceutical industry generally views pharmacists positively as potential members of its business community. Basic and advanced pharmacy education assures industry recruiters of job candidates with sound scientific training and a higher level of career dedication than most general studies or general science graduates. On the other hand, while college curriculums prepare pharmacists adequately in technical areas, two remaining potential deficiencies in this educational process are in communication and general business skills. Since success in industry requires superior skills in both of these areas, it would behoove individuals contemplating industry careers to avail themselves of elective business and communications programs. Indeed, in higher-level recruiting, pharmacists whose experience has given them both a broad understanding of the role of pharmaceuticals in health care and a perspective of industry and finance will be most in demand.

In general terms, the following sections delineate some industry areas in which tomorrow's pharmacists may find rewarding careers. Of course, the pharmaceutical industry is not homogeneous in corporate philosophy, structure, or career development. Consequently, these guidelines are meant to offer a broad perspective rather than a specific one. Major career areas for pharmacists and the levels of educational and practical experience that may be needed for entry and advancement include the following:

Technical opportunities generally require an advanced degree to assure continued advancement within the corporation. Indeed, most entry-level positions for pharmacists now require a PharmD or PhD in either an applied or basic science or in a clinical discipline.

Most corporations divide technical fields into those supporting marketing efforts, those supporting new product development, and those involving production. Scientists in marketing groups generally are responsible for working with FDA-approved products and products near approval. Development groups work with products from their design or discovery stage through late human testing. The third area, production, is somewhat self-explanatory and will be discussed in a later section.

Pharmacists support corporate marketing efforts as marketing managers or by serving as "internal consultants" in the development and implementation of marketing plans, as liaisons with professional societies, and by conducting postapproval clinical studies to further enhance basic knowledge and practitioner experience with products. Pharmacists also provide product information to practitioners over and above that generally provided by sales representatives. They are extensively involved in processing product and safety evaluation data.

For individuals with advanced degrees, opportunity abounds in such areas as medicinal chemistry, quantitative and qualitative chemistry, pharmacology (at the PhD level), pharmacokinetics, and clinical research (at the PharmD level). Pharmacists with baccalaureate degrees may qualify for work as laboratory or clinical assistants in most research areas.

An area that has boomed over the past five years is health care economics. Specialists in this area have graduate degrees – increasingly PhDs – in health care administration, economics, or related fields. Coursework generally should include theory of the health care delivery structure and, possibly, public health administration.

Pharmacoepidemiology is another relatively new discipline that fits hand in glove with the evolving environment of the pharmaceutical industry. Those who work in this discipline conduct studies or work with data from statistical studies of disease patterns and health care issues. Their efforts have great significance in safety regulation, therapeutics, and certain areas of research planning. The work of pharmacoepidemiology specialists will help determine the role pharmaceutical products will play in health care 10 to 15 years from now. Programs in pharmacoepidemiology usually are offered at the PhD level.

Corporate regulatory affairs departments are charged with making sure promotional, manufacturing, scientific, and medical activities comply with federal regulations.

Pharmacists in this specialty usually have scientific backgrounds in design and development of clinical studies, pharmacology, or scientific methodology and practice. Only a few colleges of pharmacy offer master's degrees in regulatory affairs. Usually entry-level pharmacists coordinate the day-to-day details of making drug submissions to federal agencies. Upper-level regulatory affairs positions require significant experience and a thorough understanding of both regulatory requirements and business needs. Pharmacist-attorneys are frequently employed in this area.

Opportunities in marketing are enhanced by a degree in pharmacy. However, for entry-level positions, formal training – at the MBA level – in management, marketing, or finance or significant business experience is a common prerequisite. A pharmacy education is considered helpful, but candidates will not be hired on this qualification alone. Competition for marketing positions in top corporations is keen, and persons interested in such jobs should obtain their training from the best sources possible.

Marketing managers and their assistants are responsible for developing and implementing a strategy for drug product promotion. Inherent in this process is an understanding of the marketplace, health care and business trends, manufacturing systems, distribution systems, and sales. These men and women are "movers and shakers" within the industry. High-level advancement within the industry usually requires marketing experience.

Supporting these marketing managers are staff professionals who work in market research, business and new product planning, and development. These individuals provide analytic data on business trends and practitioner prescribing habits. They also provide and analyze information about practitioner attitudes regarding products and practitioner needs and concerns relative to pharmaceuticals.

Sales is generally regarded as the most usual way for pharmacists to enter the industry. Indeed, a position in professional sales is often an extremely good place for a pharmacist to begin – to find out about career paths firsthand and gain practical business experience. By taking advantage of company-subsidized higher education programs, sales representatives often pursue graduate degrees that will help further their careers.

While certain companies appear to favor sales candidates with pharmacy backgrounds, the realities of today's job market and sales environment dictate that candidates be hired because they have the potential to be outstanding sales representatives, not because they are excellent pharmacists. Here again, a pharmacy degree may work in the candidate's favor. By itself, it will not assure a position or a successful career.

General sales positions are widely available, but more and more companies are adopting the concept of using groups of specialized representatives for certain product lines or customer bases. These representatives may require basic science degrees as well as superior sales skills. Another group of company representatives might be termed *technical service specialists*. In some corporations, these individuals report to departments other than sales and have no direct selling responsibilities or quotas. Instead, they provide technical assistance to practitioners and local general sales representatives. These individuals often have doctoral-level degrees and significant experience in the pharmaceutical industry or as clinicians.

Sales representatives need intensive training in both science and sales techniques. Practitioners demand accurate scientific information about products presented and are apt to ask complex questions on diverse aspects of products. Consequently, other opportunities exist for pharmacists in sales training.

The complexity of today's business world has opened a variety of other interesting career opportunities in industry. For example, most major pharmaceutical corporations have units that maintain liaisons with professional groups and trade associations. Most also have units that maintain relationships with such government agencies as state Medicaid boards. Both of these activities require solid communication skills. A pharmacy background that includes experience in professional associations, pharmacy management, or government can be very helpful in this work. These are seldom entry-level jobs.

In most pharmaceutical corporations there is a constant need for talented attorneys. Many with pharmacy backgrounds are employed by industry, both directly in legal practice and in areas of legal sensitivity. Their work includes contract negotiations, FDA activities, advertising counsel, and patent law. Here, too, top legal credentials are more important than a pharmacy background to successfully compete in the job market.

Health care policy specialists look at the dynamics between those who pay for and consume health care and those who determine policy and make laws – namely Congress. These specialists track and review legislative issues related to health care reimbursement, health care reform, drug product approval, government policies and procedures, and public and private research policy in the United States. Health care policy researchers delve into the interrelationship between industry, practitioners, society, regulators, and professional organizations. This area has no entry-level positions, and few pharmacists work in this arena. However, as pharmacists gain broader experience in business and marketing, the number who work in health care policy will grow.

Pharmaceutical manufacturing is a subject traditionally given cursory coverage at major pharmacy colleges. This specialized complex of activities almost always requires advanced degree training. As technology grows, particularly with the advent of new delivery systems and biotechnologically derived products, so will the need for pharmacists to implement it in the industry.

Pharmaceutical firms use consultants at many levels from various areas of business and scientific specialization. It is important for industry to keep pace with extramural views on current practice standards and opinions. Consultants from every facet of pharmacy practice help fill this need. They usually have significant levels of experience and prominence within the profession. In-house consultants and special-products consultants are also used as needed. These individuals contract with corporations to conduct specific investigative, promotional, or analytical work. Practitioners develop such contractual arrangements as a way of working in the business community while maintaining their professional practice.

Regrettably, except for individual availability and professional visibility, there are no formal mechanisms for entry into these consultant positions.

Another "industry" within the scope of this article is advertising. Independent advertising agencies provide services in marketing, publishing, and professional education. Many of the opportunities described in this article specific to the pharmaceutical industry also have some degree of applicability to advertising agency work.

Most major pharmaceutical manufacturers offer pharmacy students an opportunity to work as interns. These positions are usually available during the summer months. Some colleges of pharmacy offer formal clerkship programs that become part of certain curriculum tracks and are designed around specific industry careers, particularly in production and manufacturing. Some internships are available through the National Pharmaceutical Council or the PMA.

These programs are designed to give interested students a firsthand view of the industry. At the same time, internships give the industry an opportunity to work with potential employees.

Basic to the search for employment is keeping your eyes open for placement notices, developing contacts within the industry, and sending application after application to pharmaceutical companies. Corporate personnel managers will often be happy to discuss available openings. But just as frequently, interview opportunities depend on the luck of having your resume cross someone's desk just when he or she is looking for a person with your qualifications. Pharmacists who are truly interested in a career in industry should send initial applications to several manufacturers and update them every six or twelve months. Corporations are always on the lookout for promising talent and often review their files periodically.

There are many ways to develop a financially and personally rewarding career in the pharmaceutical industry. Career paths vary and are often unpredictable. This speaks well of the industry and indicates the range of positions and talents needed to fill them. Promotions to increased responsibility are based on outstanding performance. Moving from company to company to gain promotions is also possible, but most companies tend to promote from within.

The pharmaceutical industry has a long history of keeping pace with general salary structures for entry-level positions, both from the perspective of similar industries and of professional practice. Salary review and bonuses are tied to individual performance and corporate economic performance. Even in lean years, most corporations attempt to keep pace with economic indices in developing compensation programs. Corporations also provide stock, stock options, and other incentive programs in addition to outstanding health, savings, and pension programs.

E.F. "Gene" Fiese, PhD,
is a project leader in pharmaceutical research
and development at Pfizer Central Research
in Groton, Connecticut.

Research in the Pharmaceutical Industry

If you enjoy solving complicated problems, then research and development of new drug dosage forms may be the career for you. For me, an additional attraction is the challenge of working on the cutting edge of science and technology to solve drug delivery problems.

In 1968, I took my first job in industry working with a rather straightforward multivitamin tablet formulation. In 1974, I joined Pfizer Central Research and worked on an anti-asthma medication destined for aerosol delivery, probably the most difficult of drug delivery systems. Later, I became involved in the problem of prostaglandin delivery – not a simple issue because these are very unstable materials. I also spent six years addressing the instability of antibiotics in steam-pelletized feed for our Animal Health Division. Today, the problem we are addressing is the analytical characterization of peptides, which is quite a difficult task due to secondary and tertiary structural properties of the macromolecule. The challenges I've had to meet over the years have kept me fresh. They also have given me satisfaction with my ability to solve problems.

The lab I work in is involved in the physical and chemical characterization of new drug candidates and optimizing delivery of these candidates. In pharmaceutical research and development, our realm of responsibility extends from the time a compound is isolated in the organic chemistry laboratories until it appears in the plasma of a test species. We work to characterize the physical and chemical properties of compounds. Then we apply our formulation skills to this database to optimize a drug delivery system.

Of course, the ultimate aim of our endeavors is to produce a commercial dosage form. Sometimes this goal is elusive because many potential products enter the research and development pipeline, but very few make it to the commercial market. In fact, according to the Pharmaceutical Manufacturers Association, only one of 4,000 compounds that showed promise in preclinical testing actually made it into the marketplace in 1991. The average cost of developing each? Almost $300 million.

So, to be content in the research environment, pharmacists have to be able to accept the fact that the vast majority of the compounds they touch during their careers are fated to go nowhere. I've been at Pfizer for 18 years, working on about 15 compounds each year. During that time only three have actually entered the commercial marketplace, and two of those were marketed in 1992.

Compared with other fields of opportunity in pharmacy, research and development represents a relatively small niche for graduates. This is true because the few companies involved in R&D have relatively small departments and low attrition rates.

For example, here at Pfizer three people retired in 1992. Each of them had spent some four decades working for one company. I've been here almost 20 years. That isn't much turnover in comparison with retail pharmacy. I believe this emphasizes the fact that most researchers in the pharmaceutical industry are very satisfied with their jobs.

Speaking for myself, I appreciate the security of working for a large company with its many resources concentrated in one location. I also love the multidisciplinary aspects of my work. In fact, I tell people my job occupies a four-dimensional space because I'm working on n different compounds in x different therapeutic areas requiring y different types of chemical forms and z different types of dosage forms. In one instance, the liability may be solubility; in the next it may be instability. One agent may be a tablet, the next an aerosol. Today, LTD_4-mediated asthma may be the therapeutic challenge; tomorrow, it may be treatment of inner ear infections. Boredom is not a word that applies to my job.

Because I'm the senior person in this lab, many people look to me for guidance in one way or another. Six scientists report directly to me. As a result, a considerable part of my workday is spent motivating people to use the best of their scientific abilities and available technology to solve the drug delivery problems we encounter.

As I receive lab results I verify that the proper experiment was done and interpreted correctly. I challenge the people around me to stretch their abilities – to consider, for example, whether another approach might yield a better characterization of a compound's properties.

I convey our results to the discovery chemists or whoever our "customer" is in each case. In doing so, I attempt to relate our data to products or compounds (drugs) that already exist in this therapeutic area. With this comparative information, it is possible fully to assess the significance of our findings.

If we determine that a compound is chemically unstable, we have to describe that liability in detail. Does the instability occur during storage? During passage down the gastrointestinal track? During metabolism? Will its instability be a factor in the agent's pharmacological performance? These are critical issues, but no more critical than the data generated in other departments.

Researchers are not isolated. We work within teams, because that's the most effective use of many levels of multidisciplinary expertise. At any given time I am concerned with up to five different compounds in as many different therapeutic areas. Management of each compound occurs through a project team consisting of eight to 10 scientists representing the disciplines responsible for testing or developing each new drug candidate. At the same time, several of my assistants are busily working to characterize compounds and/or dosage forms for each therapeutic area. Lots of data and lots of people are involved in the research and development decision for each new therapeutic agent.

For every PhD, we have a BS chemist who performs the analytical endwork. In addition, we have a BS pharmacist doing the formulation endwork. The roles of these specialists are to formulate and evaluate compounds as well as dosage forms.

As firmly based on hard science as our work may be, creativity is essential in research. During school, we learned basic techniques and guidelines that taught us how to accomplish certain things. But it is the creative individual who produces a better result faster and thus makes it possible to bring a product to the marketplace first.

In the world of industrial research, characterizing compounds and developing drug delivery systems usually require creative thinking and well-organized experimentation. The first step is to access the fundamentals but after that, life can be rather freewheeling. However, as in every field, it is easy to develop one's skills to a level of comfort and then stop growing. Individuals who allow that to happen in a research environment are doomed to frustration and career stagnation.

I became interested in research and development during my second year of pharmacy school. A student in the class ahead of mine ignited my interest when he told me about his summer industrial research internship. Unfortunately, I wasn't able to find a summer internship. However, after earning my master's degree, I spent two years in the industry and then went back to school to earn my PhD.

I believe that pharmacy students who are interested in this area should gain experience in the laboratory, either at the undergraduate level or through a summer internship. Similarly, pharmacy graduates should get some experience in industry or in a research lab before making a commitment to graduate school. As in any other profession, firsthand experience in a field of interest will tell you whether that's where you want to build a career.

One of the biggest misconceptions pharmacy students have about industry is that they think the road to a research career leads through detailing drugs to physicians. In general, that's not true.

Another misconception is that a graduate degree is required for pharmacists who want to conduct research. The truth is that there are jobs in research for BS graduates. It's just a matter of finding a company that has an opening and promotional pattern compatible with your level of education. The question is how much responsibility you want. As might be expected, smaller companies tend to give BS people more responsibility than bigger companies. However, you'll generally find greater security in the big companies, and you'll find they offer more diversity in the projects you work on. Small companies often must narrow their focus to fewer products.

To succeed in research, a pharmacist must derive a lot of satisfaction from solving scientific problems. Not only do you have to perform the basic experimentation, but then you have to design the rest of the experiment to address the heart of the matter. What's wrong with the compound and how can it be fixed? It boils down to an appreciation of analytical and physical chemistry. Through physical chemistry, you identify the problem, use your formulation knowledge to solve the problem, and then employ analytical techniques to prove that the problem has been solved. In contrast, with work that is redundant or repetitive, the research pharmacist is constantly challenged to stay current scientifically and to break new ground in technology.

The Pharmacist in Marketing

Curtis L. Andrews, BS, MBA,
is manager of divisional marketing
and administration for the
Pratt Pharmaceuticals Division of Pfizer Inc.

When I began my pharmacy career I had no idea that marketing was in my future. However, my interests and experience evolved in that direction. Today, I can't imagine a more satisfying way to apply my pharmaceutical knowledge and skills.

I first became interested in the practice of pharmacy when I was in high school. Working in retail pharmacies after school and during summer vacations on Cape Cod, I came to respect the professional and business skills of my employers. They were particularly adept at helping vacationing patients who had no local physician to turn to for medical advice.

As a high school senior, I applied to pharmacy schools and enrolled at Northeastern University College of Pharmacy in Boston. Until I received my bachelor's degree, I continued my summer work on the Cape. I would recommend this balance of education and practical experience to anyone, no matter what the ultimate career goal in pharmacy may be.

After graduation, I spent nine years in retail pharmacy, first in a large, independent pharmacy, then in a small chain.

In time, I moved into a position as a staff pharmacist and store manager for several units of a large retail chain. Toward the end of my career there I opened new stores and was responsible for revitalizing others. I would make a business diagnosis of the store unit, and then I would design and implement a plan to maximize service. Finally, I would train the staff to maintain the needed changes.

This progression illustrates how I moved away from clinical pharmacy practice and toward the business side of the profession. That logically pointed me to graduate school. I spent two years at Columbia University, where I received an MBA in marketing and the management of organizations. Coupled with my pharmacy background, this experience fueled my interest in the pharmaceutical companies that were recruiting on campus.

I was recruited by the Roerig division, one of the three domestic pharmaceutical divisions of Pfizer Inc. (The other two divisions are Pfizer Laboratories and Pratt Pharmaceuticals.) I chose Pfizer because of its reputation as a leading pharmaceutical manufacturer with a high-quality research program.

Like most well-run corporations, Pfizer assigns its new marketing employees to a series of positions that both challenge and expand their skills. Marketing is a fast-track area, and it demands the efficient use of time and talent.

My first position as a marketing associate plunged me immediately into meaningful work. I assisted a product manager in developing educational and promotional materials and programs in support of a major antibiotic agent. After that, I was assigned to a sales training program, and then I was given a field assignment detailing Roerig products to physicians, pharmacists, and nurses.

Since it is a task of marketing to develop materials and programs that sales representatives use in their day-to-day contact with health professionals, marketers need to understand and appreciate the demands of successful selling. What information do health professionals need? How can sales representatives best present that information? How do health professionals respond? Does appropriate product utilization increase? While market research is essential in answering these questions, so is actual hands-on experience.

After instructive experience in the field, I was promoted to assistant product manager. The duties at this level are not drastically different from those of a marketing associate, but the degree of responsibility is greater. It is with promotion to product manager that the range of duties and degree of responsibility for completed marketing materials and programs increase significantly.

Above all else, marketing is a team activity. It depends on supervisory and subordinate staff above and below the product manager, as well as market researchers, educators, scientists, and others. The product manager must focus input from the team, develop a strategic marketing plan, and create educational and promotional programs to reach physicians, pharmacists, and nurses. If, as occurred in my own experience, FDA approval is pending, the product manager helps guide a new drug through the final stages to that approval.

Clinical research is vital to understanding any drug and to reaching the appropriate prescribing physicians. The scientific and clinical training of the pharmacist-manager may enhance his or her understanding of this critical issue.

Creating the marketing program is only part of the product manager's job. The marketing team must continually monitor the product to learn how physicians are using the drug. We look for instances in which medical professionals might not be fully aware of a product's features and benefits. We try to focus on concerns they might have in order to correct misperceptions of the drug. We address such issues in various promotional or educational materials. It's a continuing process.

As product manager in a large pharmaceutical corporation, I manage a budget and have profit-and-loss responsibilities. Moreover, I have been expected to develop marketing strategies and to execute tactics that can achieve my goals. I present information to senior management as well as to our field force.

One of the most fascinating aspects of my job is the interaction I have with medical and pharmacy experts around the world who serve as advisors and offer their expertise in educational programs. It would be hard to overstate the importance of having these notable authorities involved in projects aimed at increasing the ability of health care providers to understand, screen, diagnose and, ultimately, treat disease.

Product manager is not the highest position a marketer can achieve in a company like Pfizer. In fact, it is possible for men and women who succeed at that level to go as high as president or CEO of a corporation. I have recently been promoted to the newly created position of manager, divisional marketing and administration. Here, my job will be to develop synergistic educational and promotional programs that can support the entire drug portfolio of Pratt Pharmaceuticals – our newest marketing division. Pfizer's flair for this kind of creative management is another feature that makes employment here so attractive.

A complicated formula determines the corporate product manager's success: appropriate drug usage, effective educational and promotional programming, sales, and profits. We're judged on how well we position our products and on how well we pre-empt, anticipate, or respond to competitors. Another factor is how well we use our clinical database. Our efforts are readily assessed.

If I could go back and change any single thing about the shape my professional life has taken, I would come to Pfizer sooner. I have a good job in a great company, and I believe my efforts have an impact on the quality of patient care.

Edward Zastawny, PharmD, Capt., USAF, BSC, is chief of applied pharmacotherapy services at Malcolm Grow USAF Medical Center, Andrews Air Force Base, Maryland.

The Air Force Pharmacist

As a pharmacist in the U.S. Air Force, I believe I am providing a valued service and applying the knowledge I acquired in school. I didn't always feel that way. In fact, before I joined the military, I was quickly burning out on the pharmacy profession.

After graduating cum laude from the University of Cincinnati College of Pharmacy, I spent a frustrating six months with a large chain of drugstores. In addition to my responsibility for filling prescriptions, I was required to sell lottery tickets and to do a lot of other things that are not related to a pharmacist's professional duties. I know that many pharmacists thrive in the chain environment, but it was not for me.

When I left there, I went to work in a 550-bed medical center, where I stayed for 18 months. I rotated through every shift, working days for two weeks and nights for the next two weeks. I was low man on the totem pole, and I didn't see much potential for advancement. An assistant director's position was my only chance to move up, but several other pharmacists were senior to me, and they had advanced degrees. They would surely be chosen before me. I felt stuck.

Once I realized there were some real obstacles to my advancement, I began to think about a letter I received from the Air Force during my last year of pharmacy school. It was a recruiting letter that asked me to consider a career in the service. The job security was appealing and so were the retirement benefits. There was even a bit of glamour associated with it. But most important of all, I remembered that the letter had promised management training.

It wasn't long until I decided to call the Air Force recruiter in my home town. He put me in touch with a medical recruiter in Cleveland, who came down to my house and talked with me for a couple of hours. He convinced me to sign up for three years.

My first assignment at Wilford Hall USAF Medical Center in San Antonio, Tex., may have been the greatest learning experience of my career. Wilford Hall is the largest Air Force medical center in the world. It has 1,000 beds and several outpatient clinics that see nearly a million patients a year. From renal dialysis and bone marrow transplantation to open heart surgery, there are few limits to the procedures that can be performed at this huge medical complex.

Wilford Hall's state-of-the-art pharmacy operates 24 hours a day and provides every type of modern pharmacy service. The staff makes more than 1,000 intravenous admixtures a day with up to 30 hyperalimentation solutions and 15 chemotherapy agents.

315

I worked in all sections of the pharmacy, doing a little bit of everything. When I ran the unit-dose pharmacy, I had to make sure medication orders were accurate for 400 beds. I was responsible for policies, procedures, and ordering. I had four to six technicians working for me, and I had responsibility for an annual budget of $1 million.

From unit dose I moved to sterile products, where I was placed in charge of preparing IV solutions for the entire hospital. My responsibilities were greater than ever: I managed a staff of six to eight technicians, and my budget was between $2 million and $3 million.

Eventually, I was promoted to officer-in-charge for the inpatient pharmacy. In that capacity, I supervised six pharmacists and 30 technicians, and administered a $4 million budget. By then, it had become clear to me that the Air Force would give its people all the responsibility they could handle.

Most of the contact Wilford Hall pharmacists had with inpatients was through doctors and nurses on the medical staff. Our inpatients were on the floors of the medical center, and we communicated with them through the staff. Pharmacists who worked in the outpatient pharmacy had somewhat more personal contact with their patient population.

I was active in the Company Grade Officers Council and a member of the cardiopulmonary resuscitation/advanced cardiac life support (CPR/ACLS) committee. For the first time in my professional life, I felt that I was really making a difference. People were calling me for my opinions. Nurses would call and ask, "If my patient has an allergy to drug x, can I give him drug y?" I would catch potential problems and make recommendations. Toward the end of my tenure at Wilford Hall, I was named U.S. Air Force Junior Pharmacist of the Year. I realized then how rewarding pharmacy had become for me.

The Air Force staff pharmacists I worked with were unequalled in my experience. Almost all had advanced degrees, either an MS or a PharmD. Our clinical pharmacists provided a multitude of services, including drug information, pharmacokinetic drug dosing, and staff education.

After three years at Wilford Hall, I took advantage of one of the best benefits the Air Force offers to pharmacists – an opportunity to go to graduate school at the government's expense. I enrolled in the Air Force Institute of Technology and attended a graduate program at the University of Texas Health Science Center at San Antonio.

After earning my PharmD, I performed a one-year specialty residency in adult medicine. All this time, I continued to receive my Air Force salary and benefits, and the time I spent there counted toward my retirement. I could hardly believe I was being paid to get smart.

In return for my advanced education, I had to agree to stay in the Air Force for another five years. The commitment of time varies according to the program and the degree, but I didn't think twice about it. I planned to stay with the Air Force, no matter what.

My PharmD degree is useful in my current position as chief of applied pharmacotherapy services at Malcolm Grow USAF Medical Center at Andrews Air Force Base. Here, I am part of a clinical pharmacy service that is initiating programs that have never before been seen in the Air Force medical service.

We're training the house staff in both the family practice and internal medicine departments. Twice each week I make rounds with the intensive care team. Every day, I monitor therapeutic drug levels throughout the medical center and outpatient clinics. We also provide a counter detailing service, during which we critique manufacturer-provided product information for the medical staff.

Right now, our efforts concentrate more on physicians than nurses. Eventually, we intend to establish a clinical pharmacy program in which we will have more contact with patients. The idea is that several clinical pharmacists will be charged with teaching patients about their specific drug therapies.

I feel that I make a significant contribution at Malcolm Grow Medical Center. Even though I am part of a team here, I have my own area of expertise. And I have the continuing satisfaction of knowing that I play an important role in this facility – not only for patients who receive drug therapy, but also for the medical staff members who need to know more about the medications they prescribe and administer.

For a pharmacist right out of school, the Air Force is a gold mine of opportunities. The work is hard, but it contains plenty of challenge – and plenty of rewards. Recent graduates work with seasoned military pharmacists in full expectation that they are being groomed to accept more responsibility. And in small military hospitals or medical centers, that responsibility is not slow in coming. Air Force pharmacists command a great deal of respect for their clinical expertise.

The military is not for everyone. The biggest drawback is that it's a large organization with a correspondingly large bureaucracy. The hours spent at work can be long, and sometimes it is necessary to take work home. Occasionally, we're recalled to duty on Saturdays.

In the beginning, the Air Force pays less than a civilian employer. Fortunately, this drawback disappears in time. As a pharmacist advances in rank, the pay goes up and will eventually surpass a civilian pharmacist's salary.

The Air Force pharmacist can expect to move every three years or so. For some, this is a disadvantage. However, new assignments usually are associated with new opportunities. Current cuts in defense spending mean that moves are likely to come less often.

In general, jobs in the military have been more secure than civilian jobs. It's hard to predict what the future holds, but it's fair to say that defense budget cutbacks will have some impact on job security.

Benefits in the military are almost impossible to beat. A month's vacation is standard and is accumulated at the rate of two and a half days each month. New pharmacists don't have to wait for this benefit – it starts accruing from the first day.

Health care insurance is provided for Air Force pharmacists and their dependents. You will be able to shop at the base exchange and commissary, where the prices are lower than can be found in most civilian supermarkets.

One of the most important features of an Air Force career is that you'll be able to retire after 20 years and then receive almost 50 percent of your base pay for the rest of your life. And should you become disabled while on active duty, you'll receive the benefits of a generous disability policy.

The Air Force will pay expenses associated with continuing pharmacy education. You can attend meetings once each year. Naturally, pharmacists must have a valid state license to practice in the military, and you must submit a prescribed number of continuing education credits each year in order to maintain your license. But because officers move so often, you will not be expected to hold a license in the state where you are stationed. The Air Force will give you time to keep up with your continuing education.

An Air Force pharmacist's career may seem to start slowly in comparison with an entry-level job in the civilian world. But it doesn't take long to catch up, especially when the often-superior benefits are taken into account. After seven years in the military, I have no regrets – joining the service was the right decision for me. In the Air Force, I find few of the frustrations that dominated the jobs I had before signing up. Even better, I have the responsibility that once seemed so elusive. I think it's a great way of life.

Captain Walter L. Holt, Jr., PharmD, is Chief of the U.S. Army Centralized Allergen Extract Laboratory at the Walter Reed Army Medical Center in Washington, DC.

The Army Pharmacist

The opportunity to assume leadership is routine in the military. Pharmacists usually enter the Army as second lieutenants, and they are immediately given supervisory or managerial positions. A newly commissioned Army pharmacist will most likely supervise a hospital pharmacy section or serve as the chief pharmacist in a small community hospital. Army pharmacists must have enough flexibility to accept change, and they can be assured that boredom will not characterize their careers.

Pharmacists who are looking for diversity in their practices, like to travel, and enjoy making independent decisions should know that the Army offers career options that may meet their needs perfectly.

The Army evaluates a pharmacist's expertise and makes assignments accordingly. Working with the pharmacy consultant and a military career counselor, it is possible to have great influence in shaping your career. I enjoy my work, and I enjoy being a pharmacist in the Army.

I earned my PharmD degree at Florida A & M University and completed a miniresidency in geriatric pharmacy through the Veterans Administration. I came on active duty and was assigned to General Officer Basic Training. The task there is to learn U.S. Army doctrine. Upon completion of the officer's course I went through a two-and-a-half-week orientation course that introduced me to the different protocols and regulations involved in Army pharmacy practice. I was assigned to Walter Reed Army Medical Center for an American Society of Hospital Pharmacy (ASHP) accredited residency in hospital pharmacy practice. In 1991, at the end of this residency, I was assigned to be chief of the U.S. Army Centralized Allergen Extract Laboratory (USCAEL) at Walter Reed.

Pharmacists who enter the military with advanced clinical degrees, such as a PharmD, will be given greater responsibility at a large medical center or a medium-sized community hospital. As an example, as chief of USCAEL, I am the primary consultant on allergens to allergists in the Army, Navy, VA, U.S. Public Health Service, and at limited Air Force facilities. Even among Army pharmacists, my position is unique: I have what amounts to a worldwide practice.

Even though Walter Reed is a military hospital, it functions no differently than any other large medical teaching institution. In fact, the only difference is that we wear military uniforms. My day starts at 5:45 AM and ends at 5 PM. My technical staff and technicians begin work around 7 PM. They compound prescriptions we have received from any number of locations. My operation is purely mail order, and our daily workload is determined by the U.S. Postal Service. Allergen extract prescriptions are mailed to facilities around the world in support of active duty military personnel and their dependents, as well as to military retirees and their dependents. Thirty-three percent of our workload is devoted to active military personnel. Dependents and retirees account for the remainder. On average, two to four weeks elapse between the time we receive a prescription and the time we return it to the requesting facility. That might sound like a long time, but most of our medications are for patients on routine injection schedules. The technicians who request the prescriptions know our turn-around time and, hopefully, order accordingly. Rush orders are handled within a week.

Most of my day is spent consulting with physicians and nursing staff around the world and at Walter Reed on drug and immunotherapy and on research protocols related to patient care. I am a member of the drug utilization and evaluation committee and attend the pharmacy and therapeutics committee meetings regularly. These committees determine the criteria for drug use and regulate which drugs are added and deleted from the formulary.

In discharging my other responsibilities, I serve as a budget analyst, automation manager, and personnel director for the allergy/immunology service. I am also the class advisor for the allergy/clinical immunology specialist course. This is a Department of Defense program and is the only one of its kind in the world. The course is taught four times a year for a period of eight weeks. I coordinate the selection of students and teach a class during each course. I also coedit the course manual and *The Extract News*, a quarterly newsletter. Finally, I coordinate a biannual week-long allergy/clinical specialist short course.

The practices of Army pharmacists are no different from those of their counterparts in the civilian sector. Army pharmacists distribute medications to both inpatients and outpatients, consult with physicians on drug therapy, counsel patients, publish in the pharmacy journals, conduct research, and serve as administrative and budget coordinators of their operations. Also like their civilian colleagues, Army pharmacists are members of professional organizations, attend annual meetings, and have teaching affiliations with local schools of pharmacy.

Civilian pharmacists earn more than Army pharmacists – at least in dollars. Nevertheless, the Army allowances and other benefits tend to close the gap as one accumulates years of experience. We have 30 days of paid leave each year. We also enjoy health care benefits, housing subsidies, and no shortage of opportunities for advancement.

For sheer diversity, there is no better practice environment than the military. In a civilian setting, whether retail or hospital pharmacy, the job description seldom changes. However, military pharmacists can structure their work experience to all aspects of pharmacy practice in one institutionalized setting: from clinical, hospital, and ambulatory care to teaching, research, and administration. It is this diversity that attracts seasoned pharmacists who have grown tired of the routines in civilian practice.

Just as appealing is the military's interest in helping officers further their education and experience. Typically, the Army rotates pharmacy personnel into new positions every three to four years. In between these rotations an officer is generally afforded the opportunity for advanced education. In addition to taking the required military leadership courses, officers are expected to continue their academic and professional studies. An Army pharmacist can work toward a master's degree in pharmacy administration, a PhD in the pharmaceutical sciences, a PharmD degree, one of the three ASHP-approved residencies offered by the Army (hospital pharmacy practice, hematology/oncology, and nuclear pharmacy), or apply for a civilian specialty residency or fellowship.

Although many civilian employers encourage their employees to further their education the motivation to do so is borne by the individual. The Army helps its professionals succeed by giving them the time to pursue their graduates studies. In general, the pay-back to the government is two years of service for every year of education.

Although I was commissioned as a first lieutenant, this is the usual career progression of a pharmacy officer:

Second lieutenant – initial commission

First lieutenant – within one year

Captain – in four years of service

Major – 10 to 12 years

Lieutenant colonel – 16 years

Colonel – 20 years

My plans for the future are straightforward. I plan to go the distance and make a career in the U.S. Army. There is no place I would rather practice pharmacy.

Commander Martha B. Alexander practices in the Medical Service Corps, United States Navy.

The Navy Pharmacist

When I graduated from the University of Texas College of Pharmacy, the Vietnam War was raging. It was 1969, and some of my classmates, whose grades were not stellar, were drafted out of school. Others lived in fear of being drafted soon after graduation. Being female, I never experienced any of those concerns. Little did I know that a commission in the Navy was in my future.

Within five years of graduation, my marriage ended and I found myself with sole responsibility for supporting a family. Even though I had found community pharmacy to be stimulating, I was discontented in general and decided to look for new challenges in hospital pharmacy. Unfortunately, there were no jobs in my community for pharmacists without hospital experience or without advanced degrees in hospital pharmacy. I had neither. For a while I attempted to go to graduate school while working and being a mother, but I soon realized that all were full-time jobs that didn't leave much time at the end of the day for things like eating or sleeping.

After a couple of semesters of graduate school, I began to consider other options that would give me the experience that I lacked or that would pay for me to go to school. The military offered both: hospitals to work in and the GI bill for educational benefits. Not only could I get hospital pharmacy experience and qualify for educational benefits, but the military would provide medical coverage for me and my children. The military appeared to be tailored perfectly to my needs.

My first duty station was a small hospital at Port Hueneme, Calif. There I gained valuable, though small-scale, experience in hospital pharmacy. After two years, I became the department head and gained managerial and leadership skills that have served me well ever since.

My next duty station was a medium-size hospital in Millington, Tenn., where I was assistant department head and inpatient supervisor. At Millington, I was able to sharpen my clinical skills and to expand my managerial abilities. Off duty, I took graduate courses in pharmacy administration at the University of Tennessee at Memphis. I also earned an MS degree in operations management from the University of Arkansas.

From Tennessee, I moved to Naval Hospital, San Diego. At first, I resisted moving to San Diego; I'm a country girl and city life wasn't particularly appealing. However, as things turned out, that tour was the most professionally rewarding of my career. During my four-year stay, I worked in both outpatient and inpatient pharmacies, I served as clinical coordinator, and I was director of the drug information center. In addition,

I completed an American Society of Hospital Pharmacy (ASHP) residency. Reluctant as I was to go there, I'll always treasure my experience in a major teaching hospital.

My next assignment was a short move across the compound to the Naval School of Health Sciences, where I took over as director of the pharmacy technician training program. There I developed my teaching skills and felt proud of the part I played in training these highly skilled technicians. I was tapped for additional duties directing 15 technical training schools for the medical department of the Navy. Talk about a challenge! During my tenure several new training programs were established, including one for physician assistants.

My current job is at Naval Hospital, Bremerton, Wash., where I was assigned to head the department of pharmacy. This midsize hospital has a family practice residency program, which has been a challenge in and of itself. During Desert Shield and Desert Storm we were faced with deployment of three fourths of our pharmacy staff. We also have experienced unprecedented growth in the area due to homeporting of Navy ships in the Pacific Northwest. Currently, I serve as director for ancillary services and am responsible for pharmacy, radiology, physical therapy, laboratory, social work, nutrition, and the parent support team.

You may wonder why I didn't leave the Navy after I had fulfilled my initial obligation. I had gained the hospital experience I sought, and I had earned my GI bill to go to school. The reason is simple: I stayed for the opportunity. While my early goals in the Navy may have been narrowly focused and somewhat short-sighted, the opportunities I have been given have been almost limitless. I have served as a staff pharmacist in both ambulatory and inpatient settings, I've been a department head, directed a pharmacy technician training program, and served as director for ancillary services at a busy teaching hospital.

In addition to challenging duty assignments, the Navy offers excellent educational opportunities. I earned a master's degree in my off-duty time, using the GI bill and tuition assistance provided by the Navy. I completed an ASHP-accredited residency program while drawing full pay and allowances. Additionally, I have been fully funded to countless continuing education programs, including the annual ASHP midyear clinical meeting. As of this writing the Navy has four pharmacists attending graduate school, full time, fully funded, and the pharmacists are drawing full pay and allowances.

Many other opportunities exist and are just waiting for the right individuals. The Navy has jobs for pharmacists in Europe, the Middle East, and the Caribbean. Moreover, the chances of seeing and experiencing life in different areas of this country are excellent. Not only have my horizons been broadened by meeting and working with individuals from diverse cultural backgrounds, my children also have gained great insight into what makes the United States so great – *opportunity*.

I am surprised that there are not more women pharmacists in the Navy. Still, our numbers are growing rapidly from only six when I joined in 1976, to 27 at present. I'm afraid that many women pharmacists do not consider the military because they simply don't know enough about it.

I've had great professional experience; I've earned a master's degree and completed a residency. My job titles have ranged from staff pharmacist to director. And I've been able to do all this without sacrificing my family and friends. I go to church. I work in the yard. I do volunteer work. I do laundry and I pay my bills. On weekends, I go backpacking. I'm a naval officer, not an oddity – just a regular person pursuing my profession in a military setting.

As a Navy pharmacist, I belong to a dynamic team that delivers health care to members of the Armed Forces, their families, retirees, and their families. The needs of my patients are no different from those of civilian patients: they all want factual information. They all want to receive optimum benefit from drug therapies. They all want someone to listen to their questions and concerns. As a Navy pharmacist, I belong to a dynamic team that employs principles of total quality management in seeking ways to deliver better health care to its patients in a cost-effective manner. And as a Navy pharmacist, I have had the opportunity to be creative and innovative, and I have been given the flexibility to do things my way. I can't imagine practicing pharmacy in any other setting.

John E. Ogden, MS,
is director of pharmacy services for
the Department of Veterans Affairs
in Washington, DC.

Pharmacy in the
Veterans Administration

Entry-level pharmacy positions offer recent graduates their first chance to prove themselves and use their new skills. However, in many cases, such jobs have limited potential – they are good places to start, but they don't offer much in the way of advancement or growth. Within two or three years many who have such jobs will start searching for new ones.

At the Department of Veterans Affairs (VA) Pharmacy Services, the career outlook for a new professional is considerably different. That's because pharmacists who work here at all levels enjoy an important constant: opportunity. They are able to choose among practice sites in every state in the nation. They can pursue general or specialized clinical practices. They can follow career tracks that lead toward management and administration, or they can pursue purely clinical careers. Even more important, VA pharmacy services has taken steps to make certain our facilities and professionals remain on the cutting edge of pharmacy practice.

Students not already familiar with the VA should know that we maintain one of America's largest health care systems. Incorporating 172 hospitals, 233 outpatient clinics, and over 200,000 employees, the VA health care system provides care for millions of veterans. We provide a continuum of managed care for eligible patients.

Pharmacy services is an increasingly vital component of the VA health care system. We employ more than 6,000 staff members nationwide. Our practice sites include both hospital-based inpatient facilities and ambulatory clinics. The services we provide range from general pharmacy services to such practice specialties as geriatrics, oncology, and ambulatory care. Our patients are men and women of all ages. Because veterans of World War II and the Korean War make up a large percentage of our patient population, a growing number of our patients are elderly.

In part, the variety of career opportunities we offer is a result of the expansiveness of the VA system. However, a health care system's size alone cannot guarantee opportunities or chances for career growth. Over the last few years, VA pharmacy has instituted a farsighted transformation in our pharmacy services that is both physical and organizational. These changes are designed to keep our practitioners and services in step with changes that are taking place in the profession at large. We intend to remain in the vanguard of pharmacy through the 1990s and well into the next century.

As a federally funded agency, the VA has always had to work with limited budgets. Still, we have been able to provide high-quality care. We recognize that pharmacists possess skills and abilities that can contribute to enhanced quality of care and the more economical operation of health care facilities in general. Bringing these contributions to the attention of administrators reflects positively on our efforts towards reprofessionalization and increasing our cognitive services.

As part of our transformation, we wanted to make VA pharmacy more attractive. In doing that, we knew we had to look at types of practices and environments that currently existed within the VA system itself and see what kind of improvement could be made.

The result of all of this has been significant changes in VA pharmacy practices. To begin with, our outpatient pharmacies have become much more patient friendly.

Previously, all our clinic-based pharmacies were thick-walled structures with heavy doors that were always locked. The only way a patient could speak to a pharmacist was through a small opening in the door's glass. Obviously, this was less than conducive to friendly pharmacist-patient relations.

Government regulations prohibited us from tearing down this fortified pharmacy and, frankly, doing so would not have suited our needs. A certain level of security is prudent in dispensing and storage areas. Also, because we have a lot of support from technicians (the ratio between technicians and pharmacists in VA facilities is nearly one to one), our pharmacists don't need to spend much time in the dispensing area.

Instead, we have implemented what we refer to as "open pharmacy," which brings our pharmacists out from behind the walls. We have created counseling areas that are located in front of the pharmacies or near the patient waiting area. Depending on space constraints within the clinic, the counseling areas are either private or semiprivate installations. Each area has a computer terminal that gives pharmacists ready access to essential drug information and patient histories.

Patients appreciate our open pharmacy policy and the new level of pharmacist-patient contact. They quickly discovered that our pharmacists can do more for them than fill prescriptions. At the same time, our practitioners are challenged by the increased interaction with patients. Also, as pharmacists moved closer to the clinic's other practice areas, physicians, nurses, and other providers have benefitted from having more immediate access to professional consultations.

These physical changes may seem a small thing, but they have brought important results. Now, patients can ask questions in a private setting and get direct feedback from someone they trust. It would be difficult to overstate the value that represents.

Another physical change we have begun to implement is automation in the dispensing areas. This not only is making dispensing activities more economical and efficient, it also has the effect of concentrating practice functions on our pharmacists' knowledge and skills. Distributive functions remain pharmacy's responsibility, and our pharmacists are accountable for monitoring the accuracy and efficacy of dispensing activities. However, we recognize that the principal value of our pharmacists lies in their clinical cognitive contributions to high-quality, efficient care.

In addition to the physical changes we have implemented in our pharmacies, we have created new standards that establish separate clinical and administrative career tracks.

The impetus for these new standards came directly from our own pharmacy professionals. In many health care settings, pharmacists can advance in clinical practice only so far before their career paths must veer off in a new direction. Usually, this leads them toward administrative duties. Many very good clinicians are not drawn to administration, but they opt for those positions because that is the only way their careers can advance financially or professionally.

To resolve this conflict we have separated clinical and administrative career tracks without penalizing the practitioner for choosing one or the other. Our new qualification standards have produced a dramatic effect on our ability to recruit and retain pharmacists. In the mid-1980s we experienced double-digit vacancy and turnover rates. Today, this has been slashed to three percent. Understandably, the new system has raised the morale – and ambition – of many of our established staff pharmacists as well. And why not? We're enabling people to excel in the areas where their interests and abilities are strongest. If they don't want to be managers, they don't have to. They can be clinical specialists in oncology, nutrition, infectious disease, or other areas and reap the same financial and career rewards.

Students who will be graduating soon should be aware that the choice of a career path in the VA need not be made at the entry level, or even in the first few years of practice. Of course, all of these changes and improvements would have meant little unless they were accepted by other caregivers and administrators. Thankfully, VA health services are very proactive. Our physicians do not operate in a vacuum, and all of our health practitioners believe that teamwork produces better care. As a result, this is truly a multidisciplinary environment. And it works: We have improved quality of care, lowered costs, enhanced patients' perceptions of our health care services, and had a positive impact on staff morale.

As for the future, the 1990s and the beginning of the 21st century will see a magnitude of change in the U.S. health care system. One of VA's goals is to be a major player in American health care policy. I have no doubt that we will, because health care here mirrors trends in health care at large. I believe we are poised to share a wealth of wisdom and experience in grappling with ever-increasing health care expenditures.

I am proud that I can serve veterans through my chosen profession and help provide the vision that will effect change in VA pharmacy practice.

These are exciting times in VA pharmacy. We are facing the challenge of health care expenditures head on, and we are creating many new opportunities for qualified pharmacists and technical support staff.

I encourage students interested in a career in VA pharmacy to visit one of our medical centers or clinics. We are affiliated with all colleges of pharmacy, so there is a good chance most students will perform a rotation through one of our facilities. We also have postgraduate residences in virtually all areas of pharmacy practice. We offer job security, excellent benefits, and excellent prospects for professionalism and diversity. Applicants for professional positions may contact the nearest VA medical center or a medical center in the geographic location of interest. Students and applicants may also contact us in Washington, DC, by calling (202) 535-7302, or by writing the Department of Veterans Affairs, Pharmacy Services, (111H) 810 Vermont Avenue, Washington, DC 20420.

Richard J. Bertin, PhD,
is chief pharmacist of the
U.S. Public Health Service
in Rockville, Maryland.

Pharmacy in the
Public Health Service

The U.S. Public Health Service has provided a good career for me mainly because it offers a variety of pharmacy activities, both administrative and clinical. With the professional opportunities I have had, every day has been a new challenge. I have never been bored, and my professional knowledge and judgment have always been respected.

As the principal federal health agency, the Public Health Service (PHS) has protected and promoted the health of Americans since its founding in 1798. With eight unique agencies, the PHS continues to offer pharmacists a broad spectrum of autonomous, stimulating careers. My own experience reflects just a sampling of the service's diverse opportunities.

I entered the PHS in 1966, after graduating with an MS in hospital pharmacy administration from the University of Minnesota. My first job was in Fort Worth, Texas, and I was happy to go there as winter approached. After two years I transferred to the system's largest teaching hospital, which was on New York's Staten Island. There I was named assistant chief of the pharmacy department.

In 1971, I received approval to study pharmacy administration at the University of Minnesota through the PHS's long-term training program. My PhD minors were in public health and management, which I chose because I believed they would prepare me better for advancement than pharmacy administration would alone.

In 1974, I went back to Staten Island as deputy chief of the pharmacy department. At the time, I was one of the few PhDs in the service, and I began anticipating a move to the headquarters in Washington, DC. I soon got that chance as assistant chief of pharmacy programs for the division of hospitals and clinics. Eventually, I became director in charge of programs employing 250 pharmacists.

The beauty of the PHS is that it allows a pharmacist to have a variety of assignments without having to start over. For example, when I needed another assignment in 1981, I moved to the office of the assistant secretary for health in the federal Department of Health and Human Services. Specifically, I worked in commissioned personnel management.

I stayed there until 1988, when I was reassigned to the Food and Drug Administration as reviewing pharmacist in the Office of Orphan Products Development. This office oversees the development of products that treat rare diseases and have small markets. Early in the 1980s, Congress passed legislation calling for the FDA and industry to encourage investment in orphan drugs through academic research and grants. The hope was that, ultimately, these drugs would be brought to market to benefit this small population.

There are some 5,000 rare diseases that affect fewer than 200,000 people in the United States, so this is a program with real challenges.

In 1990, I returned to administrative work as director of the Division of Commissioned Personnel in the Office of the Surgeon General. Then, in 1992, I was selected to be chief pharmacist for the Public Health Service. There are 11 different professional categories in the PHS, and each discipline has its own adviser. Because this isn't a full-time job, I retain my FDA duties in the Office of Orphan Products.

As chief pharmacist, I advise the Surgeon General and other administrative officials on pharmacy-related issues. I consult on professional practice and personnel activities. I provide consultation to agency or program heads in the PHS or other programs that use PHS personnel. The service also provides professional health care staff members to the Coast Guard, the Federal Bureau of Prisons, and the Immigration and Naturalization Service, as well as several other non-PHS programs.

As the PHS's chief pharmacy officer, I am also the service's spokesperson to national and international pharmaceutical organizations.

In clinical practice – even in rural areas – we are known as innovators. In the Indian Health Service we pioneered the concept of patient counseling and education. We come out from behind the counter because lots of times patients are reluctant to ask questions even when their doctors tell them they should. Pharmacists in the Indian Health Service have done this for many years, and the practice has attracted national and even international attention.

The eight PHS agencies have their own unique missions and public responsibilities. They are listed in order of the size of their pharmacy programs, from largest to smallest:

- *The Indian Health Service (IHS)*. The IHS and Tribes have more than 240 sites with approximately 472 pharmacists stationed throughout the United States (in 33 states). Most of the sites are located in the Southwest. Pharmacists at all locations in the IHS practice within multidisciplinary health teams in which true peer relationships exist among the members. The clinical knowledge and skills of IHS pharmacists have long been recognized, as is evidenced by the development of many progressive clinical pharmacy services. IHS pharmacists are commonly involved in primary care programs for evaluating, treating, and monitoring ambulatory patients. Because pharmacists have direct access to the health record of each patient, the use of prescription blanks has been eliminated. The patient's health record is available for the pharmacists to review at the time of dispensing. All new clinics use private consultation rooms for providing patient counseling and other pharmacy services. For inpatient services, pharmacists actively participate in the selection, dosing, and monitoring of drug therapy. Most hospitals have unit dose, IV admixture programs, and pharmacokinetic services. The unique cultural experience of working with Native American tribes, coupled with the variety of geographical locations and professional opportunities, presents an exciting and challenging experience that cannot be found anywhere else.

- *The Food and Drug Administration (FDA)*. The FDA protects the public from harmful foods, drugs, medical devices, radiological products, and consumer products. Its pharmacists review requests for new drug applications and manufacturers' methods of preparing and testing drugs and biologics. In addition, they inspect manufacturing facilities and evaluate reported problems with medical and pharmaceutical products. FDA pharmacists also prepare *Federal Register* notices for all aspects of drug regulation.
- *The Health Resources and Services Administration (HRSA)*. The HRSA delivers health care to underserved populations and manages grant programs to improve the health of these groups. HRSA responsibilities range from facilities financing to federal employee occupational health.
- *The National Institutes of Health (NIH)*. One of the world's foremost medical research centers and the federal government's primary biomedical research agency, NIH studies all aspects of human health and illness. NIH funds nearly half of all biomedical research and development in the United States. Most NIH pharmacists work at the 540-bed clinical center in Bethesda, Md., a research hospital where top scientists and clinicians collaborate to develop cures for diseases. NIH pharmacists formulate and dispense medications, work in IV-therapy and unit-dose sections, and develop investigational formulations.
- *The Substance Abuse and Mental Health Service Administration (SAMHSA)*. Most of this agency's pharmacists work at St. Elizabeths Hospital, a large mental health and clinical research facility in Washington, DC. Their jobs are similar to those of many hospital pharmacists. Other agency pharmacists work in public affairs, informing the public about alcohol and drug abuse.
- *Agency for Health Care Policy and Research (AHCPR)*. This new agency employs a small number of pharmacists to study health care policy and outcomes research. They seek practical guidelines for health care professionals by convening panels of experts to assess treatments for such problems as postoperative pain and urinary incontinence.
- *The Centers for Disease Control and Prevention (CDC)*. Based in Atlanta, the CDC detects, tracks, controls, and eradicates disease in the United States and around the world.

- *Agency for Toxic Substances and Disease Research (ATSDR)*. An offshoot of the CDC, this agency implements health-related sections of laws in order to protect the public from hazardous wastes and substances.

The basic requirement for entry into the PHS is a pharmacy degree, either BS or PharmD. Candidates also are required to have a license to practice in one state. When I moved from Minnesota to Texas and then to New York, I retained the license I was granted by my home state of Pennsylvania.

As one of the uniformed services, the PHS gives pharmacists the choice of joining through the commissioned corps or the civil service. This is appealing to some applicants because it allows them to match their personal needs to the particular attributes or requirements of the personnel system. Most pharmacists who choose the PHS join the commissioned corps. They are likely to advance faster, but they will usually be expected to move in order to advance.

Salaries in the PHS begin a little lower than in some parts of the private sector. But with promotions and benefits, pay rates catch up in three to four years and soon bypass those of civilian pharmacists.

We are looking for young pharmacists who are challenged by our programs. Many stay with the corps for a career. It is not unusual for pharmacists to serve 20 to 30 years. But even if people decide to leave active duty, they can elect to go into the inactive reserve. Anyone in that pool can volunteer to be called back for short tours of duty. Many come back during the summer for two to three weeks to work, for example, in an Indian Health Service facility. They can brush up on their clinical skills, which academics particularly appreciate. And it's wonderful for us because it helps us cover for vacationing staff pharmacists.

Few organizations offer the variety of opportunities that the PHS does. I certainly haven't held every job in the service, but I have practiced in a clinical situation, managed large numbers of professionals, participated in making broad policy decisions, and helped improve health care in this country. The service has been good to me, and I wouldn't trade my experience for anything else.

For more information about PHS pharmacy careers, contact:
U.S. Public Health Service Recruitment
Parklawn Building, Room 7A-07
Rockville, MD 20857
1-800-221-9393
In Virginia 703-734-6855

Pharmacy Opportunities in the Supermarket

Tim Hammonds
is president and CEO of the
Food Marketing Institute.

Editor's note:

The Food Marketing Institute (FMI) is a nonprofit association that conducts programs in research, education, industry relations, and public affairs on behalf of its 1,500 members in the United States and around the world. FMI's domestic member companies operate approximately 19,000 retail food stores with a combined annual sales volume of $190 billion – more than half of all grocery store sales in the United States. FMI's retail membership is composed of large multistore chains, small regional firms, and independent supermarkets. Its international membership includes 250 members from 60 countries.

When food and pharmacy are located under one roof, the result is a time-saving convenience shoppers find hard to resist. In fact, this is the wave of the future, because what supermarket operators are hearing from their customers these days is that they want increased convenience and service. And with the grocery industry's focus on customer satisfaction, the supermarket pharmacy is well stocked, technologically advanced, and patient focused. In short, it's a great place to practice pharmacy.

Today's food store is more of a super market than ever before, offering services and products far beyond standard grocery items. Home health care items, cosmetics, carry-out meals, catering services, housewares, video rentals, photo centers, postal services, and even banks can be found in many modern supermarkets. They have evolved into community centers serving neighborhoods and providing convenient, one-stop shopping, typically offering 30,000 items. The in-store pharmacy is a natural extension of a commitment to service that has become an integral part of successful supermarket operations.

Food-drug "combo" stores are powerful economic units, with $5 billion in annual retail prescription sales. The number of U.S. supermarkets with pharmacy departments has grown tremendously over the past several years and continues to increase at a steady annual pace. The number of food stores with pharmacies jumped from 5,261 in 1991 to 5,428 in 1992, an increase of over three percent. Such growth is a strong indication that for years to come there will be plenty of career opportunities for pharmacists interested in this dynamic practice setting.

For those who choose a career in pharmacy because they enjoy interacting with people, the supermarket setting is the perfect place to practice. Consumers typically visit their local supermarket 2.2 times a week –

nearly nine times a month. This frequency offers pharmacists a great opportunity to build rewarding professional and personal relationships with their patients. With the renewed focus in the profession on pharmaceutical care and patient outcomes, the ability of supermarket pharmacists to establish ongoing, long-term relationships in which they can make a real difference in patients' lives produces a sense of job satisfaction that is not found in all practice settings.

In fact, the service-oriented environment of the typical supermarket pharmacy is a practice setting that's hard to match. Because pharmacy is fairly new in the supermarket industry, it offers pharmacists a ground-floor opportunity to grow, contribute, and advance in the industry. Pharmacies are being built in many new stores with well-designed space, state-of-the-art equipment, comfortable waiting rooms, and separate consultation areas. Moreover, the supermarket industry has long used computers to enhance efficiency, and most stores are equipped with the latest innovative, cutting-edge technology to facilitate operations. At a typical supermarket, the in-store pharmacy is part of an on-line, company-wide computer network and is equipped with sophisticated hardware and the latest in software applications. This technological support increases the pharmacist's ability to be proactive and efficient, by offering up-to-the-minute information that can enhance patient counseling and drug therapy.

The in-store pharmacy contribution to the supermarket industry's overall investment in community service is reflected in the many health-related activities that are routinely offered to consumers. Outreach programs, such as drug counseling for young people, along with health fairs and in-store screenings for diabetes, hypertension, cholesterol, and colon cancer, are a natural extension of existing customer and community service programs. Additionally, the food store is a unique setting in which patient care can incorporate the entire store, offering the creative pharmacist the chance to counsel patients about nutrition, diet, healthy eating, and improved lifestyles – and allowing patients to benefit from the pharmacist's advice immediately, on-site.

Supermarkets offer pharmacists a variety of opportunities for professional and managerial development. For the new pharmacist, an in-store position is a great place to develop communication and practice skills in a challenging, fast-paced environment. It provides experience in working with physicians and customers, as well as opportunities for business decision making. Supermarket management supports the professional growth of its pharmacists and encourages their involvement in local, state, and national professional organizations. Special training and continuing education often are offered in areas that include financial management, communication skills, and technology applications.

A career within a supermarket company can lead to a number of exciting positions. Some of the possibilities are third-party program administration and marketing, managed care sales, marketing and merchandising, procurement and distribution, systems management and training, operations management, and executive-level management.

Continual steady growth, a strong consumer focus, innovative technology, a variety of career options – these are hallmarks of supermarket pharmacy. And they are the ingredients of an exciting pharmacy practice. There are plenty of challenging and rewarding opportunities for personal and professional growth in the dynamic arena of supermarket pharmacy.

Daniel R. Brown, BA, BS,
is manager of H.E.Butts Pharmacy
in Austin, Texas.

Pharmacy in Grocery Chains

It's no exaggeration to say that I know most of my customers by their first names. We talk about fishing, golfing, hunting – you name it. That may be surprising after I say the pharmacy I manage is part of a large chain supermarket.

Of course, the number of pharmacies in superstores like mine has grown dramatically because of the conveniences they afford people who have increasing constraints on their time. However, convenience alone is not enough to keep customers coming back. The real key to success in this setting is personalized service – and lots of it. People want to feel that their pharmacist understands their special needs, and they want to be treated with dignity and respect.

In this store, we owe much of our repeat business to the fact that we work hard and give fast, reliable, and friendly service. And most important of all, we listen to our customers. Many people want nothing more than to have someone take a minute to listen to what they have to say.

Listening is difficult for many people because to do it properly it is necessary to be nonjudgmental. Pharmacists have to be able to read their patients, to understand their problems. With practice, this isn't difficult, but it's one of the most important skills in retail pharmacy.

A community internship I had with Safeway convinced me to work in retail pharmacy. While there, I worked under one of the best pharmacists I know. He was one of those superachievers who attracted everybody in the neighborhood. Everyone liked him, and everyone listened to him. He took me under his wing, and I had a great experience at Safeway. People would come in and say, "How are you today? I just came in to see you and Mike."

Later, I worked in a hospital pharmacy, which wasn't my cup of tea because I missed contact with people. As a result, I decided to go to graduate school. As a graduate student, I concentrated on drug delivery systems. Had I completed grad school, my work would have led me in a completely different direction. Almost certainly I would have wound up in research and development, probably working for a pharmaceutical manufacturer. In any event, I wouldn't be where I am today.

I never made a conscious decision to go to work for a grocery chain. I simply realized I no longer wanted to finish graduate school. I had been in college for about nine years, working on bachelor's degrees in biology and pharmacy and then on my graduate studies; I was ready to get out.

I had a friend who worked for a chain operation in Dallas, and he told me how much he enjoyed his job. He mentioned me to his boss, and they began recruiting me. They called me while I was still in graduate school, asking whether I would be interested in coming to work for them. They made an attractive offer and assigned me to a really nice store in Austin. It was too good a deal to pass up after all those years of education. I stayed for four years before I came to work for H.E.Butts.

My decision to leave school and take a job in a superstore pharmacy was fortuitous, because it confirmed what I had suspected during my earlier internship: I love the people side of pharmacy. I know I am much happier doing this than I would have been in a laboratory.

In addition to my people skills, I've discovered that I have a knack for the business side of pharmacy management. In fact, as a manager, I am also what my company calls a pacesetter. In this role, I work with 15 other pharmacists serving as communications specialists and mentors for the pharmacy managers and staff pharmacists in more than 100 stores. Each pacesetter is assigned a cluster of six or seven stores, and we are responsible for helping the pharmacy managers boost their gross profits. We accomplish this by teaching inventory management, reimbursement for service contract business, data processing – whatever it takes to make sure our cluster managers have the right information. In this day and age, as sophisticated as we have become, this support can determine success or failure.

In my own store, I have to be able to communicate effectively with managers of other departments because they are unfamiliar with details of the pharmacy side of the business. What they do understand is increased sales growth, and they're very pleased with the rise in revenues they've seen in the years since I came on board. When they realize that my pharmacy is doing almost six percent of the total business in this very busy supermarket, they're impressed. I don't think there's another department in the store that generates as many dollars per square foot as we do.

I must admit that I have sometimes felt the managers of other departments resent me because my salary is higher than theirs. I take this issue as an educational challenge. Consequently, I make it a point to attend every weekly meeting of department managers. I always chime in with my suggestions, whether they want to hear them or not. That way, the other managers know I'm paying attention to things outside my own department. I make sure they know I'm concerned about the total store: how it looks, how things should be done, and how we behave. After a great deal of hard work on my part, I hope the other managers have begun to see that I am a valuable asset to the whole operation.

Trying to position my pharmacy in the local marketplace is a constantly evolving process that I enjoy. Our direct competition includes another grocery pharmacy across the street, a chain drugstore up the road, and another one not far away.

The bottom line is that I attribute much of the growth this pharmacy has experienced over the last few years to my staff, which pays close attention to what our patients need. For example, many of the people we serve speak only Spanish. As a result, I've assembled a staff that is bilingual for the most part. It may be hard to believe, but when I came here, most of our people couldn't communicate with our Hispanic patrons at all.

To make sure our patients receive the attention they deserve, two pharmacists are on duty during a good portion of the day. This enables one pharmacist to fill prescriptions while the other is counseling patients. This system works much better than having one pharmacist try to do everything. In a busy store, that just can't be accomplished.

Another step we've taken to allow our staff pharmacists to spend more time counseling patients about their medications is to certify our technicians. This allows them to do many of the mechanical aspects of dispensing – what I call the assembly work. Our technician enters data into the computer, takes the labels out of the printer, and actually puts the medication into the containers. In Texas, technicians can do almost everything but put labels on the containers or counsel patients.

In every survey of how the public regards certain professions, pharmacists always rank highest where trust and dependability are concerned. People expect us to have integrity, and we have to behave accordingly. We simply can't violate that trust.

Because of that, H.E.Butts believes community involvement enables pharmacists to become well-rounded individuals and helps promote our pharmacies in the community. For example, we have an adopt-a-school program in which we offer counseling services on drug abuse to young people in the community.

In a chain superstore, the pharmacist must be empathetic because listening to and understanding patients is paramount in importance. The ideal pharmacist also must be able to handle stress because he or she often will be the person in the middle – among patients, the insurance company, and the doctor. Because the retail pharmacist may well be the health care professional who must put a patient's drug therapy in perspective, compassion and communication skills are essential requirements.

It's also important to understand the business side of pharmacy, because it takes solid management skills to run a chain pharmacy like this one in a highly competitive market.

But most of all, to succeed in a grocery store pharmacy you have to like people. If you don't, you won't be happy in this setting. Clearly, this practice is not for everyone because many pharmacists are uncomfortable with that kind of contact. But if you do enjoy the public – and in large numbers – superstore pharmacy may be for you.

*John A. Gans, PharmD,
is executive vice president of the
American Pharmaceutical Association
in Washington, DC.*

Careers in Associations

A wide variety of professional associations represent pharmacists and the pharmacy profession in different capacities. The American Pharmaceutical Association (APhA) serves the needs of all pharmacists, but there also are specialty organizations to serve pharmacists who practice in specific settings. For example, national associations represent independent community pharmacy owners, hospital pharmacists, nursing home consultant pharmacists, pharmacy educators, and boards of pharmacy, among others. There also are associations that represent pharmacy at the state and local levels. Often, these are affiliated with national counterparts.

During pharmacy school, future pharmacy practitioners gain exposure to associations as student members. Through their involvement in such organizations, students meet and interact with pharmacists who work in a variety of settings. They also meet students from other colleges of pharmacy and have an opportunity to make an impact on the profession.

Pharmacy associations provide important services to their members. Among these are:

Education Associations develop and administer continuing education programs – from published articles to live programs and specialized workshops to certification programs.

Publications Associations publish journals, newsletters, textbooks, and education modules, including those that can be used in presentations to community groups and schools.

Lobbying Ours is a highly regulated profession. Many decisions relating to the day-to-day practice of pharmacy are made by lawmakers in the state general assemblies, in the U.S. Congress, and by regulators in state and federal agencies. Consequently, it is imperative that professional associations make certain that pharmacy's views are reflected in laws and regulations affecting the profession, and they are very active in this effort.

Representing the profession Pharmacy associations also represent the profession and promote the value of pharmaceutical care to other professions and health care agencies. In this time of extensive health care reform, this role is more important than ever. Associations also represent the profession by implementing policies adopted through their governing bodies and by taking action on initiatives set forth through the member committees and board of directors. Moreover, pharmacy organizations serve the public through educational and health-promotion activities.

Through an understanding of the valuable services provided by organizations, one can begin to imagine the diversity of career opportunities that can be found in a professional association.

The person with primary administrative responsibility in a pharmacy organization usually has the title of executive vice president or executive director. This person serves as chief executive officer (CEO) and manages the coordination of all the association's programs and policies. This person is one of the most visible leaders of the association, works closely with the volunteer and elected leadership of the association, and directs the work of the organization's staff.

There are various other potential roles for pharmacists in a professional association. In the educational programming provided by these organizations, one might work in planning the programs and teaching sessions held during workshops, meetings, or conventions. Individuals in these positions also arrange for speakers and coordinate panels and agendas.

In preparing publications, another important role for associations, pharmacists with writing talents have the opportunity to produce articles on topics related to the profession, health care, and drug therapy, and to write chapters for textbooks. In addition, such pharmacists can look forward to serving as editors of newsletters, journals, and books published by the association.

In member services, there is challenging work to be done with the association committees and in implementing the programs and ideas generated by the members.

Public relations presents another opportunity for the pharmacist who chooses a career in a professional association. In this vital capacity, the pharmacist represents the profession in multidisciplinary public health groups in a variety of arenas. Similarly, someone interested in governmental affairs and legislation might work for an association as a lobbyist. Because the vast majority of legislators are not health professionals, it is important that they be educated in the services pharmacists provide to patients and the role pharmacists play on the health care team. This activity helps ensure that pharmacy has continuing input on legislation that may affect the profession.

There is an abundance of opportunity for pharmacists within professional associations, and the work can be extremely rewarding. It provides an excellent means for promoting and advancing the profession, and it enables pharmacists to serve their colleagues and the public.

Specialty Pharmacy Practice

Ray R. Maddox, PharmD,
is director of the Idaho Drug Information
Service, located in Pocatello.

Compared with medicine and some of the other health care disciplines, the identification and recognition of specialties is a recent development in pharmacy.

This article will describe the development of specialty recognition in pharmacy, review the process by which the Board of Pharmaceutical Specialties (BPS) was created, discuss the criteria and process for specialty recognition, and describe current existing specialties. By taking this approach, it is hoped that the pharmacy student or new pharmacist will gain an appreciation of the significance of specialization and be able to use this information in career planning.

Consideration of the prospect of practice specialization, its likely form, and the effect that such differentiation among professional activities might have began in the late 1960s and early 1970s.

In a 1968 editorial, Paul Parker described hospital pharmacists who had developed roles that were distinct from traditional dispensing responsibilities. These pharmacists, identified as part of the "generation gap" in hospital pharmacy, used their knowledge to participate with physicians in therapeutic decision making. He called them drug information specialists and suggested that their knowledge and practice skills required special academic and experiential preparation. Parker noted that these specialists, whom he identified as clinical pharmacists, sought the opportunity to practice their specialty on a full-time basis, and he said that it was unreasonable to expect that a single individual practitioner could become a good drug information specialist (or a good clinical pharmacist) as well as a good departmental administrator. Consequently, he encouraged hospital pharmacists to organize their departments in ways that recognized and used the evolving specialists. He suggested that the medical model of service organization might be applicable in pharmacy.

In 1971, the American Association of Colleges of Pharmacy (AACP) appointed the Study Commission on Pharmacy (the Millis Commission) to examine the profession. The evaluation acknowledged that differentiation in pharmacy practice was occurring and that this was generally expected and desirable. It pointed out that a clinical pharmacy movement, though poorly defined at that time, was a potent internal force in the reshaping of the profession.

In a series of editorials published between 1974 and 1976, Donald

Francke outlined a concept for a structure for the practice of pharmacy. Specialization was among the issues addressed. Francke envisioned that pharmacy would ultimately become a clinical profession with several levels of practice. In his view, the general clinical pharmacy practitioner would be the product of an entry-level program of study leading to a PharmD degree. He suggested several types of specialists whose knowledge and skills would be differentiated and would be acquired through postgraduate education. Francke outlined specific responsibilities that clinical pharmacy generalists would have, and he suggested that specialists would be able to deliver general clinical services as well as those associated with the specialty. In other words, these individuals would represent a subset of the larger practice of pharmacy. He identified anticipated specialties in pharmacotherapy, clinical radiopharmacy, drug information, pediatric clinical pharmacy, and geriatric pharmacy.

Also in 1971, the House of Delegates of the American Pharmaceutical Association (APhA) adopted a policy statement calling for the establishment of a mechanism for the recognition of specialties and certification of specialists.

In the spring of 1973, the APhA Board of Trustees appointed the Task Force on Specialties in Pharmacy. This group was given several charges: to identify existing or potential areas of specialization or to determine that there were no specialties and that the practice of pharmacy was not likely to become specialized; to propose a means by which specialties could be identified; and to develop the means by which individuals could be recognized as specialists, as well as recommendations for recertification.

The task force solicited input from a broad array of individuals and associations in pharmacy, from other health care professions, and from the public. It evaluated the policies and practices of specialty recognition and certification in other professions. The task force published its final report in November 1974. Even though no consensus was reached about whether specialties did or did not exist at that time, the task force felt that one or more specialties would develop in the near future and that there was a need to establish an independent agency responsible for recognizing specialties. The task force made specific recommendations regarding the structure of the recognition and certification process. It also recommended criteria by which practice areas should be evaluated for specialty recognition, and it recommended the establishment of BPS, which was created on January 5, 1976.

The BPS bylaws outline four primary responsibilities that constitute the board's mission. First, BPS recognizes appropriate specialties using criteria developed for this reason. Second, BPS sets standards for certification and recertification of pharmacists in designated areas of specialty practice. This work is done primarily by individual specialty councils within BPS, which recommend appropriate actions for the board. Third, BPS administers the process of examination and evaluation of individuals who seek certification and recertification as specialists. Finally, the Board of Pharmaceutical Specialties serves as an information clearinghouse and coordinating agency for organizations and pharmacists in recognized pharmacy practice specialties.

BPS bylaws call for the establishment of a specialty council for each designated area of practice. Operational guidelines for these councils were approved by BPS in July of 1976. The specialty councils are charged with developing and implementing certification processes. These processes must be legally and psychometrically defensible, and they must be consistent with sound public policy regarding the credentialing of health care professionals.

Certification of specialists by BPS is limited to seven years. Recertification is achieved through a process developed by the appropriate specialty council and approved by BPS. Failure of a BPS-certified specialist to apply for recertification automatically results in deletion of that pharmacist from the roster of certified specialists.

An important objective of the Task Force on Specialties in Pharmacy was to ensure that specialty recognition serves the public interest and meets the professional needs of pharmacy. In this regard, a set of seven criteria for evaluating and designating specialty areas was incorporated into the BPS bylaws.

A brief description of these criteria and comments on how they have been applied in the review of petitions for specialty recognition should lead to a better understanding of the relationship between the general practice of pharmacy and the specialty practice.

Demand The area of specialization shall be one in which there exists a significant and clear health demand to provide the necessary public reason for certification.

This criterion requires the petitioner to demonstrate that there is a public and professional demand for individuals in the proposed specialty. Petitioners must document the number of available positions in this area of practice, as well as the number of positions that were filled and unfilled for at least three years before submission of the petition. Additionally, the petition must include statements from pharmacy and nonpharmacy health care leaders and administrators, as well as members of the public, that such specialists are in demand.

Need The area of specialization shall be one for which specifically trained practitioners are needed to meet the responsibilities of the profession in improving the health and welfare of the public, which responsibilities may not otherwise be effectively fulfilled.

This criterion requires evidence that the proposed specialty will provide services that are germane to pharmacy and cannot be provided by pharmacy generalists or by other health care providers. The petition must demonstrate that the public health and welfare are at risk if these specialized services are not provided.

Number and time The area of specialization shall include a reasonable number of individuals who devote most of the time of their practice to the specialty area.

This criterion requires a critical mass of practitioners in the proposed specialty. An assessment of the amount of time that these individuals devote to the practice of the specialty also is required. Petitions must quantify the number of individuals who practice in the specialty and the percentage of time they devote to functions of the specialty, compared with the time they may devote to other pharmacy responsibilities.

Specialized knowledge The area of specialization shall rest on a specialized knowledge of pharmaceutical sciences, which have their basis in the biological, physical, and behavioral sciences, and not solely on the basis of managerial, procedural, or technical services, nor solely on the basis of the environment in which pharmacy is practiced.

The proposed specialty must be firmly rooted in the science and practice of pharmacy and cannot duplicate a practice role in another health care discipline. This criterion indicates that specialty practice is related more to academic and practice credentials than to the specific environment in which an individual practices. This knowledge base must be differentiated from that of pharmacy generalists and of pharmacy specialists who already have formal recognition.

Specialized functions The area of specialization shall represent an identifiable and distinct field of practice that calls for special knowledge and skills acquired by education and training and/or experience beyond the basic pharmaceutical education and training.

The petitioner must delineate specific functions that are not being and cannot be provided by a generalist or specialists in already recognized specialty practice areas. A definition of the differential professional skills used in these functions must be provided, as must a description of how the specialist acquires the education and training required for these skills. The petition must outline how the education and training programs for specialty practice differ from those for general practice and from those for recognized specialty practice areas.

Education and training The area of specialization shall be one in which schools and colleges of pharmacy and/or other organizations offer recognized education and training programs to those seeking advanced knowledge and skills in the area of specialty practice so that they may perform more competently.

A description of the nature, content, length, scope, and type of education and training necessary to practice the specialty and a list of programs that offer the needed education, training, or both, are integral parts of the petition.

Transmission of knowledge The area of specialization shall be one in which there is an adequate educational and scientific base to warrant transmission of knowledge through teaching clinics and a body of professional, scientific, and technical literature immediately related to the specialty.

Evidence of established mechanisms of transmission of scientific and practice-oriented knowledge about various aspects of the specialty is essential. These mechanisms may include books, journals, symposia, and professional meetings. The petitioner must demonstrate that these modes of knowledge transmission are designed for and used by specialists.

BPS systematically evaluates petitions against each of these seven criteria and may seek clarification or additional information from the petitioner. All petitioners are required to conduct a role-delineation study as part of the petition process.

As indicated, the board's primary activity is to review and act on petitions for specialty recognition. As of November 1992, BPS had received six such petitions and had designated four specialties in pharmacy. In 1977, the APhA Academy of Pharmacy Practice, Section on Nuclear Pharmacy, requested that nuclear pharmacy be designated a specialty. Recognition was granted in 1978, and the NUSPEX was administered for the first time in 1982. A recertification process for nuclear pharmacists was instituted in 1989.

The Committee on Clinical Pharmacy as a Specialty, which was sponsored by the American College of Clinical Pharmacy (ACCP), submitted its petition in March 1986. After being duly considered and discussed by the profession and BPS, the petition was denied. In announcing this decision, BPS commented that "... clinical pharmacy practice is too broad and too general to be recognized as a specialty ..." However, it suggested that "... an area of practice referred to as 'clinical pharmacotherapy' may be such a specialized area of pharmacy practice as to justify consideration of it for specialty recognition." In 1988, a new petition supported by ACCP requesting the recognition of pharmacotherapy was approved.

A petition sponsored jointly by the American Society of Hospital Pharmacists (ASHP) and the American Society for Parenteral and Enteral Nutrition (ASPEN) for the recognition of nutrition support pharmacy practice also was formulated during the mid-1980s. The document was reviewed concurrently with the pharmacotherapy petition. Nutrition support pharmacy practice was recognized as a specialty in 1988.

The petition for the recognition of psychopharmacy as a specialty was submitted by ASHP in October 1990. After discussion by the profession, BPS recognized psychopharmacy as a specialty in 1992.

A petition for the recognition of oncology pharmacy practice was submitted to BPS in September 1992 by ASHP. The petition is undergoing review as of this writing.

The four approved areas of specialty practice are described in the following way:

- *Pharmacotherapy* is that area of pharmacy practice which is responsible for ensuring the safe, appropriate, and economical use of drugs

353

in patient care. The pharmacotherapy specialist has responsibility for direct patient care, often functions as a member of a multidisciplinary team, and frequently is the primary source of drug information. The pharmacotherapy specialist is a licensed pharmacist with specialized education and/or structured training in pathophysiology, pharmacotherapy, pharmacokinetics, pharmacodynamics, pharmacoeconomics, research techniques, drug information, ethics, and health care regulations.

- *Nutrition support pharmacy practice* addresses the care of patients with potential or existing nutritional aberrations by utilizing pharmaceutical, pharmacologic, and clinical expertise to optimize the nutritional status and overall care of the patient. The nutrition support pharmacist has responsibility for direct patient care and often functions as a member of a multidisciplinary nutrition support team. A nutrition support pharmacist is a licensed practitioner with advanced training in pharmaceutics, pharmaceutical chemistry, pharmacology, pharmacy management, biochemistry, pathology, physiology, anatomy, and microbiology.

- *Nuclear pharmacy* is a patient-oriented service that embodies the scientific and professional knowledge required to improve and promote health through the safe and effective use of radioactive drugs for diagnosis and therapy. A nuclear pharmacist is a licensed professional with advanced training in radiation physics, instrumentation, mathematics, radiopharmaceutical chemistry, radiation biology, and health physics/radiation protection. As a member of the nuclear medicine team, the nuclear pharmacist specializes in procuring, compounding, quality control testing, dispensing, distribution, and monitoring of radiopharmaceuticals.

- *Psychopharmacy practice* addresses the pharmaceutical care of patients with psychiatric illnesses by utilizing in-depth knowledge of psychopharmacology, psychopathology, pharmacokinetics, and toxicology. The psychopharmacy practitioner's role includes designing drug therapy regimens, defining therapeutic endpoints, and addressing the effectiveness of therapy.

Interorganizational Council on Student Affairs

The Interorganizational Council on Student Affairs (ICSA) was formed in late 1991 by nine pharmacy organizations. This multiorganizational body serves as an information clearinghouse to facilitate the exchange of materials and ideas among the various pharmacy student populations. The goal of ICSA is to serve the professional needs of students and promote communications between pharmacy students and the components of pharmacy practice, education, and research represented by participating organizations.

As an example of the council's work, a publication has been developed that lists grants, scholarships, loans, awards, and experiential training available to entry-level pharmacy students and to those entering their first year of postgraduate education or training. This resource will be updated annually and made available each fall through ICSA organizations.

ICSA is composed of staff representatives from nine of the member organizations of the Joint Commission of Pharmacy Practitioners (JCPP). The participating organizations are the American Association of Colleges of Pharmacy (AACP); American College of Apothecaries (ACA); American College of Clinical Pharmacy (ACCP); American Pharmaceutical Association (APhA); American Society of Consultant Pharmacists (ASCP); American Society of Hospital Pharmacists (ASHP); NARD (representing independent retail pharmacy); National Association of Chain Drug Stores (NACDS); and the National Council of State Pharmacy Association Executives (NCSPAE). APhA serves as secretariat for ICSA.

ICSA is pleased to assist Pfizer in identifying the pharmacists profiled in this valuable career resource. With so many career directions available to today's pharmacists, you will most likely have numerous questions. If you do, don't hesitate to contact any of the individuals profiled in the book. ICSA wishes you success in identifying your career path in the pharmacy profession and knows you will find it rewarding.